GUIDE TO FOOD STORAGE

Follow this guide for food storage, and you can be sure that what's in your freezer, refrigerator, and pantry is fresh-tasting and ready to cook.

IN THE FREEZER
(At -10° to 0° F)

DAIRY

Cheese, hard	3 months
Cheese, soft	2 weeks
Egg substitute	6 months
Egg whites	6 months
Egg yolks	8 months
Ice cream, sherbet	1 month

FRUITS AND VEGETABLES

Commercially frozen fruits	1 year
Commercially frozen vegetables	8 to 12 months

MEATS, POULTRY, AND SEAFOOD

Beef, Lamb, and Veal

Ground, uncooked, and all cuts, cooked	3 months
Roasts and steaks, uncooked	9 months

Pork

Ground, uncooked, and all cuts, cooked	3 months
Roasts and chops, uncooked	6 months

Poultry

All cuts, cooked	1 month
Boneless or bone-in pieces, uncooked	6 months

Seafood

Bass, perch, trout, and shellfish	3 months
Cod, flounder, and halibut	6 months

IN THE REFRIGERATOR
(At 34° to 40° F)

DAIRY

Buttermilk, low-fat	1 to 2 weeks
Cheese, grated Parmesan	1 year
Cheeses, Cheddar and Swiss	3 to 4 weeks
Cream cheese, ⅓-less-fat and reduced-fat	2 weeks
Eggs and egg substitute	1 month
Margarine	1 month

MEATS, POULTRY, AND SEAFOOD

Beef, Lamb, Pork, and Veal

Ground and stew meat, uncooked	1 to 2 days
Roasts, uncooked	2 to 4 days
Steaks and chops, uncooked	3 to 5 days

Chicken, Turkey, and Seafood

All cuts, uncooked	1 to 2 days

FRUITS AND VEGETABLES

Apples, beets, cabbage, carrots, celery, citrus fruits, eggplant, and parsnips	2 to 3 weeks
Apricots, berries, peaches, pears, plums, asparagus, cauliflower, cucumbers, mushrooms, okra, peas, peppers, salad greens, and summer squash	2 to 4 days
Corn, husked	1 day

IN THE PANTRY
Keep these at room temperature for six to 12 months.

BAKING AND COOKING STAPLES
Baking powder
Biscuit and baking mix
Broth, canned
Cooking spray
Honey
Mayonnaise, regular, light, and fat-free (unopened)
Milk, canned evaporated skimmed
Milk, nonfat dry powder
Mustard, prepared (unopened)
Oils, olive and vegetable
Pasta, dried
Peanut butter, reduced-fat
Rice, instant and regular
Salad dressings, bottled (unopened)
Seasoning sauces, bottled
Tuna, canned

FRUITS, LEGUMES, AND VEGETABLES
Fruits, canned
Legumes (beans, lentils, peas), dried or canned
Tomato products, canned
Vegetables, canned

Tangerine Granita,
page 40

Seared Rosemary
Beef Tenderloin,
page 93

Roasted Vegetable
Salad, page 123

Triple Chocolate Cake,
page 42

Weight Watchers.

ANNUAL RECIPES
for SUCCESS

2003

Oxmoor
House.

©2002 by Oxmoor House, Inc.
Book Division of Southern Progress Corporation
P.O. Box 2463, Birmingham, Alabama 35201

ISBN: 0-8487-2545-x
ISSN: 1526-1565
Printed in the United States of America
First Printing 2002

Be sure to check with your health-care provider before making any changes in your diet. WEIGHT WATCHERS is a registered trademark of Weight Watchers International, Inc., and is used under license by Healthy Living, Inc.

OXMOOR HOUSE, INC.
Editor-in-Chief: Nancy Fitzpatrick Wyatt
Executive Editor: Katherine M. Eakin
Art Director: Cynthia R. Cooper
Copy Chief: Catherine Ritter Scholl

WEIGHT WATCHERS® ANNUAL RECIPES
FOR SUCCESS 2003
Editor: Carolyn Land, R.D., L.D.
Successes Writer: Heather Averett
Copy Editor: Jacqueline Giovanelli
Editorial Assistants: Andrea Carver, Dawn Russell
Senior Designer: Emily Albright Parrish
Director, Test Kitchens: Elizabeth Tyler Luckett
Assistant Director, Test Kitchens: Julie Christopher
Recipe Editor: Gayle Hays Sadler
Test Kitchens Staff: Kristi Carter; Jennifer Cofield; Gretchen Feldtman, R.D.;
    David Gallent; Ana Kelly; Jan A. Smith
Senior Photographer: Jim Bathie
Photographer: Brit Huckabay
Senior Photo Stylist: Kay Clarke
Photo Stylist: Ashley J. Wyatt
Publishing Systems Administrator: Rick Tucker
Director, Production and Distribution: Phillip Lee
Production Coordinator: Leslie Johnson
Production Assistant: Faye Porter Bonner

CONTRIBUTORS
Copy Editor: Dolores Hydock
Indexer: Mary Ann Laurens
Recipe Development: Rebecca Boggan, Jennifer Cofield, Nancy Hughes,
    Ana Kelly, Jean Kressy, Kathleen Royal Phillips
Test Kitchens Interns: Kelly Wilton, Tamara Zucker

COVER: Fudgy Caramel Brownies, page 56
BACK COVER: Lousianna Deviled Crab Cakes with Hot Peppered Sour Cream, page 63

To order additional publications, call 1-800-633-4910.

For more books to enrich your life, visit oxmoorhouse.com

CONTENTS

INTRODUCTION

RECIPES

SUCCESSES

WEEKLY MENU PLANNERS

Welcome!

It's amazing how simple healthy living can be.

Weight Watchers® Annual Recipes for Success 2003 offers you more than 300 brand-new, kitchen-tested recipes to fit any occasion, delicious side dish suggestions to round out your meals, step-by-step photos and helpful hints to make recipe preparation easier, plus nine "real-life" weight-loss success stories.

INSPIRING SUCCESS STORIES

Meet Gil Gilmer (page 28). To date, he's lost 208 pounds. According to Gil,

"My health is better than it has been my entire life...in short, I am a happier, healthier man because of the things Weight Watchers taught me about what to eat, how to eat, when to eat, and why to eat."

You'll find inspiration from Gil and eight other individuals as they share their weight-loss stories.

RECIPES FOR YOU AND YOUR FAMILY

As anyone who has lost weight on the Weight Watchers program will tell you, the key to getting and staying slim is learning how to make healthy choices. And with this book, that's easy to do! Flip

through, and you'll find a variety of mouthwatering recipes. Look closer, and you'll see that we've given you recipes to suit any lifestyle. If you're cooking for your family and need a dish that will please both adults and kids, try **Beef Fajita Pizza** (page 88) or **Cheese-Stuffed Italian Chicken** (page 106). You may be saving *POINTS* for a fancy dinner out and need a low-*POINT* lunch idea. Pack **Asian Chicken Salad** (page 125) and fresh orange sections for a quick 5-*POINT* brown-bag lunch. Or warm up to a bowl of **White Bean-Chicken Chili** (page 163) for only 4 *POINTS*.

TIMESAVING MENU PLANS

Take a minute to preview this year's plans on pages 164-181. You'll find nine weeks of 7-day menus planned around many of the delicious recipes that appear in this cookbook, recipes

that you as well as your family will enjoy. All you have to do is choose a recipe, and we show you what to eat for the rest of the day to stay within your *POINTS* range.

For example, look at the menu for Monday on page 164. The 24-*POINT* plan guides you to

- start the day with a 4-*POINT* **Very Berry Smoothie** (page 164) that can be made quickly in the blender;

- eat a fast-food lunch for 8 **POINTS** (a hamburger, a green salad, and an orange); then
- enjoy **Pork Tenderloin with Gingered Cranberries** (page 97). Serve it with couscous and sautéed spinach for only 8 **POINTS**.
- You'll still have 4 **POINTS** to bank or to use for snacks such as yogurt and graham crackers.
- Plus, each daily plan includes at least 2 milk servings, at least 5 servings of fruits and vegetables, and a **POINTS** total of 23–28.

It's simple to adjust each day's menu to accommodate your personal plan by adding or deleting items based on the total number of **POINTS** you have for each day. In addition, you'll

- be able to plan and cook one evening meal for you and your family;
- save time and money at the supermarket; and
- RELAX knowing that both you and your family are eating healthy meals!

Whether it's for the inspirational stories, tempting recipes, or timesaving menus, you'll definitely want to keep *Weight Watchers® Annual Recipes for Success 2003* within easy reach!

SHARE YOUR WEIGHT-LOSS SUCCESS STORY

If you have a Weight Watchers weight-loss success story, we'd love to hear from you. Send a brief account of your personal experience along with your name, address, daytime telephone number, E-mail address, and before and after snapshot to:

Weight Watchers® Annual Recipes for Success
2100 Lakeshore Drive
Birmingham, AL 35209

OUR FAVORITE RECIPES

We judge the merits of every recipe, and only the best make the cut. But a few have an indefinable quality that can only be described as the "yum factor." These recipes are so outstanding that they've become our personal favorites. We think thst they'll become yours and your family's as well.

- **Cinnamon-Raisin Sticky Buns (page 19).** Frozen roll dough, brown sugar, and butter come together in a gooey 3-*POINT* breakfast treat. Let the kids help—they're that easy to make!

- **Hot Spinach-Artichoke Dip (page 13).** We lightened this popular appetizer, and you'll love the results as much as we did. Serve it with slices of French bread or low-fat tortilla chips so your guests can scoop up every rich, cheesy bite.

- **Roasted Chicken and Corn Risotto (page 101).** The ultimate comfort food all in one dish—a creamy rice filled with flavorful roasted chicken and corn guaranteed to warm you up any night of the week.

- **Baked Shrimp in Lemony Garlic Sauce (page 66).** Your guests won't believe these buttery shrimp are light, and you won't believe how simple they are to prepare.

- **Mint-Chocolate Mousse Delight (page 37).** All your childhood favorites—Oreos, chocolate pudding, and Peppermint Patties—unite in this decadent dessert.

- **Grilled Pork Tenderloin with Black Bean Salad (page 98).** Experience South America at your dinner table. Hot, grilled pork medallions top a cool, salsa-like salad.

- **"Meaty" Meatless Double-Bean Chili (page 156).** This vegetarian recipe got our highest rating at the taste testing table. It proves that chili doesn't need meat to make it hearty and satisfying.

- **Lamb, Goat Cheese, and Roasted Pepper Calzones (page 94).** Encased in a tender, flaky crust, lamb and creamy goat cheese lend Greek flair to these traditionally Italian pockets.

About Our Recipes

Weight Watchers® Annual Recipes for Success 2003 gives you the nutrition facts you need. To make your life easier, we've provided the following useful information with every recipe:

• A number calculated through the **POINTS®** Food System, an integral part of the **Winning Points** weight-loss system from Weight Watchers International, Inc.
• Diabetic exchange values for those who use them as a guide for planning meals
• A complete nutrient analysis per serving

POINTS FOOD SYSTEM

Every recipe in the book includes a number assigned through **POINTS** value. This system uses a formula based on the calorie, fat, and fiber content of the food. Foods with more calories and fat (like a slice of pizza) receive high numbers, while fruits and vegetables receive low numbers. For more information about the **Winning Points** weight-loss system and the Weight Watchers meeting nearest you, call 1-800-651-6000 or go to *www.weightwatchers.com* on the internet.

DIABETIC EXCHANGES

Exchange values are provided for people who use them for calorie-controlled diets and for people with diabetes. All foods within a certain group contain approximately the same amount of nutrients and calories, so one serving of a food from a food group can be substituted or exchanged for one serving of any other item on the list. The food groups are starch, fruit, vegetable, milk, meat, and fat. The exchange values are based on the *Exchange Lists for Meal Planning* developed by the American Diabetes Association and The American Dietetic Association.

NUTRIENT ANALYSIS

Each recipe has a complete list of nutrients, including CAL (calories), PRO (protein), FAT (total fat), sat (saturated fat), CARB (carbohydrate), FIB (dietary fiber), CHOL (cholesterol), IRON, SOD (sodium), and CALC (calcium). Measurements are abbreviated g (grams) and mg (milligrams). Numbers are based on these assumptions:

• Unless otherwise indicated, meat, poultry, and fish refer to skinned, boned, and cooked servings.
• When we give a range for an ingredient (3 to 3½ cups flour, for instance), we calculate using the lesser amount.
• Some alcohol calories evaporate during heating; the analysis reflects that.
• Only the amount of marinade absorbed by the food is used in calculation.
• Garnishes and optional ingredients are not included in an analysis.

Nutritional values used in our calculations either come from The Food Processor, Version 7.5 (ESHA Research) or are provided by food manufacturers.

Appetizers &
Beverages

SPICY BAKED TORTILLA CHIPS

prep: 2 minutes • cook: 5 minutes

4 (8-inch) low-fat flour tortillas
Cooking spray
2 teaspoons salt-free Mexican
  seasoning
½ teaspoon garlic salt

1. Preheat oven to 400°.
2. Cut each tortilla into 8 wedges.
Arrange on a baking sheet coated
with cooking spray. Spray wedges with
cooking spray. Sprinkle with Mexican
seasoning and garlic salt.
3. Bake at 400° for 4 to 5 minutes or
until lightly browned. Remove from
pan immediately. Cool completely.
YIELD: 4 servings (serving size: 8 chips).

POINTS: 2; EXCHANGES: 1½ Starch;
PER SERVING: CAL 110 (12% from fat); PRO 3.0g;
FAT 1.5g (sat 0g); CARB 22.1g; FIB 1.0g;
CHOL 0mg; IRON 1.1mg; SOD 280mg;
CALC 60mg

QUICK PITA CHIPS

prep: 2 minutes • cook: 8 minutes

3 pita rounds, halved horizontally
Cooking spray

1. Preheat oven to 350°.
2. Cut each pita half into 8 wedges.
Spray wedges with cooking spray,
and place on an ungreased baking
sheet. Bake at 350° for 8 minutes or
until crisp. YIELD: 8 servings (serving
size: 6 chips).

POINTS: 1; EXCHANGE: 1 Starch; PER SERVING:
CAL 62 (4% from fat); PRO 2.1g; FAT 0.3g (sat 0.0g);
CARB 12.5g; FIB 0.5g; CHOL 0mg; IRON 0.6mg;
SOD 121mg; CALC 19mg

CANNELLINI BEAN SPREAD

prep: 7 minutes

*If you're a garlic lover, feel free
to add one or two extra cloves of
garlic to this creamy dip.*

1 (15.5-ounce) can cannellini
  beans, rinsed and drained
1 garlic clove
2 tablespoons minced red onion
1 tablespoon finely chopped fresh
  flat-leaf parsley
1 tablespoon extra-virgin olive oil
1 tablespoon water
2 teaspoons fresh lemon juice
¼ teaspoon salt
⅛ teaspoon pepper

1. Place all ingredients in a food
processor; process to a spreadable
consistency. Cover and chill until
ready to serve. YIELD: 10 servings
(serving size: 2 tablespoons).

POINTS: 1; EXCHANGE: ½ Starch; PER SERVING:
CAL 35 (39% from fat); PRO 1.1g; FAT 1.5g (sat 0.2g);
CARB 4.1g; FIB 1.1g; CHOL 0mg; IRON 0.4mg;
SOD 100mg; CALC 9mg

CREAMY LIME GUACAMOLE

prep: 5 minutes

1 ripe peeled avocado, seeded and
  coarsely mashed
¼ cup fat-free sour cream
2 tablespoons fresh lime juice
1 teaspoon Dijon mustard
½ teaspoon hot sauce
½ teaspoon salt
¼ teaspoon ground cumin
2 tablespoons chopped fresh
  cilantro

1. Combine all ingredients in a
medium bowl. Cover and chill until
ready to serve. YIELD: 8 servings (serving size: 2 tablespoons).

POINTS: 1; EXCHANGES: ½ Vegetable, ½ Fat;
PER SERVING: CAL 48 (69% from fat); PRO 0.8g;
FAT 3.7g (sat 0.6g); CARB 3.5g; FIB 1.2g; CHOL 1mg;
IRON 0.3mg; SOD 177mg; CALC 15mg

SPINACH-AVOCADO DIP

prep: 12 minutes

*Here's a way to speed up the ripening
process of avocados: Place avocados
in a paper bag, and set aside for 2 to
3 days at room temperature. Once
ripened, store avocados in the
refrigerator until ready to use.*

1 (10-ounce) package frozen
  chopped spinach, thawed,
  drained, and squeezed dry
1 cup diced ripe avocado (about
  1 large)
½ cup reduced-fat sour cream
¼ cup chopped red onion
1 tablespoon chopped seeded
  jalapeño pepper
1 large garlic clove
1 tablespoon fresh lime juice
½ teaspoon salt
⅛ teaspoon pepper
Dash of hot sauce

1. Place all ingredients in a food
processor; process until smooth,
scraping sides of bowl once, if neces-
sary. Cover and chill until ready to
serve. YIELD: 9 servings (serving size:
¼ cup).

POINTS: 1; EXCHANGES: 1 Vegetable, 1 Fat;
PER SERVING: CAL 58 (67% from fat); PRO 2.0g;
FAT 4.3g (sat 1.5g); CARB 4.1g; FIB 2.0g; CHOL 7mg;
IRON 0.9mg; SOD 165mg; CALC 61mg

HOT SPINACH-ARTICHOKE DIP

(pictured on page 23)
prep: 12 minutes • cook: 27 minutes

*Topped with gooey melted cheese,
this creamy appetizer will be a
hit at your next party.*

1 tablespoon light butter
1 cup finely chopped onion
2 garlic cloves, minced
1 (10-ounce) package frozen
  chopped spinach, thawed,
  drained, and squeezed dry
1 (8-ounce) can sliced water
  chestnuts, drained and coarsely
  chopped
1 (14-ounce) can quartered
  artichoke hearts, drained and
  coarsely chopped
1 (8-ounce) block ⅓-less-fat
  cream cheese, softened
1 (8-ounce) carton reduced-fat
  sour cream
1 cup (4 ounces) preshredded
  reduced-fat Cheddar cheese,
  divided
1 teaspoon hot sauce
½ teaspoon salt
¼ teaspoon pepper
Cooking spray

1. Preheat oven to 350°.
2. Melt butter in a large nonstick skillet over medium heat. Add onion and
garlic; sauté 5 minutes or until tender.
Add spinach, water chestnuts, and
artichokes; sauté 2 minutes. Add cream
cheese, sour cream, ½ cup Cheddar
cheese, and next 3 ingredients.
3. Spoon into an 11 x 7-inch baking
dish coated with cooking spray. Top
with remaining ½ cup Cheddar
cheese. Bake at 350° for 18 to 20
minutes or until thoroughly heated.
Serve with baked tortilla chips. YIELD:
18 servings (serving size: ¼ cup).

POINTS: 2; **EXCHANGES:** 1 Vegetable, 1 Fat;
PER SERVING: CAL 95 (63% from fat); PRO 4.4g;
FAT 6.6g (sat 4.1g); CARB 4.5g; FIB 1.1g; CHOL 22mg;
IRON 2.7mg; SOD 230mg; CALC 95mg

ROASTED RED PEPPER HUMMUS

prep: 8 minutes • chill: 2 hours

*This hummus is even tastier after
being refrigerated overnight.*

2 (15-ounce) cans chickpeas
  (garbanzo beans)
1 (7-ounce) bottle roasted red bell
  peppers, drained
3 garlic cloves
3 tablespoons tahini (sesame seed
  paste)
1 tablespoon olive oil
6 tablespoons fresh lemon juice
1 teaspoon curry powder
½ teaspoon ground cumin
½ teaspoon ground coriander
1¼ teaspoons salt
½ teaspoon freshly ground pepper

1. Drain chickpeas, reserving ¼ cup
liquid.
2. Place chickpeas, reserved liquid,
and remaining ingredients in a food
processor; process 2 minutes or until
very smooth. Cover and chill 2
hours. Serve with pita wedges or
baked tortilla chips. YIELD: 14 servings
(serving size: ¼ cup).

POINTS: 1; **EXCHANGES:** 1 Starch, ½ Fat;
PER SERVING: CAL 84 (35% from fat); PRO 2.9g;
FAT 3.3g (sat 0.5g); CARB 11.6g; FIB 2.3g;
CHOL 0mg; IRON 1.0mg; SOD 384mg; CALC 32mg

EAST INDIAN BEAN DIP

(pictured on page 27)
prep: 12 minutes • cook: 1 minute

*Don't skip heating the spices; the heat
brings out their pungent flavors.
Then the warm spice mix enlivens the
flavors in this chunky dip.*

1 teaspoon curry powder
¼ teaspoon ground ginger
¼ teaspoon ground cumin
¼ teaspoon ground allspice
1 (16-ounce) can navy beans,
  rinsed and drained
1 small zucchini, chopped
¾ cup chopped yellow bell pepper
  (about 1 small)
⅓ cup chopped red onion
1 large garlic clove, minced
½ teaspoon salt
¼ cup hot mango chutney
2 tablespoons chopped fresh mint
2 tablespoons plain fat-free yogurt

1. Cook first 4 ingredients in a small
skillet, stirring constantly, over low
heat 1 minute; remove from heat.
2. Combine beans and next 5 ingredients in a bowl; add spice mixture,
stirring well. Stir in chutney, mint,
and yogurt. Serve with Quick Pita
Chips (page 12) or commercial baked
pita chips. YIELD: 24 servings
(serving size: 2 tablespoons).

POINTS: 0; **EXCHANGE:** 1 Vegetable;
PER SERVING: CAL 25 (3% from fat); PRO 1.1g;
FAT 0.1g (sat 0.0g); CARB 5.1g; FIB 0.8g; CHOL 0mg;
IRON 0.3mg; SOD 142mg; CALC 10mg

SALMON PÂTÉ

prep: 6 minutes

2 (6-ounce) cans skinless, boneless
  pink salmon in water, drained
1 (8-ounce) block fat-free
  cream cheese
2 tablespoons minced red onion
2 teaspoons minced fresh dill
2 teaspoons fresh lemon juice
2 teaspoons prepared horseradish
⅛ teaspoon salt
¼ teaspoon freshly ground pepper

1. Combine all ingredients in a large
bowl; beat with a mixer until well
blended. Cover and chill until ready
to serve. YIELD: 16 servings (serving
size: 2 tablespoons).

POINTS: 1; EXCHANGE: ½ Very Lean Meat;
PER SERVING: CAL 44 (31% from fat); PRO 6.3g;
FAT 1.5g (sat 0.5g); CARB 1.1g; FIB 0.1g; CHOL 13mg;
IRON 0.2mg; SOD 114mg; CALC 72mg

TOMATO AND ARUGULA CROSTINI

(pictured on page 23)

prep: 12 minutes • stand: 20 minutes
cook: 2 to 3 minutes

1⅓ cups chopped seeded plum
  tomato (about 4 tomatoes)
2 cups chopped fresh arugula
½ cup (2 ounces) freshly grated
  Parmesan cheese
1 tablespoon extra-virgin olive oil
2 teaspoons white balsamic
  vinegar
¼ teaspoon kosher salt
¼ teaspoon freshly ground pepper
4 (1.25-ounce) slices Italian bread
  (about ¾ inch thick)
1 large garlic clove, halved

1. Combine first 7 ingredients. Let
stand 20 minutes.
2. Preheat broiler or prepare grill.
3. Rub bread with cut side of garlic
clove. Place bread slices on a baking
sheet or grill rack; cook 2 to 3 minutes on each side or until lightly
browned.
4. Top bread slices with tomato
mixture. Serve immediately. YIELD: 4
servings (serving size: 1 slice bread
and ½ cup tomato mixture).

POINTS: 4; EXCHANGES: 1 Starch, 1 Vegetable,
½ Medium-Fat Meat, 1 Fat; PER SERVING: CAL 188
(41% from fat); PRO 8.7g; FAT 8.6g (sat 3.2g);
CARB 19.4g; FIB 1.7g; CHOL 10mg; IRON 1.5mg;
SOD 535mg; CALC 217mg

BABY TWICE-BAKED POTATOES

prep: 14 minutes • cook: 10 minutes

These potatoes can be assembled
one day ahead, refrigerated,
and baked just before serving.

8 small red potatoes (about 1
  pound)
2 green onions, finely chopped
⅓ cup reduced-fat sour cream
⅓ cup fat-free milk
2 bacon slices, cooked and
  crumbled
½ cup (2 ounces) preshredded
  reduced-fat sharp Cheddar cheese
⅛ teaspoon garlic powder
½ teaspoon salt
⅛ teaspoon pepper

1. Preheat oven to 350°.
2. Pierce potatoes with a fork; arrange
on paper towels in microwave oven.
Microwave at HIGH 6 minutes or
until tender. Let stand 5 minutes. Cut
each potato in half; scoop out pulp,
reserving shells. Combine potato pulp,
onions, and remaining ingredients
with a mixer at medium speed.
3. Spoon potato mixture into shells.
Place on a baking sheet; bake at
350° for 10 minutes or until thoroughly heated. YIELD: 8 servings
(serving size: 1 potato).

POINTS: 2; EXCHANGES: 1 Starch, ½ Fat;
PER SERVING: CAL 87 (27% from fat); PRO 4.0g;
FAT 2.6g (sat 1.4g); CARB 12.0g; FIB 1.1g; CHOL 8mg;
IRON 0.6mg; SOD 230mg; CALC 63mg

ANTIPASTO TOSS

prep: 13 minutes • chill: 8 hours

This combine-and-chill dish can be
made ahead and pulled out of the
refrigerator just before serving.

12 green olives
1 (14.4-ounce) bottle hearts of
  palm, drained and sliced
1 (7-ounce) bottle roasted red bell
  peppers, drained and sliced
3 ounces part-skim mozzarella
  cheese, cubed
1 garlic clove, minced
¼ cup chopped fresh basil
1 tablespoon chopped fresh parsley
¼ teaspoon dried rosemary
1 tablespoon olive oil
1 tablespoon fresh lemon juice
¼ teaspoon freshly ground pepper

1. Combine all ingredients; toss to
coat. Cover and chill 8 hours. Serve
chilled or at room temperature. YIELD:
8 servings (serving size: ½ cup).

POINTS: 2; EXCHANGES: 1 Vegetable, 1 Fat;
PER SERVING: CAL 83 (67% from fat); PRO 3.5g;
FAT 6.2g (sat 2.2g); CARB 4.1g; FIB 1.0g; CHOL 8mg;
IRON 1.3mg; SOD 457mg; CALC 82mg

GREEK OYSTERS

(pictured on page 27)

prep: 30 minutes • **cook:** 8 minutes

Rock salt steadies the oyster shells and keeps them from tipping over as they bake.

2 dozen fresh oysters
Rock salt
1 teaspoon olive oil
¼ cup finely chopped onion
1 (6-ounce) jar marinated quartered artichoke hearts, drained and finely chopped
1 (10-ounce) package frozen chopped spinach, thawed, drained, and squeezed dry
1¼ teaspoons Greek seasoning
3 ounces ⅓-less-fat cream cheese, softened
¼ cup (1 ounce) freshly grated Parmesan cheese

1. Bring water to a boil in a saucepan. Loosen oysters from shells; add oysters to boiling water. Simmer 3 to 5 minutes or until oysters are plump and opaque; drain. Return oysters to shells. Discard top shells, keeping oysters in the deeper bottom shells.
2. Sprinkle a thin layer of rock salt in a jelly roll pan. Arrange oysters in shells over rock salt; set aside.
3. Preheat broiler.
4. Heat oil in a skillet over medium heat. Add onion; cook 2 minutes, stirring often, until onion is soft. Add artichoke hearts and spinach; sauté 2 minutes. Stir in Greek seasoning and cream cheese.
5. Top each oyster with 1 heaping tablespoon of spinach mixture; sprinkle oysters evenly with

Parmesan cheese. Broil oysters 4 minutes or until cheese melts. **YIELD:** 8 servings (serving size: 3 oysters).

POINTS: 2; **EXCHANGES:** 1 Vegetable, ½ Very Lean Meat, 1 Fat; **PER SERVING:** CAL 91 (56% from fat); PRO 5.5g; FAT 5.7g (sat 2.5g); CARB 6.0g; FIB 1.6g; CHOL 22mg; IRON 3.1mg; SOD 264mg; CALC 108mg

POT STICKERS

prep: 22 minutes • **cook:** 15 minutes

To save time, ask the butcher for ½ pound lean ground pork.

¼ cup plum sauce
2 tablespoons low-sodium soy sauce
3 green onions
1 tablespoon chopped peeled fresh ginger
2 garlic cloves
⅓ cup fresh cilantro leaves, loosely packed
2 (¾-inch-thick) center-cut boneless pork loin chops
1 large egg, separated
¼ teaspoon salt
¼ teaspoon crushed red pepper
24 won ton wrappers
2 teaspoons sesame oil, divided
1 (14-ounce) can fat-free, less-sodium chicken broth

1. Combine plum sauce and soy sauce in a small bowl; stir well. Cover and chill.
2. Place green onions and next 3 ingredients in a food processor; pulse 10 times or until mixture is finely chopped. Remove from food processor, and place in a large bowl.

3. Trim fat from pork; slice pork into thin slices. Place pork in food processor; pulse until pork is finely ground. Add pork to green onion mixture. Stir in egg yolk, salt, and pepper until thoroughly combined.
4. Working with 1 won ton wrapper at a time (cover remaining wrappers with a damp towel to keep from drying), spoon 1 rounded teaspoon pork mixture onto center of each wrapper. Moisten edges of dough with beaten egg white, and bring 2 opposite corners together. Pinch edges together to seal, forming a triangle. Place pot sticker on a platter; cover loosely with a towel to keep from drying. Repeat procedure with remaining pork mixture and won ton wrappers.
5. Heat 1 teaspoon sesame oil in a large nonstick skillet over medium-low heat. Arrange half of pot stickers in pan. Cook 3 minutes on each side or until lightly browned. Remove from pan; set aside. Repeat procedure with remaining sesame oil and pot stickers.
6. Return pot stickers to pan; add broth. Bring to a boil. Cover, reduce heat, and simmer 3 minutes. Remove pot stickers from pan using a slotted spoon; serve with plum sauce mixture. **YIELD:** 6 servings (serving size: 4 pot stickers and 1 tablespoon plum sauce mixture).

POINTS: 4; **EXCHANGES:** 1½ Starch, 1 Medium-Fat Meat; **PER SERVING:** CAL 206 (25% from fat); PRO 13.6g; FAT 5.7g (sat 1.6g); CARB 23.7g; FIB 0.9g; CHOL 61mg; IRON 1.8mg; SOD 657mg; CALC 29mg

SKEWERED CHICKEN WITH SPICY PEANUT DIP

(pictured on page 22)
prep: 14 minutes
chill/marinate: 2 hours • **cook:** 13 minutes

Leftover peanut dip is tasty on fresh celery and carrot sticks for a quick snack. It can be stored in an airtight container and refrigerated for up to a week.

Cooking spray
1 shallot, minced (about 1 tablespoon)
1½ tablespoons minced peeled fresh ginger, divided
2 teaspoons minced garlic, divided
½ teaspoon curry powder
½ teaspoon crushed red pepper, divided
¾ cup fat-free, less-sodium chicken broth
⅓ cup reduced-fat creamy peanut butter
¼ cup fresh lime juice, divided
3 tablespoons low-sodium soy sauce, divided
1 teaspoon light brown sugar
½ teaspoon salt, divided
3 (4-ounce) skinless, boneless chicken breast halves
¼ teaspoon sesame oil
12 (8-inch) wooden skewers

1. Coat a large nonstick skillet with cooking spray. Add shallot, 1 tablespoon ginger, and 1 teaspoon garlic; sauté 3 minutes or until shallot is tender. Add curry powder and ¼ teaspoon crushed red pepper; sauté 1 minute. Stir in broth, peanut butter, 2 tablespoons lime juice, 1 tablespoon soy sauce, brown sugar, and ¼ teaspoon salt. Simmer 3 to 5 minutes, or until mixture thickens, stirring constantly. Transfer mixture to a bowl; cover and chill at least 2 hours.
2. Cut each chicken breast half lengthwise into 4 strips. Place strips between 2 pieces of heavy-duty plastic wrap, and flatten to ¼-inch thickness, using a meat mallet or rolling pin. Combine remaining ginger, garlic, crushed red pepper, lime juice, soy sauce, salt, and sesame oil in a heavy-duty zip-top plastic bag. Add chicken, and seal bag securely. Marinate in refrigerator 1½ hours, turning once.
3. Soak wooden skewers in water 30 minutes; drain.
4. Preheat broiler.
5. Remove chicken from marinade, discarding marinade. Thread chicken onto wooden skewers. Place skewers on a baking sheet coated with cooking spray. Broil 2 to 3 minutes on each side or until done. Serve with peanut dip. YIELD: 6 servings (serving size: 2 skewers and 2½ tablespoons sauce).

POINTS: 3; **EXCHANGES:** ½ Starch, 2 Lean Meat; **PER SERVING:** CAL 152 (34% from fat); PRO 18.0g; FAT 5.7g (sat 1.1g); CARB 8.0g; FIB 1.1g; CHOL 33mg; IRON 1.0mg; SOD 655mg; CALC 18mg

SWEET CRANBERRY ICED TEA

prep: 2 minutes • **steep:** 3 minutes

Chill out on a hot summer day with this refreshing fruit tea.

2 cups water
2 regular-sized tea bags
2 cups cranberry-apple juice drink
2 packets sugar substitute with aspartame
4 cups ice cubes
Mint sprigs (optional)

1. Bring water to a boil in a small saucepan; remove from heat. Add tea bags; cover and let steep 3 minutes. Discard tea bags.
2. Combine tea, cranberry-apple juice drink, and sugar substitute in a pitcher; stir well.
3. Place 1 cup ice in each of 4 glasses; add 1 cup tea mixture. Garnish drinks with mint sprigs, if desired. Serve immediately. YIELD: 4 servings (serving size: 1 cup).

POINTS: 2; **EXCHANGES:** 1½ Fruit; **PER SERVING:** CAL 85 (0% from fat); PRO 0.1g; FAT 0.0g (sat 0.0g); CARB 21.7g; FIB 0.1g; CHOL 0mg; IRON 0.1mg; SOD 6mg; CALC 9mg

STRAWBERRY-PEACH SMOOTHIE

(pictured on page 25)
prep: 5 minutes

You can enjoy this fruit-filled smoothie year-round. Use fresh or frozen unsweetened strawberries and peaches. For a thicker smoothie, let the frozen fruit stay a little icy.

⅔ cup strawberry fat-free frozen yogurt or ice cream
½ cup peach nectar, chilled
1 cup quartered strawberries
½ cup sliced peeled peaches

1. Combine all ingredients in a blender; process until smooth. Serve immediately. YIELD: 2 servings (serving size: 1 cup).

POINTS: 3; **EXCHANGES:** 1½ Starch, 1 Fruit; **PER SERVING:** CAL 155 (2% from fat); PRO 3.6g; FAT 0.3g (sat 0.0g); CARB 35.4g; FIB 3.0g; CHOL 0mg; IRON 0.5mg; SOD 58mg; CALC 116mg

PEANUT BUTTER-BANANA HEALTH SHAKE

prep: 4 minutes

This yummy shake features soy milk, an excellent source of disease-preventing isoflavones. It can also be made with fat-free milk.

2 cups refrigerated vanilla fat-free soy milk (such as Silk)
1 cup vanilla fat-free frozen yogurt or ice cream
3 small ripe bananas, sliced and frozen
3 tablespoons creamy peanut butter
2 tablespoons wheat germ
1 tablespoon honey
Crushed ice

1. Combine first 6 ingredients in a blender; process until smooth. Add ice to blender to raise level to 5 cups; process until smooth. Serve immediately. YIELD: 4 servings (serving size: 1 cup).

POINTS: 5; EXCHANGES: 2 Starch, 1 Fruit, 1 High-Fat Meat; PER SERVING: CAL 275 (23% from fat); PRO 9.4g; FAT 6.9g (sat 1.5g); CARB 48.2g; FIB 3.5g; CHOL 2mg; IRON 1.5mg; SOD 112mg; CALC 261mg

BANANA-CARAMEL MILKSHAKE

prep: 5 minutes

Almost too thick to sip with a straw—you'll need a spoon to get every bite.

½ cup 1% low-fat milk
2 teaspoons fat-free caramel sundae syrup
1 large banana, sliced and frozen
¼ cup vanilla low-fat ice cream

1. Combine all ingredients in a blender; process until smooth. Serve immediately. YIELD: 2 servings (serving size: ¾ cup).

POINTS: 2; EXCHANGES: 1 Starch, 1 Fruit; PER SERVING: CAL 131 (10% from fat); PRO 3.6g; FAT 1.5g (sat 0.8g); CARB 27.5g; FIB 1.9g; CHOL 4mg; IRON 0.2mg; SOD 62mg; CALC 107mg

CINNAMON-CRANBERRY STEAMER

prep: 2 minutes • cook: 8 minutes

2 cups cranberry-apple juice drink
1 cup water
3 tablespoons cinnamon decorator candies (such as Red Hots)
1 tablespoon lemon juice

1. Combine cranberry-apple juice drink, water, and candies in a small saucepan. Bring to a boil, stirring until candies dissolve. Remove from heat; stir in lemon juice. YIELD: 3 cups (serving size: 1 cup).

POINTS: 3; EXCHANGES: 1 Starch, 2 Fruit; PER SERVING: CAL 172 (0% from fat); PRO 0.2g; FAT 0.0g (sat 0.0g); CARB 43.1g; FIB 0.2g; CHOL 0mg; IRON 0.1mg; SOD 9mg; CALC 14mg

---

KEEP ON SNACKIN'

Think snacks are the first thing that have to go when you're trying to lose weight? Well, before you clean out the pantry, read on!

Research has shown over the past years that snacking actually helps you succeed in weight loss. It may seem contradictory to consume extra calories between meals to lose weight, but there's a good reason why: snacking helps keep your blood sugar stable between mealtimes.

Several hours after a meal, blood sugar has a tendency to dip. This dip can make you feel sluggish and give you the urge to binge on any food in sight. When frequent healthy snacks are built into your diet, your blood glucose stays much more stable and prevents you from going on an eating binge or overeating at meals. By snacking, you feel satisfied, and you consume fewer *POINTS* and calories over the total day.

Below are some quick, on-the-go snacks that are both low in *POINTS* and good for you.   *POINTS*
- 1 (8-ounce) carton fat-free yogurt with ½ cup high-fiber cereal 3
- 1 sheet reduced-fat graham crackers with 1 tablespoon peanut butter 3
- 1 (1-ounce) mozzarella cheese stick 2
- 1 small apple with 1 tablespoon peanut butter 3
- 4 cups 97%-fat-free popcorn with 1 tablespoon Parmesan cheese 2

Breads

CINNAMON-RAISIN STICKY BUNS

(pictured on page 24)
prep: 8 minutes • **rise:** 45 minutes
cook: 20 minutes

These yummy sticky buns can easily be prepared the night before. To make them ahead, let the buns rise as directed in step 2, refrigerate, and bake as directed the next morning.

Cooking spray
⅓ cup raisins
9 (1-ounce) frozen bread dough rolls, thawed (such as Rich's)
¼ cup fat-free evaporated milk
½ cup packed light brown sugar
2 tablespoons dark corn syrup
2 tablespoons light butter
½ teaspoon ground cinnamon

1. Coat a Bundt pan or an 8-inch square baking pan with cooking spray. Sprinkle raisins in bottom of pan. Arrange rolls over raisins.
2. Combine milk and remaining 4 ingredients in a 2-cup glass measure. Microwave at HIGH 2 minutes, stirring every 30 seconds until sugar dissolves. Pour over rolls. Cover with plastic wrap; let rise in a warm place (85°), free from drafts, 45 minutes or until doubled in size.
3. Preheat oven to 375°.
4. Bake at 375° for 18 to 20 minutes or until golden. Run a knife around outside edges of pan. Place a plate upside down on top of pan; invert onto plate. YIELD: 9 servings (serving size: 1 bun).

POINTS: 3; **EXCHANGES:** 2 Starch, ½ Fat;
PER SERVING: CAL 171 (13% from fat); PRO 3.9g;
FAT 2.7g (sat 0.9g); CARB 35.2g; FIB 1.2g;
CHOL 5mg; IRON 1.4mg; SOD 194mg; CALC 43mg

CINNAMON BREADSTICKS

prep: 10 minutes • **cook:** 12 minutes

Nothing smells better than warm cinnamon rolls. Here's a quick, low-fat, hand-held version for mornings on the go.

3 tablespoons sugar
1½ teaspoons ground cinnamon
1 (11-ounce) can refrigerated soft breadstick dough
2 tablespoons light butter, melted
Cooking spray

1. Preheat oven to 375°.
2. Combine sugar and cinnamon in a small bowl; set aside.
3. Unroll dough, separating along perforations into 12 breadsticks. Brush both sides of breadsticks with melted butter. Sprinkle evenly with sugar mixture. Twist each breadstick about 3 times, and place on a large baking sheet coated with cooking spray.
4. Bake at 375° for 12 minutes or until golden. Serve warm. YIELD: 12 servings (serving size: 1 breadstick).

POINTS: 2; **EXCHANGES:** 1 Starch, ½ Fat;
PER SERVING: CAL 95 (22% from fat); PRO 2.2g;
FAT 2.3g (sat 0.7g); CARB 16.0g; FIB 0.5g;
CHOL 3mg; IRON 0.7mg; SOD 205mg; CALC 3mg

CINNAMON SAVES CALORIES

You'll notice that cinnamon is used in all three recipes on this page and throughout the book. The sweet and spicy flavor of this popular spice enhances the sweetness in foods so that you can use less sugar. Less sugar means fewer calories, and that's one thing that helps keep *POINTS* low.

CHUNKY APPLE PANCAKES

prep: 5 minutes • **cook:** 10 minutes

For an even heftier cinnamon punch, substitute cinnamon-flavored chunky applesauce.

1 cup all-purpose flour
1 tablespoon light brown sugar
2 teaspoons baking powder
¼ teaspoon ground cinnamon
⅛ teaspoon salt
1 large egg, lightly beaten
2 teaspoons vegetable oil
⅔ cup 1% low-fat milk
½ cup chunky applesauce
Cooking spray

1. Lightly spoon flour into a dry measuring cup; level with a knife. Combine flour, sugar, and next 3 ingredients in a large bowl; stir with a whisk. Combine egg, oil, milk, and applesauce; stir with a whisk until blended. Add to flour mixture, and stir until dry ingredients are moistened.
2. Spoon about ¼ cup batter onto a hot nonstick griddle or nonstick skillet coated with cooking spray. Turn pancakes when tops are covered with bubbles and edges look cooked. YIELD: 4 servings (serving size: 2 pancakes).

POINTS: 4; **EXCHANGES:** 2 Starch, 1 Fat;
PER SERVING: CAL 193 (20% from fat); PRO 6.2g;
FAT 4.3g (sat 1.0g); CARB 32.3g; FIB 1.3g;
CHOL 55mg; IRON 2.0mg; SOD 356mg;
CALC 200mg

BLUEBERRY-CORNMEAL PANCAKES

prep: 8 minutes • cook: 10 minutes

Frozen berries can be substituted in this recipe. Just be sure to defrost them first and drain well before adding them to the batter.

½ cup all-purpose flour
½ cup yellow cornmeal
2 tablespoons sugar
1 teaspoon baking powder
½ teaspoon baking soda
⅛ teaspoon salt
1 cup low-fat buttermilk (1%)
1 large egg, lightly beaten
1 tablespoon vegetable oil
1 cup blueberries
Cooking spray

1. Lightly spoon flour into a dry measuring cup; level with a knife. Combine flour, cornmeal, and next 4 ingredients in a large bowl. Combine buttermilk, egg, and oil; add to flour mixture, stirring until smooth. Gently stir in blueberries.
2. Spoon about ¼ cup batter onto a hot nonstick griddle or nonstick skillet coated with cooking spray. Turn pancakes when tops are covered with bubbles and edges look cooked. YIELD: 5 servings (serving size: 2 pancakes).

POINTS: 4; **EXCHANGES:** 2 Starch, 1 Fat; **PER SERVING:** CAL 193 (22% from fat); PRO 5.7g; FAT 4.7g (sat 1.1g); CARB 32.3g; FIB 2.1g; CHOL 46mg; IRON 1.5mg; SOD 349mg; CALC 117mg

HEARTY WHEAT AND OAT PANCAKES

prep: 12 minutes • cook: 10 minutes
stand: 10 minutes

This wholesome breakfast provides a double dose of whole grains and heart-healthy fiber.

1¼ cups 1% low-fat milk
½ cup quick-cooking oats
2 tablespoons dark brown sugar
1 tablespoon vegetable oil
1 large egg
¾ cup all-purpose flour
¼ cup whole wheat flour
1½ teaspoons baking powder
¼ teaspoon salt
Cooking spray

1. Combine first 4 ingredients in a bowl; let stand 10 minutes. Add egg, and beat well.
2. Lightly spoon flours into dry measuring cups; level with a knife. Combine flours, baking powder, and salt; stir with a whisk. Add oat mixture to flour mixture; stir until blended.
3. Spoon about ¼ cup batter onto a hot nonstick griddle or nonstick skillet coated with cooking spray. Turn pancakes when tops are covered with bubbles and edges look cooked. YIELD: 5 servings (serving size: 2 pancakes).

POINTS: 4; **EXCHANGES:** 2 Starch, 1 Fat; **PER SERVING:** CAL 206 (23% from fat); PRO 7.3g; FAT 5.2g (sat 1.2g); CARB 32.9g; FIB 2.1g; CHOL 45mg; IRON 1.9mg; SOD 310mg; CALC 175mg

GINGERBREAD PANCAKES

prep: 9 minutes • cook: 8 minutes

Take a break from syrup—try these hotcakes with applesauce or lemon curd.

1 cup all-purpose flour
1 teaspoon baking powder
¼ teaspoon baking soda
⅛ teaspoon salt
2 tablespoons sugar
1 teaspoon ground ginger
½ teaspoon ground cinnamon
⅛ teaspoon ground cloves
⅛ teaspoon ground nutmeg
1 large egg, lightly beaten
1 cup low-fat buttermilk (1%)
¼ cup molasses
1 tablespoon vegetable oil
Cooking spray

1. Lightly spoon flour into a dry measuring cup; level with a knife. Combine flour, baking powder, and next 7 ingredients in a large bowl; stir with a whisk.
2. Combine egg and next 3 ingredients in a small bowl; stir well. Add to flour mixture, stirring until smooth.
3. Spoon about ¼ cup batter onto a hot nonstick griddle or nonstick skillet coated with cooking spray. Turn pancakes when tops are covered with bubbles and edges look cooked. YIELD: 6 servings (serving size: 2 pancakes).

POINTS: 4; **EXCHANGES:** 2 Starch, ½ Fat; **PER SERVING:** CAL 182 (18% from fat); PRO 4.7g; FAT 3.8g (sat 0.9g); CARB 32.5g; FIB 0.7g; CHOL 38mg; IRON 1.8mg; SOD 239mg; CALC 133mg

Crazy for Cookbooks

DODIE BURKETT • **HEIGHT** 5'5" • **BEFORE** 224 LBS. • **AFTER** 149 LBS.

Motto: Does this food taste as good as thin will feel?

While visiting her brother in California in October 2001—and with a little bit of prodding on his part—Dodie Burkett, a retired food services worker, and her sister-in-law bit the bullet and joined Weight Watchers. For someone who considered herself chubby most of her life, Dodie says it was a positive step in the right direction.

Both Dodie and her sister-in-law each immediately purchased a Weight Watchers cookbook and vowed to cook nothing but those recipes for the next two weeks.

"On my first week of weigh-in I was really nervous," Dodie recalls. "We ate delicious meals every day and stayed within our *POINTS*, but I just couldn't believe that we would lose any weight because of how well we were eating."

But sure enough, they did lose. And it was at that moment that Dodie was convinced she could go all the way to her goal of losing 75 pounds. "It was just so wonderful," Dodie says. "I really didn't miss all that other food once I got in the groove of cooking strictly from the cookbooks and realized that this wasn't a diet but a true lifestyle change."

Dodie especially likes to brag about her husband, Mike, to whom she has been married 40 years. "He's just extremely wonderful," she says with deep pride. "He's always looking for ways to make our meals lighter, and he would never put an ounce more of butter or anything else in our food than the books call for. He never complained when I weighed 224 pounds, but now I think he really enjoys the new me—he can't seem to stop taking my picture!"

Fifteen months later Dodie triumphantly reached her goal of losing 75 pounds. "Reaching my goal was my happiest moment," Dodie says. "I know it's probably trivial to a lot of people, but it sure meant a lot to me. My life has come full circle. I have more energy, more self-esteem, and more confidence in myself than I ever had before. And most importantly, I just really like who I am!"

"If I can do it, anybody can do it!"

There's one thing that people who spend time with Dodie realize: She tells it like it is. "If I can do it, anybody can do it," she says. And she's not kidding around. "Sometimes I feel like people get sick of hearing my story. But I'm a real person who has met the weight-loss challenge, and I hope that it inspires people."

21

Skewered Chicken
with Spicy Peanut
Dip, page 16

Hot Spinach-
Artichoke Dip,
page 13

Tomato and
Arugula Crostini,
page 14

Cornmeal Scones with Sage
and Cheddar, page 30

Cinnamon-Raisin
Sticky Buns, page 19

Strawberry-Peach
Smoothie, page 16

Swedish Rye Bread,
page 34

26

East Indian Bean Dip,
page 13

Greek Oysters,
page 15

Finding His Motivation

GIL GILMER • HEIGHT 6'1" **• BEFORE** 391 LBS. **• AFTER** 183 LBS.

Tip: Losing weight is more of a mind thing than just eating the right stuff. Find your motivation. Luckily mine was something—or someone—I could see every day.

Until he was 13 years old Gil Gilmer was always a really skinny kid. But with the onset of puberty, the pounds came creeping. "From then on I was always overweight," he says. And by the time Gil reached college, his weight had really become a problem.

Over the years Gil would try different diets and would sometimes even starve himself to lose weight. But he just couldn't seem to find the motivation to stick with it. Then one day in November 1999, Gil finally found the answer. If ever there was something that would keep Gil Gilmer motivated to lose weight, it was the birth of his son Landon.

"The day my son was born was the day I realized I needed to change my life," Gil says. "I wanted to do everything in my control to be around as long as possible for my wife and child."

With a determination to succeed, Gil went to his first Weight Watchers meeting in February 2000, weighing in at 391 pounds. "There was no turning back after that day," he says. "I consistently lost weight for the next year and a half until I had lost a total of 208 pounds. I actually lost more weight than I now weigh."

Gil glories in the fact that he's never hungry. "Weight

Watchers taught me how to eat, the portions to eat, and when to eat," he says. "The **POINTS** have definitely made the difference. It's so easy because you can eat anything in the world you want as long as you stay within your **POINTS**."

As for exercise, Gil works out Monday through Friday by alternating cardiovascular work and weight training. His favorite heart-healthy workout is the elliptical trainer, which he has found is a great alternative to the treadmill.

Most importantly, Gil is now the healthiest he's ever been and has the energy to keep up with Landon—now an active two-year-old. Gil's best advice to those considering weight loss is to find some motivation.

"The day my son was born was the day I realized I needed to change my life."

"Losing weight is more of a mind game than it is just eating the right stuff," he says. "You need some kind of motivation. For me this was really easy to do. Luckily my motivation was something—or someone—I could see every day."

PUMPKIN WAFFLES

prep: 12 minutes • cook: 20 minutes

These thin, crispy waffles have a wonderful pumpkin-spice flavor!

1 cup all-purpose flour
2 teaspoons baking powder
½ teaspoon baking soda
⅛ teaspoon salt
¾ teaspoon ground cinnamon
¼ teaspoon ground nutmeg
1 large egg, lightly beaten
¼ cup packed dark brown sugar
1 tablespoon vegetable oil
½ cup canned pumpkin
1¼ cups low-fat buttermilk (1%)
Cooking spray

1. Lightly spoon flour into a dry measuring cup; level with a knife. Combine flour, baking powder, and next 4 ingredients in a large bowl; stir well with a whisk.
2. Combine egg, brown sugar, oil, pumpkin, and buttermilk in a bowl; stir with a whisk until blended. Add pumpkin mixture to flour mixture, and stir until well combined.
3. Coat a waffle iron with cooking spray; preheat. Spoon about ¼ cup of batter per waffle onto hot waffle iron, spreading batter to edges. Cook 5 to 7 minutes or until steaming stops; repeat with remaining batter. YIELD: 5 servings (serving size: 2 waffles).

POINTS: 4; EXCHANGES: 2½ Starch, 1 Fat; **PER SERVING:** CAL 210 (20% from fat); PRO 6.4g; FAT 4.7g (sat 1.2g); CARB 35.9g; FIB 1.6g; CHOL 46mg; IRON 2.1mg; SOD 463mg; CALC 203mg

MARMALADE SWIRL BISCUITS

prep: 12 minutes • cook: 22 minutes

To keep dough from flattening while cutting, place a long piece of dental floss or string under dough roll. Cross ends of floss over top of roll; slowly pull ends to neatly cut through dough.

1¾ cups all-purpose flour
2 tablespoons granulated sugar
2 teaspoons baking powder
¼ teaspoon salt
3 tablespoons chilled butter, cut into small pieces
⅔ cup 1% low-fat milk
¼ cup orange marmalade
Cooking spray
⅔ cup sifted powdered sugar
2 teaspoons 1% low-fat milk

1. Preheat oven to 425°.
2. Lightly spoon flour into dry measuring cups; level with a knife. Combine flour, granulated sugar, baking powder, and salt in a bowl; cut in butter with a pastry blender or 2 knives until mixture resembles coarse meal. Add ⅔ cup milk; stir just until moist.
3. Turn dough out onto a heavily floured surface; knead lightly 5 times. Roll dough into a 10 x 7-inch rectangle on a lightly floured surface. Spread marmalade to within ½ inch of edges.
4. Beginning at long side, roll up dough tightly, jelly roll fashion; pinch seam to seal. (Do not seal ends of roll.) Cut roll into 9 slices. Place slices, cut sides up, in an 8-inch square baking pan coated with cooking spray.
5. Bake at 425° for 22 minutes or until golden. Remove biscuits from pan, and place on a wire rack.
6. Combine powdered sugar and 2 teaspoons milk in a small bowl; stir until smooth. Drizzle over warm biscuits. Serve immediately. YIELD: 9 servings (serving size: 1 biscuit).

POINTS: 4; EXCHANGES: 2½ Starch, 1 Fat; **PER SERVING:** CAL 192 (20% from fat); PRO 3.2g; FAT 4.3g (sat 2.6g); CARB 35.8g; FIB 0.7g; CHOL 11mg; IRON 1.3mg; SOD 228mg; CALC 92mg

HOW TO CUT DOUGH ROLLS

1. With dental floss under dough, cross ends of floss over top of dough.

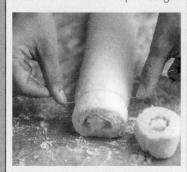

2. Gently pull ends downward until dough is completely cut through.

BANANA-OATMEAL MUFFINS

prep: 8 minutes • cook: 18 minutes

*These easy-to-pack 2-**POINT** muffins make a great on-the-run breakfast or afternoon snack.*

1 cup all-purpose flour
1 cup quick-cooking oats
1 tablespoon baking powder
½ teaspoon baking soda
¼ teaspoon salt
1 teaspoon ground cinnamon
1 large egg
1 cup low-fat buttermilk (1%)
1 cup chopped ripe banana
⅓ cup packed light brown sugar
2 teaspoons vegetable oil
1 teaspoon vanilla extract
Cooking spray
1½ teaspoons bottled cinnamon-sugar

1. Preheat oven to 425°.
2. Lightly spoon flour into a dry measuring cup; level with a knife. Combine flour, oats, and next 4 ingredients in a bowl; stir well.
3. Combine egg and next 5 ingredients; stir well with a whisk. Add to flour mixture, stirring just until moist.
4. Spoon batter into 12 muffin cups coated with cooking spray. Sprinkle batter evenly with cinnamon-sugar.
5. Bake at 425° for 18 minutes or until muffins spring back when touched lightly in center.
6. Remove muffins from pan immediately; place on a wire rack. YIELD: 12 servings (serving size: 1 muffin).

POINTS: 2; EXCHANGES: 1½ Starch;
PER SERVING: CAL 130 (14% from fat); PRO 3.6g;
FAT 2.0g (sat 0.5g); CARB 24.9g; FIB 1.6g;
CHOL 19mg; IRON 1.2mg; SOD 253mg;
CALC 106mg

CORNMEAL SCONES WITH SAGE AND CHEDDAR

(pictured on page 24)
prep: 15 minutes • cook: 17 minutes

1⅔ cups all-purpose flour
⅓ cup yellow cornmeal
2½ teaspoons baking powder
½ teaspoon salt
1 teaspoon dried rubbed sage
⅛ teaspoon ground red pepper
3½ tablespoons chilled butter, cut into small pieces
½ cup (2 ounces) preshredded reduced-fat Cheddar cheese
½ cup 1% low-fat milk
1 large egg, lightly beaten
Cooking spray

1. Preheat oven to 400°.
2. Lightly spoon flour into dry measuring cups; level with a knife. Combine flour, cornmeal, and next 4 ingredients in a large bowl. Cut in butter with a pastry blender or 2 knives until mixture resembles coarse meal. Stir in cheese. Add milk and egg, stirring just until moist.
3. Turn dough out onto a lightly floured surface, and knead 3 or 4 times. Transfer dough to a baking sheet coated with cooking spray; pat into a 7-inch circle. Cut into 10 wedges, cutting to, but not through, bottom of dough. (Do not separate wedges.)
4. Bake at 400° for 17 minutes or until golden. Transfer scones to a wire rack. Serve warm. YIELD: 10 servings (serving size: 1 scone).

POINTS: 3; EXCHANGES: 1½ Starch, 1 Fat;
PER SERVING: CAL 152 (31% from fat); PRO 5.1g;
FAT 5.3g (sat 3.0g); CARB 20.7g; FIB 0.9g;
CHOL 34mg; IRON 1.3mg; SOD 327mg; CALC 113mg

LEMON-POPPY SEED SCONES

prep: 17 minutes • cook: 21 minutes

2 cups all-purpose flour
2½ teaspoons baking powder
¼ teaspoon baking soda
¼ teaspoon salt
⅓ cup granulated sugar
3½ tablespoons chilled butter or stick margarine, cut into small pieces
1½ tablespoons poppy seeds
1½ tablespoons grated lemon rind
1 large egg, lightly beaten
½ cup low-fat buttermilk (1%)
Cooking spray
1 teaspoon powdered sugar

1. Preheat oven to 375°.
2. Lightly spoon flour into dry measuring cups; level with a knife. Combine flour, baking powder, and next 3 ingredients in a large bowl; stir well with a whisk. Cut in butter with a pastry blender or 2 knives until mixture resembles fine crumbs. Add poppy seeds, lemon rind, egg, and buttermilk; stir with a fork until dry ingredients are moistened. Transfer to a lightly floured surface; pat into a 7-inch circle.
3. Transfer dough to a baking sheet coated with cooking spray; cut into 8 wedges, cutting to, but not through, bottom of dough. (Do not separate wedges.) Bake at 375° for 21 to 23 minutes or until golden brown. Transfer to a wire rack; sift powdered sugar over top. YIELD: 8 servings (serving size: 1 scone).

POINTS: 5; EXCHANGES: 2½ Starch, 1 Fat;
PER SERVING: CAL 218 (28% from fat); PRO 4.9g;
FAT 6.9g (sat 3.6g); CARB 34.3g; FIB 1.1g;
CHOL 41mg; IRON 1.9mg; SOD 342mg;
CALC 136mg

ALMOND-APRICOT LOAF

prep: 20 minutes • cook: 45 minutes

1⅓ cups all-purpose flour
⅔ cup whole wheat flour
1½ teaspoons baking powder
½ teaspoon baking soda
¼ teaspoon salt
1 cup sugar
¼ cup vegetable oil
1 large egg
2 teaspoons grated orange rind
⅔ cup apple cider
⅓ cup chopped dried apricots
Cooking spray
2 teaspoons sugar
1 tablespoon sliced almonds

1. Preheat oven to 350°.
2. Lightly spoon flours into dry measuring cups; level with a knife. Combine flours, baking powder, baking soda, and salt in a bowl; stir with a whisk.
3. Combine 1 cup sugar, oil, egg, and orange rind in a bowl; stir well. Gradually add cider to sugar mixture, stirring well. Add flour mixture, stirring just until moist. Stir in apricots. Pour into a 9 x 5-inch loaf pan coated with cooking spray; sprinkle top with 2 teaspoons sugar and almonds.
4. Bake at 350° for 45 minutes or until a wooden pick inserted in center comes out clean. Cool in pan on a wire rack 10 minutes. Remove loaf from pan, and let cool completely on wire rack. YIELD: 14 servings (serving size: 1 slice).

POINTS: 4; EXCHANGES: 2 Starch, 1 Fat;
PER SERVING: CAL 179 (24% from fat); PRO 2.7g;
FAT 4.7g (sat 0.7g); CARB 32.5g; FIB 1.4g;
CHOL 15mg; IRON 1.1mg; SOD 145mg; CALC 38mg

LEMON-GLAZED GINGER LOAF

prep: 14 minutes • cook: 57 minutes

5 tablespoons butter
1 cup granulated sugar
2 large eggs
1 tablespoon grated peeled fresh ginger
1 teaspoon vanilla extract
1⅓ cups all-purpose flour
⅓ cup whole wheat flour
1 teaspoon baking powder
¼ teaspoon baking soda
⅛ teaspoon salt
¾ cup plain fat-free yogurt
Cooking spray
½ cup sifted powdered sugar
1 tablespoon fresh lemon juice

1. Preheat oven to 350°.
2. Beat butter and granulated sugar in a large bowl with a mixer at medium speed until well blended. Add eggs, ginger, and vanilla; beat well.
3. Lightly spoon flours into dry measuring cups; level with a knife. Combine flours, baking powder, baking soda, and salt. Add flour mixture and yogurt alternately to sugar mixture, ending with flour mixture.
4. Pour batter into an 8 x 4-inch loaf pan coated with cooking spray. Bake at 350° for 57 minutes or until a wooden pick inserted in center comes out clean.
5. Combine powdered sugar and lemon juice in a small bowl; stir until smooth. Spread over top of loaf, and cool in pan on a wire rack. YIELD: 12 servings (serving size: 1 slice).

POINTS: 4; EXCHANGES: 2½ Starch, 1 Fat;
PER SERVING: CAL 205 (25% from fat); PRO 3.6g;
FAT 5.8g (sat 3.3g); CARB 35.4g; FIB 0.8g;
CHOL 49mg; IRON 1.0mg; SOD 160mg; CALC 50mg

PUMPKIN-DATE-NUT LOAF

prep: 6 minutes • cook: 55 minutes

1⅔ cups all-purpose flour
¾ teaspoon baking soda
¼ teaspoon baking powder
¼ teaspoon salt
¾ teaspoon ground cinnamon
½ teaspoon ground ginger
¼ teaspoon ground nutmeg
¾ cup sugar
¾ cup canned pumpkin
½ cup low-fat buttermilk (1%)
3 tablespoons vegetable oil
1 large egg
1 large egg white
⅓ cup chopped dates
3 tablespoons chopped walnuts, toasted
Cooking spray

1. Preheat oven to 350°.
2. Lightly spoon flour into dry measuring cups; level with a knife. Combine flour, baking soda, and next 5 ingredients; stir with a whisk.
3. Combine sugar and next 5 ingredients in a large mixing bowl; beat with a mixer at medium speed just until smooth. Gradually add flour mixture, beating just until moist.
4. Stir in dates and walnuts. Pour batter into an 8 x 4-inch loaf pan coated with cooking spray. Bake at 350° for 55 minutes or until a wooden pick inserted in center comes out clean. Remove bread from pan immediately; cool on a wire rack. YIELD: 14 servings (serving size: 1 slice).

POINTS: 3; EXCHANGES: 2 Starch, 1 Fat;
PER SERVING: CAL 159 (25% from fat); PRO 3.2g;
FAT 4.5g (sat 0.7g); CARB 27.2g; FIB 1.3g;
CHOL 16mg; IRON 1.1mg; SOD 137mg; CALC 26mg

RASPBERRY-ALMOND COFFEE CAKE

prep: 13 minutes • cook: 40 minutes

Puddles of sweet icing and the flavor of brown sugar and almonds will make this pastry a new family breakfast favorite.

    1 cup fresh raspberries
    3 tablespoons brown sugar
    1 cup all-purpose flour
    ⅓ cup granulated sugar
    ½ teaspoon baking powder
    ¼ teaspoon baking soda
    ⅛ teaspoon salt
    ½ cup plain low-fat yogurt
    2 tablespoons butter or stick
      margarine, melted
    1 teaspoon vanilla extract
    1 large egg, lightly beaten
Cooking spray
    1 tablespoon sliced almonds
    ¼ cup sifted powdered sugar
    1 teaspoon fat-free milk
    ¼ teaspoon vanilla extract

1. Preheat oven to 350°.
2. Combine raspberries and brown sugar in a bowl. Set aside.
3. Lightly spoon flour into a dry measuring cup; level with a knife. Combine flour and next 4 ingredients in a large bowl. Combine yogurt, margarine, 1 teaspoon vanilla, and egg; add to flour mixture, stirring just until moist.
4. Spoon two-thirds of batter into an 8-inch round cake pan coated with cooking spray. Top with raspberry mixture. Spoon remaining batter over raspberry mixture; top with almonds.
5. Bake at 350° for 40 minutes or until a wooden pick inserted in

center comes out clean. Cool on a wire rack. Combine powdered sugar, milk, and ¼ teaspoon vanilla. Drizzle over cake. Serve warm or at room temperature. YIELD: 8 servings (serving size: 1 wedge).

POINTS: 4; EXCHANGES: 2 Starch, 1 Fat; PER SERVING: CAL 176 (23% from fat); PRO 3.5g; FAT 4.5g (sat 1.0g); CARB 30.4g; FIB 1.7g; CHOL 28mg; IRON 1.1mg; SOD 131mg; CALC 59mg

CHIPOTLE SPOON BREAD

prep: 30 minutes • cook: 45 minutes
stand: 15 minutes

Freeze any remaining chipotles in ice cube trays. Once frozen, store in a heavy-duty zip-top plastic bag.

    2 cups fat-free, less-sodium
      chicken broth
    1 cup yellow cornmeal
    1 (15.25-ounce) can whole-kernel
      corn, drained and divided
  1¼ cups 1% low-fat milk
    2 tablespoons light butter, melted
    2 tablespoons honey
    2 canned chipotle chiles in adobo
      sauce, drained and chopped
    ¾ teaspoon ground cinnamon
  1½ teaspoons salt
    2 large egg yolks
    2 teaspoons baking powder
    ½ cup chopped fresh cilantro
    4 large egg whites
Cooking spray

1. Preheat oven to 350°.
2. Bring broth to a boil; pour over cornmeal in a large bowl. Stir and let stand 5 minutes.
3. Place 1 cup corn, milk, and next 7 ingredients in a blender; process until smooth. Whisk together corn

mixture and cornmeal mixture; stir in remaining corn and cilantro.
4. Beat egg whites with a mixer at high speed until stiff peaks form; fold egg whites into cornmeal mixture. Spoon mixture into an 11 x 7-inch baking dish coated with cooking spray. (Dish will be very full but will not bubble over.)
5. Bake at 350° for 45 to 50 minutes or until puffed and golden. Remove from oven; let stand 10 minutes before serving. YIELD: 8 servings (serving size: ⅛ of spoon bread).

POINTS: 3; EXCHANGES: 2 Starch, 1 Fat; PER SERVING: CAL 167 (21% from fat); PRO 7.2g; FAT 3.9g (sat 1.7g); CARB 27.4g; FIB 2.3g; CHOL 60mg; IRON 0.9mg; SOD 876mg; CALC 127mg

BLUE CHEESE AND CARAMELIZED ONION PIZZA BREAD

prep: 18 minutes • rise: 45 minutes
cook: 27 minutes

    1 package dry yeast (about 2¼
      teaspoons)
    ½ teaspoon sugar
    1 cup warm water (100° to 110°)
    1 tablespoon olive oil
  2½ cups all-purpose flour
  1½ teaspoons salt, divided
    ¼ cup crumbled blue cheese
Olive oil-flavored cooking spray
    1 red onion, cut into thin rings
    1 tablespoon cornmeal
    1 teaspoon olive oil
    1 teaspoon freshly ground pepper

1. Combine yeast, sugar, and water in a large bowl; let stand 5 minutes. Stir 1 tablespoon olive oil into yeast mixture.

2. Lightly spoon flour into dry measuring cups; level with a knife. Combine flour and 1 teaspoon salt. Gradually stir flour mixture into yeast mixture, using a wooden spoon. Stir dough 2 minutes with wooden spoon. (Dough will be sticky.)

3. Turn dough out onto a lightly floured surface. Gradually knead blue cheese into dough until smooth and elastic. Place dough in a large bowl coated with cooking spray, turning to coat top. Cover and let rise in a warm place (85°), free from drafts, 45 minutes or until doubled in size.

4. Place a large nonstick skillet over medium-high heat until hot. Coat with cooking spray; add onion. Reduce heat to medium-low; cook, stirring often, 12 to 15 minutes or until onion is tender and browned. Set aside.

5. Preheat oven to 450°.

6. Coat a 12-inch pizza pan with cooking spray; sprinkle with 1 tablespoon cornmeal. Turn dough out onto a lightly floured surface; roll into a 12-inch circle, and place into pan, patting dough to edge. Brush 1 teaspoon olive oil over dough. Make fingertip indentations at 1-inch intervals over dough. Sprinkle remaining ½ teaspoon salt and pepper over dough. Top with onion.

7. Bake at 450° for 15 to 17 minutes or until edges are lightly browned. Cut into 10 slices. Serve warm. YIELD: 10 servings (serving size: 1 slice).

POINTS: 3; EXCHANGES: 2 Starch, ½ Fat; PER SERVING: CAL 157 (18% from fat); PRO 4.6g; FAT 3.2g (sat 0.9g); CARB 27.2g; FIB 1.5g; CHOL 3mg; IRON 1.7mg; SOD 394mg; CALC 29mg

---

YEAST 101

Does the thought of making yeast bread overwhelm you? Relax! With these quick tips, it's easy to get breads to rise to the occasion.

• **TIP #1: Warm It Up!** Yeast needs a warm environment to be activated, but not too warm or it will die. Water at the right temperature (about 100° to 110°) should feel warm but not hot. For guaranteed success, test the water temperature with an instant-read thermometer.

• **TIP #2: Check Its Pulse.** Make sure the yeast is alive. Combine the yeast and warm water. Give the mixture 5 minutes to activate or "grow." You will actually see the yeast bubble and expand while it activates.

• **TIP #3: Start Over.** If there's no activity in the mixture, the yeast is dead and can't make the bread rise. Throw out the mixture, and start over with a new package of yeast.

OATMEAL-MOLASSES BREAD

prep: 15 minutes • rise: 70 minutes
cook: 35 minutes

1 package dry yeast (about 2¼ teaspoons)
1 cup warm water (100° to 110°)
3 tablespoons molasses
2½ cups all-purpose flour
1 cup regular oats
1 tablespoon vegetable oil
1½ teaspoons salt
Cooking spray

1. Dissolve yeast in warm water in a large bowl. Add molasses; let stand 5 minutes. Lightly spoon flour into dry measuring cups; level with knife. Combine 1 cup flour, oats, oil, and salt. Add flour mixture to yeast mixture, stirring to form a soft dough. Gradually add remaining flour.

2. Turn dough out onto a lightly floured surface. Knead until smooth and elastic (about 2 minutes). Place dough in a large bowl coated with cooking spray, turning to coat top. Cover and let rise in a warm place (85°), free from drafts, 35 minutes or until doubled in size. (Press two fingers into dough. If indentation remains, the dough has risen enough.)

3. Punch dough down; place on a lightly floured surface. Knead about 10 times; roll into a 12 x 7-inch rectangle. Roll up rectangle tightly, starting with a short side, pressing firmly to eliminate air pockets; pinch seam and ends to seal. Place roll, seam side down, in an 8 x 4-inch loaf pan coated with cooking spray. Cover; let rise 35 minutes or until doubled in size.

4. Preheat oven to 375°.

5. Uncover dough. Bake at 375° for 35 minutes or until loaf is browned and sounds hollow when tapped. Remove from pan; cool on a wire rack. YIELD: 14 servings (serving size: 1 slice).

POINTS: 2; EXCHANGES: 1½ Starch; PER SERVING: CAL 125 (12% from fat); PRO 3.4g; FAT 1.6g (sat 0.2g); CARB 24.2g; FIB 1.3g; CHOL 0mg; IRON 1.6mg; SOD 253mg; CALC 18mg

SWEDISH RYE BREAD

(pictured on page 26)

prep: 25 minutes • rise: 95 minutes
cook: 25 minutes

Whole-grain flours such as whole wheat and rye contain a small amount of fat which can quickly turn rancid. Store these flours in an airtight container in the refrigerator. Allow flour to warm to room temperature before using.

1 package active dry yeast (about 2¼ teaspoons)
1 cup warm water (100° to 110°)
1¾ cups all-purpose flour
1¼ cups rye flour
2 tablespoons dark brown sugar
1 tablespoon vegetable oil
1 tablespoon molasses
2 teaspoons grated orange rind
1½ teaspoons salt
½ teaspoon caraway seeds
½ teaspoon aniseed
Cooking spray

1. Dissolve yeast in warm water in a large bowl; let stand 5 minutes.
2. Lightly spoon flours into dry measuring cups; level with a knife. Combine flours in a bowl. Add 1 cup flour mixture, sugar, and next 6 ingredients to yeast mixture; beat with a mixer at medium speed until blended. Gradually beat in remaining flour mixture to form a dough. Turn dough out onto a lightly floured surface. Knead until smooth and elastic (about 10 minutes).
3. Place dough in a large bowl coated with cooking spray, turning to coat top. Cover and let rise in a warm place (85°), free from drafts, 35 minutes or until doubled in size. (Press two fingers into dough. If indentation remains, dough has risen enough.)
4. Punch dough down; place on a lightly floured surface. Knead 10 times, and shape into a 7-inch round. Place on a baking sheet coated with cooking spray. Let rise 1 hour or until doubled in size.
5. Preheat oven to 375°.
6. Bake at 375° for 25 minutes or until loaf is lightly browned and sounds hollow when tapped. Remove from baking sheet; cool on a wire rack. YIELD: 12 servings (serving size: 1 slice).

POINTS: 2; **EXCHANGES:** 1 ½ Starch;
PER SERVING: CAL 127 (11% from fat); PRO 3.1g; FAT 1.6g (sat 0.2g); CARB 25.2g; FIB 2.3g; CHOL 0mg; IRON 1.3mg; SOD 293mg; CALC 13mg

WHOLE WHEAT BREAD WITH WHEAT GERM AND HONEY

prep: 18 minutes • rise: 90 minutes
cook: 35 minutes

Wheat germ is packed full of vitamins, minerals, and protein. Sprinkling extra wheat germ on yogurt, salads, smoothies, or fruit adds a nutty burst of flavor and extra nutrients.

1 package dry yeast (about 2¼ teaspoons)
1 cup plus 3 tablespoons warm water (100° to 110°)
2 cups all-purpose flour
1 cup whole wheat flour
⅓ cup wheat germ
2 tablespoons honey
1½ teaspoons salt
Cooking spray

1. Dissolve yeast and warm water in a large bowl; let stand 5 minutes.
2. Lightly spoon flours into dry measuring cups; level with a knife. Combine flours in a bowl. Add 1 cup flour mixture, wheat germ, honey, and salt to yeast mixture. Stir until blended. Gradually add remaining flour mixture.
3. Turn dough out onto a lightly floured surface. Knead until smooth and elastic (about 6 to 8 minutes). Place dough in a large bowl coated with cooking spray, turning to coat top. Cover and let rise in a warm place (85°), free from drafts, 45 minutes or until doubled in size. (Press two fingers into dough. If indentation remains, dough has risen enough.)
4. Punch dough down; place on a lightly floured surface. Knead about 10 times, and roll into a 12 x 7-inch rectangle. Starting at short side, roll up jelly roll fashion to form a loaf. Place loaf, seam side down, in an 8 x 4-inch loaf pan coated with cooking spray. Cover and let rise 45 minutes or until doubled in size.
5. Preheat oven to 375°.
6. Bake at 375° for 35 to 40 minutes or until loaf sounds hollow when tapped. Remove from pan, and cool on a wire rack. YIELD: 14 servings (serving size: 1 slice).

POINTS: 2; **EXCHANGES:** 1 ½ Starch;
PER SERVING: CAL 115 (5% from fat); PRO 4.0g; FAT 0.7g (sat 0.1g); CARB 23.9g; FIB 2.0g; CHOL 0mg; IRON 1.5mg; SOD 253mg; CALC 8mg

Desserts

PINK GRAPEFRUIT COMPOTE

prep: 4 minutes

1 (24-ounce) jar pink grapefruit sections in juice, drained
2 tablespoons honey
2 teaspoons fresh lemon juice
2 tablespoons minced fresh mint

1. Combine all ingredients in a bowl. Cover and chill until ready to serve. YIELD: 4 servings (serving size: ½ cup).

POINTS: 1; EXCHANGE: 1 Fruit; PER SERVING: CAL 76 (1% from fat); PRO 0.9g; FAT 0.1g (sat 0.0g); CARB 19.7g; FIB 0.6g; CHOL 0mg; IRON 0.3mg; SOD 9mg; CALC 20mg

SWEET MELON AND BERRY TOSS

prep: 7 minutes

To save time, buy precubed cantaloupe from the produce section of your grocery store.

½ cup fresh orange juice
¼ cup honey
2 teaspoons chopped fresh mint
2 cups cubed peeled fresh cantaloupe
1 cup fresh blueberries
1 cup halved fresh strawberries

1. Combine first 3 ingredients. Combine cantaloupe, blueberries, and strawberries in a bowl. Pour orange juice mixture over fruit; toss gently. YIELD: 4 servings (serving size: 1 cup).

POINTS: 2; EXCHANGES: 1 Starch, 1½ Fruit; PER SERVING: CAL 138 (3% from fat); PRO 1.5g; FAT 0.6g (sat 0.1g); CARB 35.2g; FIB 2.1g; CHOL 0mg; IRON 0.5mg; SOD 11mg; CALC 22mg

---

> ### AS SWEET AS...HONEY
> Honey just may be the most forgotten about of all sweeteners. It's the same *POINTS* per serving as sugar but imparts a more mellow sweet flavor so that it can be used in a variety of dishes. You'll see honey used throughout this book, from desserts to marinades to salads and soups.

ROSEMARY AMBROSIA

(pictured on page 49)
prep: 29 minutes • cook: 8 minutes

You get prettier orange and grapefruit sections if you peel the skin and pith (white layer covering fruit) from the fruit at the same time. Then cut between the membranes separating each section.

½ cup sugar
¼ cup water
3 tablespoons fresh rosemary leaves
4 large naval oranges
3 pink grapefruit
1 small cored fresh pineapple
4 large firm bananas, sliced
½ cup flaked sweetened coconut
Rosemary sprigs (optional)

1. Combine sugar, water, and rosemary leaves in a small saucepan. Cook over medium heat, stirring constantly, until mixture comes to a boil. Reduce heat, and simmer, uncovered, 8 minutes or until slightly thickened. Cool completely. Pour syrup through a wire mesh strainer into a cup; discard rosemary.
2. Peel and section oranges and grapefruit over a large bowl to catch juices. Cut pineapple into bite-sized chunks. Add pineapple and banana to orange mixture. Pour rosemary syrup over fruit; stir gently. Pour fruit mixture into a large, shallow dish; sprinkle with coconut. Garnish with rosemary, if desired. YIELD: 12 servings (serving size: 1 cup).

POINTS: 2; EXCHANGES: ½ Starch, 2 Fruit; PER SERVING: CAL 154 (8% from fat); PRO 1.5g; FAT 1.6g (sat 1.0g); CARB 36.9g; FIB 3.6g; CHOL 0mg; IRON 0.6mg; SOD 10mg; CALC 37mg

MANGO MELBA

prep: 5 minutes • cook: 2 minutes

Melba sauce is a classic sweet raspberry sauce and is often used as a dessert sauce for fruits, cakes, custards, and chocolate desserts.

1 cup fresh raspberries
2 tablespoons water
3 tablespoons sugar
1 cup chopped mango
1⅓ cups vanilla low-fat ice cream

1. Combine raspberries and water in a blender; process until smooth. Strain into a small saucepan; discard seeds. Stir in sugar. Cook over medium heat 2 minutes or until sugar dissolves, stirring often. Chill, if desired.
2. Divide mango evenly among each of 4 dessert bowls; top each with ice cream and raspberry sauce. YIELD: 4 servings (serving size: ¼ cup mango, ⅓ cup ice cream, and 2 tablespoons raspberry sauce).

POINTS: 2; EXCHANGES: 1 Starch, 1 Fruit; PER SERVING: CAL 151 (9% from fat); PRO 2.5g; FAT 1.6g (sat 0.7g); CARB 32.6g; FIB 3.5g; CHOL 3mg; IRON 0.2mg; SOD 31mg; CALC 78mg

BAKED NECTARINES
WITH CREAM

prep: 5 minutes • cook: 20 minutes

To ripen nectarines, place the fruit in a basket, at room temperature, for 2 or 3 days or until soft. The nectarines will get sweeter the longer they stand.

  1 tablespoon sugar
⅓ cup peach nectar
  4 nectarines, each cut into 4
    wedges
½ cup vanilla low-fat ice cream
Ground nutmeg (optional)

1. Preheat oven to 400°.
2. Combine sugar and peach nectar in a 9-inch pie plate. Place nectarine wedges, skin side up, in pie plate. Bake at 400° for 20 minutes or until tender. Spoon hot fruit and syrup evenly into 4 individual serving bowls. Top each evenly with ice cream. Sprinkle with nutmeg, if desired. YIELD: 4 servings (serving size: 4 nectarine wedges, 2 tablespoons syrup, and 2 tablespoons ice cream).

POINTS: 3; **EXCHANGES:** 1 Starch, 1 Fruit;
PER SERVING: CAL 117 (6% from fat); PRO 2.1g;
FAT 1.1g (sat 0.3g); CARB 26.8g; FIB 2.6g;
CHOL 1.3mg; IRON 0.3mg; SOD 13mg; CALC 33mg

SHOPPING FOR NECTARINES

While this sweet and colorful fruit is available during the spring and summer months, the best-quality nectarines are found during July and August. Choose those that are golden yellow with generous blushes of red. Try to avoid overly green, bruised, or blemished nectarines.

MINT-CHOCOLATE
MOUSSE DELIGHT

prep: 10 minutes • chill: 2 hours

Crème de menthe is a cool, minty liqueur. If you prefer not to use it, substitute ½ teaspoon mint extract.

  8 reduced-fat cream-filled
    chocolate sandwich cookies
    (such as reduced-fat Oreos),
    coarsely crushed
2½ cups 1% low-fat milk
  1 (2.1-ounce) package chocolate
    sugar-free instant pudding mix
  2 tablespoons crème de menthe
  1 (8-ounce) container frozen fat-
    free whipped topping, thawed
    and divided
  3 (1.5-ounce) chocolate-covered
    peppermint patties (such as
    York), chopped
½ (1-ounce) square semisweet
    chocolate

1. Sprinkle crushed cookies in bottom of an 8-inch square baking dish.
2. Combine milk, pudding mix, and crème de menthe in a blender. Process until smooth. Pour into a bowl. Let stand 1 to 2 minutes or until pudding mixture thickens. Fold in half of container of whipped topping and peppermint patties. Spoon into prepared dish. Cover and chill 2 hours.
3. Shave chocolate with a vegetable peeler to get 2 tablespoons chocolate curls. Spread remaining whipped topping over mousse, and sprinkle with chocolate curls. YIELD: 8 servings (serving size: ¾ cup).

POINTS: 5; **EXCHANGES:** 2½ Starch, ½ Fat;
PER SERVING: CAL 240 (14% from fat); PRO 4.0g;
FAT 3.8g (sat 1.5g); CARB 40.2g; FIB 1.2g;
CHOL 5mg; IRON 1.0mg; SOD 314mg; CALC 103mg

BANANA PUDDING

(pictured on page 51)

prep: 15 minutes • cook: 10 minutes

⅓ cup all-purpose flour
¾ cup sugar
¼ teaspoon salt
  2 large egg yolks, lightly beaten
2½ cups 1% low-fat milk
  3 tablespoons butter, divided
  1 tablespoon vanilla extract
36 reduced-fat vanilla wafers
  3 large ripe bananas, sliced
  2 cups frozen fat-free whipped
    topping, thawed

1. Lightly spoon flour into a dry measuring cup; level with a knife.
2. Combine flour, sugar, and salt in a 3-quart saucepan. Combine egg yolks and milk; stir with a whisk. Gradually add egg mixture to dry ingredients, stirring well. Add 2 tablespoons butter. Cook over medium heat until thick and bubbly (about 10 minutes), stirring constantly. Remove from heat; add remaining 1 tablespoon butter and vanilla, stirring until butter melts.
3. Place 12 vanilla wafers in bottom of an 8-inch square baking dish. Arrange one-third of banana over cookies. Spoon one-third of pudding mixture over banana; repeat procedure with remaining cookies, banana, and pudding, ending with pudding. Spoon whipped topping over pudding, and spread evenly. Cover and chill until ready to serve. YIELD: 12 servings (serving size: about ¾ cup).

POINTS: 4; **EXCHANGES:** 2 Starch, ½ Fruit, 1 Fat;
PER SERVING: CAL 212 (19% from fat); PRO 3.6g;
FAT 4.4g (sat 2.2g); CARB 37.7g; FIB 0.9g;
CHOL 11mg; IRON 0.6mg; SOD 163mg; CALC 60mg

RAISIN BREAD PUDDING WITH APPLES

prep: 15 minutes • cook: 40 minutes
stand: 45 minutes

9 (1-ounce) slices cinnamon-
   raisin bread
1 large egg
1 large egg white
⅔ cup sugar
1 (12-ounce) can fat-free
   evaporated milk
½ cup fat-free half-and-half
1 teaspoon vanilla extract
¾ cup chopped peeled apple
Cooking spray
3 cups vanilla low-fat ice cream
¾ cup fat-free caramel syrup

1. Tear bread into 1-inch pieces.
Spread evenly on a jelly roll pan;
place in a cool oven. Let stand
overnight or until dried.
2. Combine egg and next 5 ingredients in a large bowl, beating with a
whisk until well blended. Add dried
bread and apple to egg mixture,
tossing gently to moisten; let stand
30 minutes.
3. Preheat oven to 350°.
4. Spoon bread mixture into a 9-
inch square baking dish coated with
cooking spray. Bake at 350° for 40
minutes or until a knife inserted in
center comes out clean. Let stand 15
minutes. Serve warm with ice cream
and caramel sauce. YIELD: 12 servings
(serving size: 1 square bread pudding, ¼ cup ice cream, and 1 tablespoon syrup).

POINTS: 5; EXCHANGES: 3 Starch; **PER SERVING:**
CAL 255 (9% from fat); PRO 6.9g; FAT 2.6g (sat 0.6g);
CARB 49.4g; FIB 1.4g; CHOL 20mg; IRON 1.4mg;
SOD 213mg; CALC 140mg

PEACH MELBA TART

prep: 23 minutes • cook: 14 minutes
chill: 9½ hours

*Crush gingersnaps in a food processor
or in a zip-top plastic bag with a mallet.*

30 gingersnaps, crushed
3 tablespoons butter, melted
Cooking spray
1 (16-ounce) package frozen
   sliced peaches, thawed
⅓ cup sugar
1 envelope unflavored gelatin
2 tablespoons boiling water
1 cup frozen raspberries, thawed
1 tablespoon minced peeled fresh
   ginger
2 tablespoons fresh lime juice
2 tablespoons sugar
1 cup frozen fat-free whipped
   topping, thawed

1. Preheat oven to 350°.
2. Combine gingersnaps and butter;
stir well. Press mixture into a 9-inch
round removable-bottom tart pan
coated with cooking spray. Bake at
350° for 9 minutes or until lightly
browned. Cool on a wire rack.
3. Place peaches and ⅓ cup sugar in
a blender; process until smooth.
Combine gelatin and boiling water;
stir until gelatin dissolves. Add gelatin
mixture to blender; process 15 seconds. Transfer peach mixture to a
large bowl; cover and chill 1 hour.
4. Combine raspberries and next 3
ingredients in a small saucepan; bring
to a boil. Reduce heat, and simmer 5
minutes or until mixture thickens.
Strain mixture through a sieve into a
bowl; discard solids. Cover and chill
30 minutes.

5. Fold whipped topping into peach
mixture. Pour onto prepared crust.
Spoon raspberry mixture over peach
mixture; swirl mixtures together using
a knife. Cover and chill 8 hours.
Remove sides of pan before serving.
YIELD: 10 servings (serving size: 1 slice).

POINTS: 5; EXCHANGES: 3 Starch, 1 Fat;
PER SERVING: CAL 237 (26% from fat); PRO 1.9g;
FAT 6.8g (sat 3.0g); CARB 42.4g; FIB 2.2g;
CHOL 9mg; IRON 1.1mg; SOD 115mg; CALC 12mg

APPLE TART

prep: 24 minutes • cook: 1 hour
cool: 5 minutes

1½ cups all-purpose flour
6 tablespoons granulated sugar,
   divided
⅛ teaspoon salt
5 tablespoons chilled butter, cut
   into small pieces
5 tablespoons ice water
6 cups thinly sliced peeled apples
2 teaspoons fresh lemon juice
3 tablespoons light brown sugar
2½ tablespoons cornstarch
¼ teaspoon ground cinnamon
Cooking spray

1. Lightly spoon flour into dry measuring cups; level with a knife.
Combine flour, 1 tablespoon granulated sugar, and salt in a bowl. Cut
in butter with pastry blender or 2
knives until mixture resembles
coarse meal. Sprinkle with ice water,
1 tablespoon at a time; toss with a
fork until moist. Press pastry into a
4-inch circle on plastic wrap; cover
with another sheet of plastic wrap.
Roll dough, still covered, into a

14-inch circle. Freeze 10 minutes or until wrap can be easily removed.

2. Preheat oven to 425°.

3. Toss apple slices with lemon juice. Combine brown sugar, cornstarch, cinnamon, and 3 tablespoons sugar in a bowl. Add apple slices, toss well.

4. Unwrap pastry, and place on a baking sheet coated with cooking spray. Arrange apple slices over dough, leaving a 3-inch border. Sprinkle tops of apples with remaining 2 tablespoons sugar. Fold 3-inch border of dough over apples, pressing to seal.

5. Bake at 425° for 20 minutes. Reduce oven temperature to 350°, and bake 40 minutes or until pastry is golden brown and apples are tender. Cool tart in pan 5 minutes. YIELD: 10 servings (serving size: 1 slice).

POINTS: 4; EXCHANGES: 2 Starch, ½ Fruit, 1 Fat; PER SERVING: CAL 211 (26% from fat); PRO 2.1g; FAT 6.1g (sat 3.7g); CARB 37.9g; FIB 1.8g; CHOL 16mg; IRON 1.0mg; SOD 90mg; CALC 12mg

CHOCOLATE MERINGUE PIE

(pictured on page 50)
prep: 15 minutes • cook: 43 minutes
cool: 1 hour • chill: 3 hours

½ (15-ounce) refrigerated pie
  crust dough (such as Pillsbury)
⅓ cup all-purpose flour
2 cups chocolate 1% low-fat milk
¼ cup sugar
⅓ cup cocoa
2 teaspoons vanilla extract
1 large egg, lightly beaten
4 large egg whites
1 teaspoon cornstarch
¼ teaspoon cream of tartar
⅓ cup sugar

1. Preheat oven to 450°.

2. Fit dough into a 9-inch pie plate. Fold edges of dough under, and flute. Pierce bottom and sides of dough with a fork. Bake at 450° for 10 minutes or until lightly browned. Reduce oven temperature to 350°.

3. Lightly spoon flour into a dry measuring cup; level with a knife. Combine flour, milk, and next 3 ingredients in a saucepan, stirring until smooth. Bring to a boil over medium heat. Reduce heat, and simmer, stirring constantly, 5 minutes.

4. Gradually stir about one-fourth of milk mixture into beaten egg, stirring constantly with a whisk; add to remaining milk mixture. Cook 3 minute. Pour into prepared crust; cover with plastic wrap.

5. Place egg whites, cornstarch, and cream of tartar in a large bowl. Beat at high speed until foamy. Gradually add ⅓ cup sugar, 1 tablespoon at a time, beating until stiff peaks form.

6. Remove plastic wrap from filling; spread meringue evenly over filling, sealing to edge of crust. Bake at 350° for 25 minutes; cool on a wire rack 1 hour. Chill 3 hours or until set. YIELD: 10 servings (serving size: 1 slice).

POINTS: 5; EXCHANGES: 2 Starch, 1 Fat; PER SERVING: CAL 213 (29% from fat); PRO 5.4g; FAT 7.0g (sat 3.1g); CARB 33.0g; FIB 1.1g; CHOL 27mg; IRON 0.8mg; SOD 144mg; CALC 58mg

LEMON CREAM PIE

prep: 30 minutes • chill: 4 hours

Cooling the filling in a saucepan set in ice water keeps prep time to half an hour.

⅔ cup sugar
⅓ cup cornstarch
⅛ teaspoon salt
2 cups 1% low-fat milk
1 large egg, beaten
1 tablespoon butter or stick
  margarine, softened
1 tablespoon grated lemon rind
⅓ cup fresh lemon juice
1 (6-ounce) reduced-fat graham
  cracker crust
1½ cups frozen fat-free whipped
  topping, thawed

1. Combine first 3 ingredients in a saucepan; gradually stir in milk. Cook over medium heat, stirring constantly, until mixture comes to a boil. Cook 2 minutes. Remove from heat. Gradually stir about ¼ of hot milk mixture into beaten egg; add to remaining hot mixture, stirring constantly. Cook over medium heat, stirring constantly, 3 minutes or until thickened. Remove from heat; stir in butter, lemon rind, and lemon juice.

2. Set saucepan in a bowl of ice water. Cool completely (about 5 minutes), stirring often. Pour mixture into crust. Cover and chill 4 hours. Spread whipped topping over pie before serving. YIELD: 8 servings (serving size: 1 slice).

POINTS: 5; EXCHANGES: 3 Starch, 1 Fat; PER SERVING: CAL 250 (22% from fat); PRO 4.1g; FAT 6.2g (sat 2.0g); CARB 42.8g; FIB 0.2g; CHOL 34mg; IRON 0.5mg; SOD 185mg; CALC 73mg

CARAMEL-TOFFEE-ICE CREAM PIE

(pictured on page 48)
prep: 14 minutes • cook: 8 minutes
freeze: 6½ hours

1½ cups chocolate graham cracker
  crumbs (about 10 sheets)
2 tablespoons sugar
2 tablespoons butter, melted
1 large egg white
Cooking spray
4 cups vanilla fat-free ice cream,
  divided
2 (1.4-ounce) milk chocolate
  crisp butter toffee bars (such as
  Hershey's Skor), coarsely
  chopped and divided
½ cup fat-free caramel sundae
  syrup, divided

1. Preheat oven to 375°.
2. Combine graham cracker crumbs,
sugar, butter, and egg white in a large
bowl; stir well. Press crumb mixture
into a 9-inch pie plate coated with
cooking spray. Bake at 375° for 8
minutes; cool on a wire rack. Cover
and freeze 30 minutes.
3. Place ice cream in refrigerator 30
minutes to soften. Spread 2⅔ cups
ice cream into crust, covering bottom.
Sprinkle with half of toffee; drizzle
with half of syrup. Spoon remaining
1⅓ cups ice cream over syrup; sprinkle with remaining toffee bar; drizzle
with remaining syrup.
4. Cover and freeze 6 hours or until
firm. Place pie in refrigerator 20 minutes before serving to soften. YIELD: 10
servings (serving size: 1 slice).

POINTS: 6; **EXCHANGES:** 3 Starch, 1½ Fat;
PER SERVING: CAL 279 (25% from fat); PRO 4.7g;
FAT 7.8g (sat 3.7g); CARB 47.7g; FIB 0.1g;
CHOL 10mg; IRON 0.1mg; SOD 192mg; CALC 83mg

LIGHT ICE CREAM *POINTERS*

How many *POINTS* are in your favorite light ice cream? Check out the
chart below to determine how these frozen treats can fit into your daily
POINTS range. The following nutritional values are based on a ½-cup
serving:

Brand	POINTS
Ben & Jerry's Lowfat Mocha Latte	3
Breyers All Natural Light Strawberry	3
Breyers Fat-Free Vanilla	2
Dreyer's (Edy's) Fat Free Chocolate Peanut Butter	2
Dreyer's (Edy's) Light S'mores n' More	3
Haägen-Daz Lowfat Chocolate	2
Healthy Choice Butter Pecan Crunch	2
Healthy Choice Turtle Fudge Cake	2

PEACH GRANITA

prep: 5 minutes • freeze: 8 hours

*So light and sweet, this 1-POINT
frozen dessert is the perfect way
to end a summer day.*

2 cups peach nectar
2 tablespoons sugar
1 tablespoon fresh lemon juice

1. Combine peach nectar and sugar
in a saucepan over medium-high
heat; cook, stirring often, until sugar
dissolves. Remove from heat; stir in
lemon juice. Pour mixture into a
13 x 9-inch baking dish; cover and
freeze 8 hours or until firm.
2. Remove mixture from freezer;
scrape entire mixture with a fork
until fluffy. Serve immediately, or store
in a covered container in freezer. YIELD:
6 servings (serving size: ½ cup).

POINTS: 1; **EXCHANGE:** 1 Starch; **PER SERVING:**
CAL 62 (0% from fat); PRO 0.2g; FAT 0.0g (sat 0.0g);
CARB 15.9g; FIB 0.5g; CHOL 0mg; IRON 0.2mg;
SOD 6mg; CALC 62mg

TANGERINE GRANITA

(pictured on page 1)
prep: 5 minutes • freeze: 2 hours
stand: 30 minutes

*Substitute 2 tablespoons of tangerine
juice, lemon juice, lime juice, or orange
juice for the Grand Marnier if you prefer.*

2 cups fresh tangerine juice
  (about 6 large tangerines)
¾ cup sugar
2 tablespoons Grand Marnier

1. Combine juice, sugar, and Grand
Marnier. Let stand 30 minutes, stirring often. Pour mixture into an 8-
inch square baking pan. Freeze 2
hours or until firm, stirring after 1
hour. Remove mixture from freezer;
scrape entire mixture with a fork
until fluffy. YIELD: 6 servings (serving
size: about ½ cup).

POINTS: 3; **EXCHANGES:** 2 Starch; **PER SERVING:**
CAL 133 (0% from fat); PRO 0.5g; FAT 0.1g (sat 0.0g);
CARB 33.6g; FIB 0.0g; CHOL 0mg; IRON 0.2mg;
SOD 1mg; CALC 16mg

BROWNIE-BERRY BLAST

(pictured on page 46)
prep: 14 minutes • cook: 25 minutes

Freezing the raspberries before folding them into the yogurt helps them hold their shape.

1 pint fresh raspberries
1 (13.7-ounce) package fat-free brownie mix (such as Krusteaz or No Pudge!)
1 (1.75-quart) container vanilla low-fat ice cream, softened (such as Healthy Choice)

1. Freeze raspberries in a single layer on a cookie sheet.
2. Prepare and bake brownies according to package directions. Cool brownies completely on a wire rack. Cut into small chunks.
3. Combine brownie chunks and softened ice cream; stir until brownie is evenly distributed. Add raspberries; stir gently. Serve immediately, or transfer mixture to a freezer-safe container and freeze until ready to serve. Let soften at room temperature 5 minutes before serving. YIELD: 16 servings (serving size: ½ cup).

POINTS: 4; **EXCHANGES:** 2 Starch, 1 Fat; **PER SERVING:** CAL 201 (24% from fat); PRO 6.0g; FAT 5.5g (sat 2.3g); CARB 33.7g; FIB 2.0g; CHOL 22mg; IRON 0.8mg; SOD 117mg; CALC 164mg

SUMMER BERRY-CINNAMON SHORTCAKES

(pictured on page 51)
prep: 30 minutes • cook: 12 minutes

Plan your day ahead so that you can enjoy this yummy dessert. For a more traditional shortcake, substitute 4 cups sliced fresh strawberries and omit the other berries.

¾ cup fresh blueberries
¾ cup fresh raspberries
¾ cup fresh blackberries
¾ cup sliced fresh strawberries
2 tablespoons sugar
2 cups self-rising flour
3 tablespoons sugar
½ teaspoon ground cinnamon
⅓ cup chilled butter, cut into small pieces
⅔ cup low-fat buttermilk (1%)
Cooking spray
2 teaspoons sugar
1 (10-ounce) package frozen sliced strawberries in light syrup, thawed
8 tablespoons frozen reduced-calorie whipped topping, thawed

1. Combine first 5 ingredients in a bowl; set aside.
2. Preheat oven to 425°.
3. Lightly spoon flour into dry measuring cups; level with a knife.

Combine flour, 3 tablespoons sugar, and cinnamon in a bowl; cut in butter with a pastry blender or 2 knives until mixture resembles coarse meal. Add buttermilk, stirring just until dry ingredients are moist.
4. Turn dough out onto a heavily floured surface; knead lightly 5 times. Roll dough to ½-inch thickness; cut with a 2¾-inch biscuit cutter. Place shortcakes on a baking sheet coated with cooking spray. Sprinkle evenly with 2 teaspoons sugar.
5. Bake at 425° for 12 minutes or until golden. Remove shortcakes from baking sheet, and cool on a wire rack.
6. Place thawed strawberries in a blender or food processor. Process 20 seconds. Strain puree through a sieve into a bowl; discard solids. Stir strawberry puree into berry mixture.
7. Cut shortcakes in half. Spoon ¼ cup fruit mixture over bottom of each shortcake. Place top of shortcakes over fruit mixture; spoon ¼ cup fruit mixture over tops. Dollop 1 tablespoon whipped topping onto each shortcake. Serve immediately. YIELD: 8 servings (serving size: 1 shortcake).

POINTS: 6; **EXCHANGES:** 2 Starch, 1 Fruit, 1½ Fat; **PER SERVING:** CAL 285 (27% from fat); PRO 4.5g; FAT 8.5g (sat 5.0g); CARB 49.0g; FIB 3.8g; CHOL 22mg; IRON 2.0mg; SOD 500mg; CALC 146mg

---

BROWNIE-BERRY BLAST VARIATIONS

This decadent ice cream dessert was a huge hit in our Test Kitchens. Everyone had their own favorite way to serve the ice cream. We thought we'd share some of the serving ideas with you!

Serve ½ cup in a small waffle cone - 4 *POINTS*
Serve ½ cup topped with 1 tablespoon fat-free fudge sauce - 4 *POINTS*
Serve ½ cup in a small waffle cone, drizzle with 1 tablespoon fat-free fudge sauce (and serve with lots of napkins!) - 5 *POINTS*

APPLESAUCE SNACK CAKE WITH CREAM CHEESE FROSTING

(pictured on page 47)
prep: 11 minutes • cook: 22 minutes
cool: 10 minutes

3 tablespoons vegetable oil
⅓ cup granulated sugar
⅓ cup firmly packed light brown
  sugar
1 large egg
1 large egg white
1 teaspoon vanilla extract
½ cup chunky applesauce
1 cup all-purpose flour
¾ teaspoon baking powder
⅛ teaspoon baking soda
¾ teaspoon ground cinnamon
¼ teaspoon ground ginger
⅛ teaspoon ground nutmeg
Dash of ground cloves
¼ teaspoon salt
Cooking spray
Cream Cheese Frosting
1 tablespoon finely chopped
  walnuts

1. Preheat oven to 350°.
2. Combine oil and sugars in a large bowl; beat with a mixer at medium speed until well blended. Add egg and egg white; beat well. Beat in vanilla and applesauce. Lightly spoon flour into a dry measuring cup; level with a knife. Combine flour and next 7 ingredients, stirring well with a whisk. Add flour mixture to applesauce mixture.
3. Pour batter into an 8-inch square baking pan coated with cooking spray. Bake at 350° for 22 minutes or until a wooden pick inserted in center comes out clean. Cool in pan 10 minutes.

4. Spread top of cake with Cream Cheese Frosting, and sprinkle with walnuts. Cut into 9 equal squares. YIELD: 9 servings (serving size: 1 square).

CREAM CHEESE FROSTING
prep: 6 minutes

⅓ cup (3 ounces) light cream
  cheese, softened
½ teaspoon vanilla extract
1¼ cups sifted powdered sugar

1. Combine cream cheese and vanilla in a mixing bowl; beat with a mixer at low until blended. Gradually add sugar; beat at medium-high speed until smooth and creamy. YIELD: ½ cup.

POINTS: 5; EXCHANGES: 3 Starch, 1 Fat;
PER SERVING: CAL 249 (26% from fat); PRO 3.6g;
FAT 7.3g (sat 2.0g); CARB 42.4g; FIB 0.8g;
CHOL 28mg; IRON 1.2mg; SOD 184mg; CALC 50mg

TRIPLE CHOCOLATE CAKE

(pictured on page 4)
prep: 12 minutes • cook: 1 hour
cool: 15 minutes

1 (18.25-ounce) package chocolate
  cake mix
1 (1.4-ounce) package chocolate
  sugar-free, fat-free pudding mix
¾ cup semisweet chocolate chips
1 (8-ounce) carton fat-free sour
  cream
1 cup egg substitute
½ cup water
⅓ cup vegetable oil
Cooking spray
1 cup light fudge topping, (such as
  Smucker's)

1. Preheat oven to 350°.
2. Combine first 7 ingredients in a large bowl; stir well with a wire whisk until ingredients are blended. Pour batter into a 12-cup Bundt pan coated with cooking spray.
3. Bake at 350° for 1 hour or until cake begins to pull away from sides of pan. Cool in pan on a wire rack 15 minutes; remove cake from pan, and cool completely on wire rack. To serve, cut cake into 16 slices. Drizzle each slice with 1 tablespoon fudge topping. YIELD: 16 servings (serving size: 1 slice cake and 1 tablespoon topping).

POINTS: 6; EXCHANGES: 3 Starch, 2 Fat;
PER SERVING: CAL 289 (33% from fat); PRO 6.0g;
FAT 10.6g (sat 3.3g); CARB 44.9g; FIB 2.5g;
CHOL 1mg; IRON 1.9mg; SOD 387mg; CALC 63mg

WARM BROWNIE SUNDAE CAKE

(pictured on page 47)
prep: 10 minutes • cook: 18 minutes

After cutting into squares, wrap brownies individually in plastic wrap, and freeze. When a chocolate craving hits, pull a brownie from the freezer, and prepare your sundae.

Cooking spray
⅔ cup all-purpose flour
¾ cup sugar
¼ cup cocoa
¼ teaspoon baking soda
¼ cup applesauce
3 tablespoons vegetable oil
1 large egg
1 large egg white
1 teaspoon vanilla extract
3 cups vanilla fat-free ice cream
¾ cup fat-free chocolate syrup

1. Preheat oven to 350°.

2. Line an 8-inch square baking pan with aluminum foil. Coat foil with cooking spray; set aside.

3. Lightly spoon flour into a dry measuring cup; level with a knife.

4. Combine flour, sugar, cocoa, and soda in a medium bowl. Combine applesauce and next 4 ingredients, and stir with a whisk; gradually add to dry ingredients, stirring just until blended. Pour batter into prepared pan. Bake at 350° for 18 minutes. (Wooden pick will not come out clean.)

5. Cool in pan on a wire rack. Cut into 16 squares; cut each square in half diagonally, creating triangles. Arrange 2 triangles on each serving plate. Spoon ¼ cup ice cream on top of each serving. Drizzle each serving with 1 tablespoon chocolate syrup. Serve immediately. YIELD: 12 servings (serving size: 1 brownie sundae).

POINTS: 4; EXCHANGES: 3 Starch, 1 Fat; PER SERVING: CAL 220 (17% from fat); PRO 3.8g; FAT 4.3g (sat 0.7g); CARB 42.9g; FIB 1.4g; CHOL 18mg; IRON 0.9mg; SOD 69mg; CALC 49mg

PINEAPPLE CRUMB CAKE

prep: 10 minutes • cook: 35 minutes

This tender, crumbly sweet treat smells delicious while baking.

¼ cup (2 ounces) fat-free cream cheese
2 tablespoons sugar
1¼ cups all-purpose flour
½ cup sugar
⅛ teaspoon salt
¼ cup chilled butter, cut into small pieces
½ teaspoon baking powder
¼ teaspoon baking soda
1 large egg, beaten
1 teaspoon grated lemon rind
1 teaspoon vanilla extract
½ cup 1% low-fat milk
Cooking spray
¼ cup pineapple preserves

1. Preheat oven to 350°.

2. Combine cream cheese and 2 tablespoons sugar, and stir until blended. Set aside.

3. Lightly spoon flour into dry measuring cups; level with a knife. Combine flour, ½ cup sugar, and salt in a bowl; cut in butter with a pastry blender or 2 knives until mixture resembles coarse meal. Remove ⅓ cup crumb mixture; set aside.

4. Add baking powder and baking soda to remaining crumb mixture; stir well with a whisk. Add egg and next 3 ingredients. Beat with a mixer at medium speed until blended. Pour into an 8-inch round cake pan coated with cooking spray. Spread cheese mixture over batter. Spoon pineapple preserves over cheese mixture; sprinkle with remaining crumb mixture.

5. Bake at 350° for 35 minutes or until edges of cake just begin to pull away from sides of pan. Serve warm or at room temperature. YIELD: 8 servings (serving size: 1 wedge).

POINTS: 5; EXCHANGES: 2½ Starch, 1 Fat; PER SERVING: CAL 232 (26% from fat); PRO 4.5g; FAT 6.7g (sat 3.9g); CARB 39.1g; FIB 0.6g; CHOL 43mg; IRON 1.1mg; SOD 224mg; CALC 67mg

HOW TO PREPARE CRUMB CAKE

1. Cut chilled butter into flour mixture using a pastry blender or 2 knives until mixture resembles course meal.

2. Gently spoon pineapple mixture evenly over cream cheese mixture.

3. Sprinkle reserved crumb mixture over cake before baking.

UPSIDE-DOWN APPLE-SPICE CAKE

prep: 20 minutes • cook: 25 minutes
cool: 5 minutes

Cooking spray
1½ tablespoons butter, melted
2 tablespoons dark brown sugar
1 small Golden Delicious apple,
   peeled and thinly sliced
1⅓ cups all-purpose flour
1 teaspoon baking soda
2 teaspoons apple pie spice
¼ teaspoon salt
1 tablespoon butter, softened
¼ cup apple butter
⅔ cup firmly packed dark brown
   sugar
1 large egg
1 teaspoon vanilla extract
½ cup low-fat buttermilk (1%)

1. Preheat oven to 350°.
2. Coat a 9-inch round cake pan with cooking spray. Place 1½ tablespoons melted butter in pan. Quickly tilt pan in all directions so butter covers pan with a thin film. Sprinkle butter with 2 tablespoons brown sugar. Arrange apple slices spokelike over brown sugar. Set aside.
3. Lightly spoon flour into dry measuring cups; level with a knife. Combine flour and next 3 ingredients in a medium bowl.
4. Beat softened butter, apple butter, and ⅔ cup brown sugar in a large bowl with a mixer at medium speed until well blended. Add egg, vanilla, and buttermilk; beat well. Gradually stir in flour mixture. Spread batter over apples.
5. Bake at 350° for 23 to 25 minutes or until a wooden pick inserted in center comes out clean. Cool in

pan 5 minutes. Loosen cake from sides of pan using a narrow metal spatula. Place a plate upside down on top of cake pan; invert cake onto plate. Serve warm. YIELD: 10 servings (serving size: 1 slice).

POINTS: 4; *EXCHANGES:* 2½ Starch, ½ Fat; *PER SERVING:* CAL 187 (18% from fat); PRO 2.9g; FAT 3.7g (sat 2.1g); CARB 35.7g; FIB 0.9g; CHOL 30mg; IRON 1.2mg; SOD 240mg; CALC 38mg

UPSIDE-DOWN PLUM CAKE

prep: 8 minutes • cook: 35 minutes
cool: 5 minutes

While the cake layer is cooking, the butter, sugar, and fruit combine to form a rich sauce that soaks into the cake after it is turned out onto the serving plate.

1 tablespoon light butter, melted
¼ cup packed light brown sugar
2 cups thinly sliced plums
1 cup all-purpose flour
¾ teaspoon baking powder
¼ teaspoon baking soda
⅛ teaspoon salt
¼ cup light butter, softened
⅔ cup granulated sugar
2 teaspoons grated orange rind
1 teaspoon vanilla extract
1 large egg
⅔ cup low-fat buttermilk (1%)

1. Preheat oven to 350°.
2. Coat bottom of a 9-inch round cake pan or 9-inch cast iron skillet with melted butter. Sprinkle with brown sugar. Top with plums, arranging in a circular pattern; set aside.
3. Lightly spoon flour into a dry measuring cup; level with a knife. Combine flour, baking powder,

baking soda, and salt in a large bowl. Beat softened butter and sugar with a mixer at medium speed until blended. Add orange rind, vanilla, and egg, beating until well blended. Add flour mixture to sugar mixture alternately with buttermilk, beating well after each addition. Pour batter over plums.
4. Bake at 350° for 35 minutes or until a wooden pick inserted in center comes out clean. Cool in pan 5 minutes on a wire rack. Loosen cake from sides of pan using a narrow metal spatula. Place a plate upside down on top of cake pan; invert cake onto plate. Serve warm. YIELD: 8 servings (serving size: 1 slice).

POINTS: 5; *EXCHANGES:* 3 Starch, 1 Fat; *PER SERVING:* CAL 222 (19% from fat); PRO 4.1g; FAT 5.0g (sat 2.9g); CARB 42.1g; FIB 1.1g; CHOL 40mg; IRON 1.1mg; SOD 198mg; CALC 62mg

TURNING UPSIDE-DOWN INTO RIGHT-SIDE UP

• Let the cake cool for 5 minutes, then run a small spatula around the side to loosen the cake.

• Put a serving plate on top of the cake pan; wearing an oven mitt, firmly hold the cake pan, and invert it onto the plate. Remove the pan.

Reclaiming Her Health

GLORIA CANNON • **HEIGHT** 5'2" • **BEFORE** 205.5 LBS. • **AFTER** 120.6 LBS.

Biggest Accomplishment: I didn't give up what I wanted most for what I wanted at the moment.

Before starting Weight Watchers in April 2001, Gloria Cannon was taking two different medications to control her high blood pressure. "I kept thinking 'I'm killing myself'," she says. "I realized that if I didn't do something to better my health I would die young like my father, who died at the age of 65 from heart disease."

After talking with a friend who had success with Weight Watchers, Gloria decided that it was time for her to lose weight and reclaim her health. So on April 4, 2001 Gloria walked through the doors of a Weight Watchers center and committed to making it work.

For Gloria the weight came off fast. By January 2002 she had lost 75 pounds—just 10 pounds shy of her goal. While the **POINTS** program and tips helped with the initial weight loss, it's the emphasis on exercise that Gloria credits for the quick loss. "You can lose weight on the meal plan alone, but with exercise you can lose it more quickly," she says.

"Being overweight is like any other bad habit to be broken."

Gloria loves the fact that Weight Watchers is not a diet, but a true lifestyle change. "It's something I can live with for the rest of my life," she says. "It's a wonderful, healthy program. While it does take some determination, anybody can do it if they want it bad enough. Being overweight is like any other bad habit to be broken."

By April 2002, Gloria had reached her personal goal of 120 pounds. "Getting to my goal was definitely my proudest moment," she says. "I had tears in my eyes because I was so overwhelmed!"

To celebrate her huge accomplishment, Gloria's husband of 28 years bought her a sapphire and diamond ring, as well as some new clothes for his "new" bride. "He tells everybody he's married a new woman without having to go through a divorce," Gloria says. "He's been so supportive and has also lost 47 pounds as a result of our better food choices and daily exercise."

Gloria doesn't need to take blood pressure medication anymore and says that she feels years younger. "I no longer let everyday situations take over my life," she says. "And my energy has skyrocketed!"

Because of her great weight-loss success and her newfound passion for Weight Watchers, Gloria has joined the team as a group leader. "I am so excited about the program and really enjoy telling everyone about its benefits," she says. "It's a great feeling for me to be able to help someone else."

Perhaps her greatest accomplishment in her weight-loss endeavor is summed up in her own words, which she has inscribed on a plaque with her "before" and "after" photos: "I didn't give up what I wanted most for what I wanted at the moment."

Brownie-Berry Blast,
page 41

Warm Brownie
Sundae Cake,
page 42

Applesauce Snack Cake
with Cream Cheese
Frosting, page 42

47

Spicy Molasses Crackles
and Chocolate Chocolate
Chip Cookies, page 54

Caramel-Toffee-Ice
Cream Pie, page 40

Rosemary Ambrosia,
page 36

49

Chocolate Meringue Pie,
page 39

Date-Nut Blondies,
page 56

Summer Berry-
Cinnamon Shortcakes,
page 41

Banana Pudding,
page 37

Fudgy Caramel Brownies,
page 56

COFFEE CHEESECAKE

prep: 37 minutes • cook: 1 hour
stand: 1 hour • chill: 8 hours

Cooking spray
 ¾ cup graham cracker crumbs
 2 tablespoons sugar
 2 tablespoons reduced-calorie
   stick margarine, melted
 1 tablespoon unsweetened cocoa
 ⅔ cup sugar
 ⅓ cup all-purpose flour
 1 tablespoon cornstarch
 1 teaspoon vanilla extract
 1 (8-ounce) block ⅓-less-fat
   cream cheese, softened
 1 (8-ounce) block fat-free cream
   cheese, softened
 2 large eggs
 ½ cup fat-free milk
2½ tablespoons instant coffee granules
 ⅓ cup fat-free sour cream
 3 large egg whites
 ¼ cup sugar

1. Preheat oven to 300°.
2. Coat a 9-inch springform pan
with cooking spray. Combine
graham cracker crumbs and next 3
ingredients, and stir well. Firmly press
crumb mixture into bottom and 2
inches up sides of pan; set pan aside.
3. Combine ⅔ cup sugar and next 6
ingredients in a large bowl; beat with
a mixer at high speed until blended.
Combine milk and coffee granules;
stir well. Add milk mixture and sour
cream to cream cheese mixture; beat
until smooth.
4. Beat egg whites at high speed
with a mixer until soft peaks form.
Gradually add ¼ cup sugar, 1 tablespoon at a time, beating until stiff
peaks form. Gently fold egg white
mixture into cheese mixture.

5. Pour batter into prepared pan. Bake
at 300° for 1 hour or until almost set.
Turn oven off; loosen cheesecake from
sides of pan using a narrow metal
spatula or knife. Let cheesecake stand
in oven with door slightly open for 1
hour. Remove cheesecake from oven;
cover and chill 8 hours. YIELD: 12 servings (serving size: 1 slice).

POINTS: 5; EXCHANGES: 2 Starch, 1 High-Fat
Meat; **PER SERVING:** CAL 211 (30% from fat);
PRO 8.2g; FAT 7.0g (sat 3.4g); CARB 27.8g;
FIB 0.1g; CHOL 53mg; IRON 0.7mg; SOD 286mg;
CALC 90mg

MOCHA FUDGE TORTE

prep: 18 minutes • cook: 35 minutes
chill: 2 hours

1½ cups chocolate-flavored bear-
   shaped graham crackers, crushed
 2 tablespoons sugar
 2 tablespoons butter, melted
Cooking spray
 ½ cup (4 ounces) block-style
   ⅓-less-fat cream cheese, softened
 1 large egg
 1 (14-ounce) can fat-free
   sweetened condensed milk
 ⅓ cup unsweetened cocoa
 3 tablespoons fat-free chocolate
   syrup
 1 tablespoon instant coffee granules
 1 teaspoon vanilla extract
1½ cups frozen fat-free whipped
   topping, thawed
 ½ teaspoon unsweetened cocoa

1. Preheat oven to 350°.
2. Combine cookie crumbs, sugar,
and butter. Press into bottom of a
9-inch springform pan coated with
cooking spray. Bake at 350° for 10
minutes.

3. Beat cream cheese and next 6
ingredients with a mixer at medium
speed 30 seconds or until smooth.
Pour into prepared crust. Bake at
350° for 25 minutes. Cool on a wire
rack. Cover and chill 2 hours.
4. Remove sides of pan; dollop torte
with whipped topping, and sprinkle
with cocoa. YIELD: 10 servings (serving size: 1 slice and 2 tablespoons
whipped topping).

POINTS: 6; EXCHANGES: 3 Starch, 1 Fat;
PER SERVING: CAL 268 (23% from fat); PRO 7.0g;
FAT 7.0g (sat 3.5g); CARB 45.2g; FIB 1.1g;
CHOL 36mg; IRON 0.6mg; SOD 211mg; CALC 136mg

CRISPY PEANUT BUTTER SQUARES

prep: 6 minutes • cook: 4 minutes

 3 tablespoons light butter
Cooking spray
 4 cups miniature marshmallows
 ⅓ cup reduced-fat creamy peanut
   butter
 6 cups oven-toasted rice cereal
   (such as Rice Krispies)

1. Melt butter in a large saucepan
coated with cooking spray over
medium-low heat. Add marshmallows, stirring until melted. Add
peanut butter, and cook until melted. Remove from heat.
2. Immediately add rice cereal; stir
until cereal is coated. Press mixture
into a 13 x 9-inch pan coated with
cooking spray. Cool completely.
Store in an airtight container. YIELD:
18 servings (serving size: 1 square).

POINTS: 2; EXCHANGES: 1 Starch, ½ Fat;
PER SERVING: CAL 98 (24% from fat); PRO 2.2g;
FAT 2.7g (sat 1.0g); CARB 17.5g; FIB 0.4g;
CHOL 3mg; IRON 0.7mg; SOD 137mg; CALC 3mg

CHOCOLATE CHOCOLATE CHIP COOKIES

(pictured on page 48)
prep: 11 minutes • cook: 40 minutes

Indulge your sweet tooth by biting into crisp chocolate cookies packed with melted pockets of chocolate chips.

  1 cup all-purpose flour
  ¼ teaspoon baking soda
  ⅛ teaspoon salt
  ¼ cup butter, softened
  ½ cup packed dark brown sugar
  ½ cup granulated sugar
  ⅓ cup unsweetened cocoa
  2 large egg whites
  ⅓ cup semisweet chocolate minichips
Cooking spray

1. Preheat oven to 350°.
2. Lightly spoon flour into a dry measuring cup; level with a knife. Combine flour, baking soda, and salt in a large bowl.
3. Beat butter and brown sugar with a mixer at medium speed until light and fluffy; gradually add granulated sugar, beating well. Add cocoa and egg whites, beating well. Gradually add flour mixture, beating until blended. Stir in chocolate minichips.
4. Drop by rounded teaspoonfuls 1½ inches apart onto baking sheets coated with cooking spray. Bake at 350° for 10 minutes. Cool on pans 2 minutes or until firm. Remove cookies from pans; cool completely on wire racks. YIELD: 40 cookies (serving size: 1 cookie).

POINTS: 1; **EXCHANGE:** ½ Starch; **PER SERVING:** CAL 52 (27% from fat); PRO 0.7g; FAT 1.6g (sat 1.1g); CARB 9.1g; FIB 0.4g; CHOL 3mg; IRON 0.3mg; SOD 32mg; CALC 4mg

SPICY MOLASSES CRACKLES

(pictured on page 48)
prep: 24 minutes • cook: 24 minutes

For easy cleanup, line baking sheets with parchment paper.

  2 cups all-purpose flour
  2 teaspoons baking soda
  1¼ teaspoons ground cinnamon
  ¾ teaspoon ground ginger
  ¼ teaspoon ground nutmeg
  ⅛ teaspoon ground cloves
  ⅛ teaspoon salt
  ⅓ cup butter, softened
  1 cup packed dark brown sugar
  1 large egg
  2 tablespoons molasses
  2½ tablespoons granulated sugar
Cooking spray

1. Preheat oven to 350°.
2. Lightly spoon flour into dry measuring cups; level with a knife. Combine flour, baking soda, and next 5 ingredients in a medium bowl.
3. Beat butter with a mixer at medium speed until creamy; gradually add 1 cup brown sugar, beating well. Add egg and molasses; beat well. Add flour mixture; beat until smooth. (Dough will be slightly crumbly.)
4. Shape dough into 1-inch balls. Roll balls in 2½ tablespoons sugar. Place balls 1½ inches apart on baking sheets coated with cooking spray. Bake at 350° for 8 minutes. Cool 2 minutes on pans. Remove from pans; cool completely on wire racks. YIELD: 38 cookies (serving size: 1 cookie).

POINTS: 1; **EXCHANGE:** 1 Starch; **PER SERVING:** CAL 68 (24% from fat); PRO 0.9g; FAT 1.8g (sat 1.1g); CARB 12.3g; FIB 0.2g; CHOL 10mg; IRON 0.5mg; SOD 95mg; CALC 10mg

EASY PEANUT BUTTER COOKIES

prep: 25 minutes • cook: 28 minutes

  1⅔ cups all-purpose flour
  1½ tablespoons cornstarch
  1¾ teaspoons baking powder
  ½ teaspoon baking soda
  ¾ cup packed brown sugar
  ¼ cup vegetable oil
  ¼ cup granulated sugar
  ¼ cup creamy peanut butter
  1½ tablespoons light-colored corn syrup
  2½ teaspoons vanilla extract
  1 large egg
Cooking spray
  3 tablespoons granulated sugar

1. Preheat oven to 375°.
2. Lightly spoon flour into dry measuring cups; level with a knife. Combine flour and next 3 ingredients in a bowl. Beat brown sugar and next 3 ingredients with a mixer at medium speed until well blended. Add corn syrup, vanilla, and egg; beat well. Stir in flour mixture.
3. Coat hands lightly with cooking spray, and shape dough into 48 (1-inch) balls. Roll balls in 3 tablespoons granulated sugar, and place 2 inches apart on baking sheets coated with cooking spray. Flatten cookies with the bottom of a glass.
4. Bake at 375° for 7 minutes or until cookies are lightly browned. Remove from pans, and cool cookies on wire racks. YIELD: 4 dozen (serving size: 1 cookie).

POINTS: 1; **EXCHANGES:** ½ Starch, ½ Fat; **PER SERVING:** CAL 59 (31% from fat); PRO 1.0g; FAT 2g (sat 0.4g); CARB 9.5g; FIB 0.2g; CHOL 5mg; IRON 0.3mg; SOD 23mg; CALC 14mg

PB AND J CHEESECAKE BARS

prep: 10 minutes • cook: 20 minutes
cool: 30 minutes • chill: 1½ hours

  15 reduced-fat vanilla wafers,
      crushed
    2 tablespoons butter, melted
    1 teaspoon sugar
Cooking spray
    1 (8-ounce) block ⅓-less-fat
      cream cheese
    ¼ cup creamy peanut butter
    ⅓ cup sugar
    1 large egg
    1 teaspoon vanilla extract
    ⅓ cup seedless blackberry fruit
      spread
    1 reduced-fat vanilla wafer,
      crushed

1. Preheat oven to 350°.
2. Combine first 3 ingredients; press into bottom of an 8-inch square baking pan coated with cooking spray. Bake at 350° for 6 minutes.
3. Beat cream cheese and peanut butter with a mixer at medium speed until creamy. Add sugar and egg, beating well. Stir in vanilla.
4. Spread blackberry spread evenly over crust. Pour cream cheese mixture over fruit spread; sprinkle with remaining crushed vanilla wafer. Bake at 350° for 14 minutes or until almost set. Cool 30 minutes. Cover and chill 1½ hours. YIELD: 16 servings (serving size: 1 bar).

POINTS: 3; EXCHANGES: 1 Starch, 1 Fat;
PER SERVING: CAL 121 (46% from fat); PRO 2.9g;
FAT 6.3g (sat 3.0g); CARB 13.2g; FIB 0.4g;
CHOL 24mg; IRON 0.2mg; SOD 121mg; CALC 21mg

CREAM CHEESE BROWNIES

prep: 15 minutes • cook: 37 minutes

Full of swirls of sweet cream cheese, these fudgy brownies are sure to be a new favorite with your family.

Cooking spray
    ½ cup (4 ounces) tub light cream
      cheese, softened
    ⅓ cup sugar
    ⅔ cup all-purpose flour
    ⅔ cup unsweetened cocoa
    ¼ teaspoon baking powder
    ¼ teaspoon baking soda
    ⅛ teaspoon salt
    1 large egg
    1 large egg white
    1 cup sugar
    ¼ cup butter, melted
    1 teaspoon vanilla extract
    3 tablespoons water

1. Preheat oven to 350°.
2. Line an 8-inch square baking pan with aluminum foil. Coat foil with cooking spray; set aside.
3. Beat cream cheese and ⅓ cup sugar with a mixer at medium speed until thoroughly blended. Set aside.
4. Lightly spoon flour into a dry measuring cup; level with a knife. Combine flour, cocoa, baking powder, baking soda, and salt in a large bowl; stir well. Combine egg and remaining 5 ingredients in a small bowl. Add egg mixture to flour mixture, and beat with a mixer at medium speed until well blended.
5. Set aside ½ cup chocolate mixture. Spread remaining chocolate mixture into prepared pan. Spread cream cheese mixture over chocolate. Dollop remaining chocolate mixture over top. Swirl batters together using a knife.

6. Bake at 350° for 35 to 37 minutes or until a wooden pick inserted in center comes out clean. Cool on a wire rack. Remove brownies from pan using foil; cut into squares. Remove from foil using spatula. YIELD: 16 servings (serving size: 1 brownie).

POINTS: 3; EXCHANGES: 1½ Starch, 1 Fat;
PER SERVING: CAL 141 (30% from fat); PRO 2.6g;
FAT 5.0g (sat 3.1g); CARB 23.2g; FIB 1.3g;
CHOL 25mg; IRON 0.8mg; SOD 121mg; CALC 22mg

BROWNIE EASE

Press a piece of aluminum foil into the baking pan so that the foil makes a smooth lining.

Once cooled, gently lift the brownies out of the pan using edges of foil.

Cut brownies into squares, and remove from foil lining using a spatula.

FUDGY CARAMEL BROWNIES

(pictured on cover and on page 52)
prep: 13 minutes • cook: 30 minutes

Substitute 16 small quartered chocolate-covered peppermint patties (such as York) for the caramels to get a 4-POINT fudgy mint treat.

  5 tablespoons stick margarine
  1 ounce unsweetened chocolate
1½ cups sugar
 ⅔ cup Dutch process cocoa or
    unsweetened cocoa
  3 large egg whites, lightly beaten
  1 large egg, lightly beaten
  1 cup all-purpose flour
 ½ teaspoon baking powder
Cooking spray
 20 small soft caramel candies,
    quartered

1. Preheat oven to 325°.
2. Place margarine and chocolate in a microwave-safe bowl. Microwave at HIGH 1 minute, stirring after 30 seconds, or until melted. Add sugar and cocoa; stir well. (Batter will be stiff.) Add egg whites and egg; stir well.
3. Lightly spoon flour into a dry measuring cup; level with a knife. Combine flour and baking powder; add to margarine mixture, stirring until smooth.
4. Pour batter into a 9-inch square pan coated with cooking spray. Sprinkle with caramels; swirl caramels into batter using the tip of a knife. Bake at 325° for 30 minutes. Cool in pan on a wire rack. YIELD: 16 servings (serving size: 1 brownie).

POINTS: 4; **EXCHANGES:** 2½ Starch, 1 Fat;
PER SERVING: CAL 198 (25% from fat); PRO 3.3g;
FAT 5.6g (sat 2.4g); CARB 37.0g; FIB 0.6g;
CHOL 14mg; IRON 1.1mg; SOD 106mg; CALC 36mg

DATE-NUT BLONDIES

(pictured on page 51)
prep: 20 minutes • cook: 22 minutes

Cooking spray
 ⅔ cup all-purpose flour
 ½ teaspoon baking powder
 ⅛ teaspoon salt
  1 large egg
  1 cup packed light brown sugar
  3 tablespoons butter or stick
    margarine, melted
  1 teaspoon vanilla extract
 ½ cup chopped dates
 ¼ cup chopped walnuts, toasted

1. Preheat oven to 350°.
2. Coat an 8-inch square baking pan with cooking spray; line with aluminum foil, letting ends of foil extend over sides of pan. Coat foil with cooking spray; set aside.
3. Lightly spoon flour into a dry measuring cup; level with a knife. Combine flour, baking powder, and salt in a large bowl; stir with a whisk. Set aside.
4. Beat egg, sugar, butter, and vanilla with a mixer at medium speed until smooth and creamy. Gradually add flour mixture, beating well. Stir in dates and walnuts. Spread mixture into prepared pan. Bake at 350° for 22 minutes or until golden. Cool completely on a wire rack.
5. Remove brownies from pan using foil; cut into squares. Remove from foil using a spatula. YIELD: 16 servings (serving size: 1 square).

POINTS: 3; **EXCHANGES:** 1½ Starch, ½ Fat;
PER SERVING: CAL 123 (27% from fat); PRO 1.4g;
FAT 3.8g (sat 1.6g); CARB 21.8g; FIB 0.7g;
CHOL 19mg; IRON 0.7mg; SOD 65mg; CALC 27mg

GRANOLA BISCOTTI

prep: 22 minutes • cook: 40 minutes
cool: 10 minutes

1¼ cups all-purpose flour
 ¾ teaspoon baking powder
 ¼ teaspoon baking soda
 ⅛ teaspoon salt
  3 tablespoons butter
 ½ cup sugar
 ¼ teaspoon almond extract
  1 large egg
 ½ cup low-fat granola without
    raisins (such as Kellogg's)
Cooking spray

1. Preheat oven to 325°.
2. Lightly spoon flour into dry measuring cups; level with a knife. Combine flour, baking powder, baking soda, and salt in a large bowl; stir with a whisk. Beat butter, sugar, almond extract, and egg with a mixer at medium speed until blended. Add flour mixture and granola; beat until well blended.
3. Turn dough out onto a baking sheet coated with cooking spray. Shape dough into an 11-inch-long roll; pat to 1-inch thickness. Bake at 325° for 30 minutes.
4. Place baking sheet on a wire rack to cool 10 minutes. Remove roll from baking sheet; cut roll diagonally into 18 (½-inch) slices. Place slices, cut sides up, on baking sheet. Bake at 325° for 10 minutes. Remove from baking sheet; cool completely on wire rack. YIELD: 18 servings (serving size: 1 biscotto).

POINTS: 2; **EXCHANGES:** 1 Starch, ½ Fat;
PER SERVING: CAL 85 (26% from fat); PRO 1.5g;
FAT 2.4g (sat 1.3g); CARB 14.5g; FIB 0.4g;
CHOL 17mg; IRON 0.6mg; SOD 84mg; CALC 16mg

Fish & Shellfish

BLACKENED CATFISH FILLETS

prep: 5 minutes • cook: 12 minutes

We followed tradition and cooked the fish in a cast iron skillet. A large nonstick skillet could also be used. Just reduce the starting temperature from high to medium-high.

1 tablespoon paprika
1½ teaspoons dried oregano
½ teaspoon salt
½ teaspoon pepper
¼ teaspoon ground cumin
⅛ teaspoon garlic powder
4 (6-ounce) catfish fillets
1 tablespoon light butter
Lemon slices (optional)

1. Combine first 6 ingredients in a small bowl; stir well.
2. Rinse fillets, and pat dry with paper towels to remove excess moisture. Sprinkle paprika mixture evenly on both sides of fillets; rub seasonings in gently.
3. Place a 12-inch cast iron skillet over high heat until hot. Add ½ tablespoon butter, and tilt pan to coat bottom. Add 2 fillets, and cook 2 minutes. Reduce heat to medium; turn, and cook 4 minutes or until fish flakes easily when tested with a fork. Remove from pan, and keep warm. Repeat procedure with remaining butter and fillets. Serve with lemon slices, if desired. YIELD: 4 servings (serving size: 1 fillet).

POINTS: 4; **EXCHANGES:** 4 Lean Meat; **PER SERVING:** CAL 183 (33% from fat); PRO 28.5g; FAT 6.6g (sat 2.3g); CARB 1.6g; FIB 0.7g; CHOL 104mg; IRON 1.3mg; SOD 383mg; CALC 38mg

FLOUNDER FILLETS WITH BÉARNAISE SAUCE

prep: 6 minutes • cook: 19 minutes

To keep the fillets in one piece when turning them, place one spatula under the fillet and one spatula on top and gently flip.

4 (6-ounce) flounder fillets
¼ teaspoon pepper
Cooking spray
½ cup dry white wine
2 tablespoons minced fresh onion
1 garlic clove, minced
½ teaspoon dried tarragon
3 tablespoons light butter
1 tablespoon chopped fresh parsley
¼ teaspoon salt

1. Sprinkle fillets with pepper.
2. Heat a large nonstick skillet over medium-high heat. Coat fillets with cooking spray. Add 2 fillets to pan; cook 3 to 4 minutes on each side or until fish flakes easily when tested with a fork. Remove from pan, and keep warm. Repeat procedure with remaining fillets.
3. Add wine, onion, garlic, and tarragon to pan; bring to a boil. Reduce heat to medium-high, and cook 5 to 7 minutes or until liquid evaporates. Reduce heat to low; add butter, parsley, and salt. Cook 2 minutes or until butter melts.
4. Spoon sauce over fillets. Serve immediately. YIELD: 4 servings (serving size: 1 fillet and about 1½ tablespoons sauce).

POINTS: 4; **EXCHANGES:** 4 Very Lean Meat, ½ Fat; **PER SERVING:** CAL 181 (32% from fat); PRO 29.4g; FAT 6.3g (sat 3.4g); CARB 1.4g; FIB 0.2g; CHOL 95mg; IRON 0.7mg; SOD 324mg; CALC 30mg

BAKED GROUPER FILLETS WITH KALAMATA MUSTARD

prep: 6 minutes • cook: 12 minutes

Orange roughy or sea bass may be substituted for the grouper.

4 (6-ounce) grouper or other firm white fish fillets
Cooking spray
¼ teaspoon pepper
⅛ teaspoon paprika
8 chopped pitted kalamata olives
½ teaspoon dried basil
1½ tablespoons coarse-grain Dijon mustard
2 tablespoons light butter, softened
2 tablespoons chopped fresh parsley

1. Preheat oven to 425°.
2. Arrange fillets on a baking sheet coated with cooking spray. Lightly coat tops of each fillet with cooking spray; sprinkle with pepper and paprika. Bake, uncovered, at 425° for 12 minutes or until fish flakes easily when tested with a fork.
3. Combine olives and next 3 ingredients in a small bowl.
4. Remove fillets from baking sheet, and top evenly with mustard mixture. Sprinkle with parsley. Serve immediately. YIELD: 4 servings (serving size: 1 fillet and about 2 teaspoons mustard mixture).

POINTS: 5; **EXCHANGES:** 5 Very Lean Meat, ½ Fat; **PER SERVING:** CAL 210 (30% from fat); PRO 33.8g; FAT 6.7g (sat 2.6g); CARB 1.1g; FIB 0.2g; CHOL 73mg; IRON 1.8mg; SOD 384mg; CALC 55mg

CRUSTY BAKED GROUPER WITH CUCUMBER SALSA

prep: 10 minutes • cook: 27 minutes

⅔ cup plain fat-free yogurt
½ cup chopped seeded cucumber
¼ teaspoon dried mint, crushed
¼ cup finely chopped red onion
⅛ teaspoon salt
⅛ teaspoon freshly ground black
   pepper
4 (6-ounce) grouper fillets or
   other firm white fish fillets
   (about 1 inch thick)
Cooking spray
1 (1-ounce) slice white bread
1 tablespoon butter, melted

1. Preheat oven to 450°.
2. Combine first 6 ingredients in a bowl; stir until blended. Cover mixture, and chill.
3. Place fillets in an 11 x 7-inch baking dish coated with cooking spray.
4. Place bread in a food processor; pulse 10 times or until coarse crumbs measure ½ cup. Combine crumbs and butter in a bowl; stir well. Spoon over fillets.
5. Bake at 450° for 15 minutes or until crumbs are browned; cover loosely with foil, and bake an additional 12 to 15 minutes or until fish flakes easily when tested with a fork. Serve with chilled cucumber salsa. YIELD: 4 servings (serving size: 1 fillet and ¼ cup cucumber salsa).

POINTS: 5; **EXCHANGES:** ½ Starch, 5 Very Lean Meat; **PER SERVING:** CAL 221 (20% from fat); PRO 35.5g; FAT 4.8g (sat 2.2g); CARB 8.1g; FIB 0.7g; CHOL 72mg; IRON 1.7mg; SOD 251mg; CALC 106mg

GROUPER WITH ROASTED ASPARAGUS AND PEPPERS

prep: 10 minutes • cook: 18 minutes

24 asparagus spears (about ½
   pound)
1 cup red bell pepper strips
   (¼ inch thick), cut in half
   crosswise
1 tablespoon olive oil
Cooking spray
1 tablespoon fresh lemon juice
1 teaspoon dried dill, divided
½ teaspoon salt, divided
4 (6-ounce) grouper or other
   firm white fish fillets
⅛ teaspoon black pepper

1. Preheat oven to 425°.
2. Snap off tough ends of asparagus. Cut asparagus into 2-inch pieces. Toss asparagus and peppers with olive oil, and place on a jelly roll pan coated with cooking spray. Bake at 425° for 8 to 10 minutes or until crisp-tender, stirring occasionally. Remove from oven. Sprinkle with lemon juice, ¾ teaspoon dill, and ¼ teaspoon salt, tossing gently to coat. Set aside, and keep warm.
3. Arrange fillets on a jelly roll pan coated with cooking spray. Sprinkle fillets evenly with remaining ¼ teaspoon dill, remaining ¼ teaspoon salt, and black pepper. Bake at 425° for 10 to 12 minutes or until fish flakes easily when tested with a fork. Top with asparagus mixture. Serve immediately. YIELD: 4 servings (serving size: 1 fillet and ½ cup asparagus mixture).

POINTS: 4; **EXCHANGES:** 1 Vegetable, 5 Very Lean Meat; **PER SERVING:** CAL 207 (24% from fat); PRO 34.7g; FAT 5.3g (sat 0.9g); CARB 4.3g; FIB 1.4g; CHOL 63mg; IRON 2.2mg; SOD 388mg; CALC 64mg

GRILLED HALIBUT WITH LEMON SAUCE

prep: 8 minutes • cook: 12 minutes

We preferred the flavor of freshly squeezed lemon juice. Generally, one lemon yields 2 to 3 tablespoons of juice.

¾ cup fat-free, less-sodium chicken
   broth
¼ cup fresh lemon juice
1 tablespoon cornstarch
1 tablespoon minced fresh parsley
½ teaspoon salt
¼ teaspoon dried oregano
¼ teaspoon dried rosemary
8 (6-ounce) halibut fillets
Cooking spray

1. Prepare grill.
2. Combine first 3 ingredients in a small saucepan. Bring to a boil; cook 1 minute, stirring constantly. Remove from heat. Stir in parsley, salt, oregano, and rosemary; set mixture aside, and keep warm.
3. Place fillets on grill rack coated with cooking spray; cover and grill 6 minutes on each side or until fish flakes easily when tested with a fork. Serve with warm lemon sauce. YIELD: 8 servings (serving size: 1 fillet and 2 tablespoons sauce).

POINTS: 4; **EXCHANGES:** 5 Very Lean Meat; **PER SERVING:** CAL 197 (19% from fat); PRO 35.6g; FAT 4.2g (sat 0.6g); CARB 1.7g; FIB 0.0g; CHOL 80mg; IRON 1.5mg; SOD 251mg; CALC 82mg

BROILED SALMON WITH CUCUMBER-DILL SAUCE

prep: 8 minutes • cook: 14 minutes

The crisp coolness of cucumber and the bite of fresh dill make a refreshing summer sauce for salmon.

¾ cup reduced-fat sour cream
1 small cucumber, peeled, seeded, and chopped (about ¾ cup)
1 small shallot, peeled and finely chopped
2 tablespoons chopped fresh dill
½ teaspoon salt, divided
½ teaspoon freshly ground black pepper, divided
4 (6-ounce) salmon fillets
Cooking spray
Lemon wedges (optional)

1. Preheat broiler.
2. Combine first 4 ingredients in a small serving bowl; stir in ¼ teaspoon each of salt and pepper. Cover and chill until ready to serve.
3. Sprinkle fillets with remaining salt and pepper. Place fillets, skin side up, on broiler rack coated with cooking spray. Broil 7 minutes; turn fillets, and broil 5 to 7 minutes or until fish flakes easily when tested with a fork. Remove skin from fillets. Serve fillets with sauce and lemon wedges, if desired. YIELD: 4 servings (serving size: 1 fillet and ⅓ cup sauce).

POINTS: 6; **EXCHANGES:** ½ Starch, 5 Lean Meat; **PER SERVING:** CAL 262 (32% from fat); PRO 35.8g; FAT 9.3g (sat 3.8g); CARB 7.9g; FIB 0.4g; CHOL 95mg; IRON 1.0mg; SOD 421mg; CALC 134mg

SALMON WITH FIERY SWEET CUCUMBER SALSA

prep: 12 minutes • cook: 12 minutes

Four medium limes should yield enough juice for this recipe.

1 cup chopped seeded cucumber
3 tablespoons finely chopped red onion
1 medium jalapeño, seeded and finely chopped
3 tablespoons chopped fresh mint
3 tablespoons fresh lime juice
1 tablespoon sugar
⅛ teaspoon salt
4 (6-ounce) salmon fillets
Cooking spray
2 tablespoons fresh lime juice
½ teaspoon salt
¼ teaspoon freshly ground black pepper

1. Preheat broiler.
2. Combine first 7 ingredients in a small bowl. Cover and chill.
3. Place fillets on rack of a broiler pan coated with cooking spray. Drizzle with 2 tablespoons lime juice; sprinkle with ½ teaspoon salt and pepper. Broil 12 minutes or until fish flakes easily when tested with a fork. Serve salmon with cucumber mixture. YIELD: 4 servings (serving size: 1 fillet and ¼ cup salsa).

POINTS: 5; **EXCHANGES:** ½ Fruit, 5 Very Lean Meat; **PER SERVING:** CAL 230 (26% from fat); PRO 34.5g; FAT 6.4g (sat 1.6g); CARB 7.3g; FIB 0.8g; CHOL 80mg; IRON 1.5mg; SOD 450mg; CALC 82mg

BROILED SALMON WITH CITRUS SALSA

prep: 20 minutes • cook: 10 minutes

Jarred citrus salad, available in the produce section of the supermarket, can be substituted for the orange and grapefruit sections.

4 (6-ounce) salmon fillets
Cooking spray
1 teaspoon olive oil
½ teaspoon salt
⅛ teaspoon black pepper
1 cup coarsely chopped orange sections (about 1 large)
1 cup coarsely chopped grapefruit sections (about 1 large)
2 tablespoons minced fresh cilantro
½ cup chopped red bell pepper
¼ cup finely chopped red onion
1 jalapeño pepper, seeded and finely chopped
1 tablespoon sugar

1. Preheat broiler.
2. Place fillets on rack of a broiler pan coated with cooking spray. Brush fillets with olive oil; sprinkle with salt and pepper. Broil 10 to 12 minutes or until fish flakes easily when tested with a fork.
3. While fillets cook, combine orange sections and remaining ingredients in a bowl. Serve with fillets. YIELD: 4 servings (serving size: 1 fillet and about ⅔ cup salsa).

POINTS: 6; **EXCHANGES:** 1 Starch, 5 Very Lean Meat, ½ Fat; **PER SERVING:** CAL 274 (25% from fat); PRO 35.1g; FAT 7.6g (sat 1.7g); CARB 15.7g; FIB 2.3g; CHOL 80mg; IRON 1.1mg; SOD 376mg; CALC 95mg

SZECHUAN SALMON STIR-FRY

prep: 17 minutes • cook: 15 minutes

1 pound salmon fillets, skinned
   and cut into 2-inch pieces
1 tablespoon minced garlic
1 tablespoon grated peeled fresh
   ginger
1 (5-ounce) package Japanese
   curly noodles
1 teaspoon sesame oil
½ cup fat-free, less-sodium
   chicken broth, divided
1 tablespoon cornstarch
⅓ cup low-sodium teriyaki sauce
½ teaspoon crushed red pepper
¼ teaspoon salt
2 teaspoons vegetable oil
1 cup matchstick-cut carrots
1 large orange bell pepper,
   cut into ⅛-inch-thick strips
½ cup green onions, cut into
   2-inch pieces

1. Combine first 3 ingredients in a bowl; toss well, and set aside.
2. Prepare noodles according to package directions, omitting salt and fat; drain well. Return noodles to pan; toss with sesame oil. Set aside, and keep warm.
3. Combine ¼ cup broth and cornstarch, stirring until smooth. Stir in remaining broth, teriyaki sauce, red pepper, and salt; set aside.
4. Heat oil in a wok or large non-stick skillet over high heat. Add salmon mixture; stir-fry 4 minutes or until fish flakes easily when tested with a fork. Remove salmon. Add carrots, bell pepper, and green onions to pan; stir-fry 4 minutes or until crisp-tender.

5. Reduce heat; return salmon to pan. Stir in broth mixture; bring to a boil. Cook, stirring constantly, 1 to 2 minutes, or until sauce thickens. Top noodles with salmon mixture.
YIELD: 4 servings (serving size: ¾ cup noodles and 1 cup salmon mixture).

POINTS: 7; **EXCHANGES:** 2½ Starch, 1 Vegetable, 3 Lean Meat; **PER SERVING:** CAL 354 (21% from fat); PRO 29.0g; FAT 8.4g (sat 1.4g); CARB 40.3g; FIB 3.0g; CHOL 53mg; IRON 1.5mg; SOD 921mg; CALC 60mg

HONEY-GLAZED SALMON

(pictured on page 70)
prep: 6 minutes • cook: 12 minutes

2 tablespoons honey
1 tablespoon fresh orange juice
1 tablespoon fresh lemon juice
1 tablespoon hoisin sauce
2 teaspoons Dijon mustard
¼ teaspoon salt
¼ teaspoon pepper
4 (6-ounce) salmon fillets (about
   1 inch thick)
Cooking spray

1. Preheat broiler.
2. Combine first 7 ingredients, and stir well with a whisk.
3. Place fillets on a broiler pan coated with cooking spray. Brush with honey mixture; cook 12 minutes or until fish flakes easily when tested with a fork, basting frequently with honey mixture. YIELD: 4 servings (serving size: 1 fillet).

POINTS: 5; **EXCHANGES:** 1 Starch, 5 Very Lean Meat; **PER SERVING:** CAL 248 (24% from fat); PRO 34.2g; FAT 6.4g (sat 1.6g); CARB 11.3g; FIB 0.2g; CHOL 80mg; IRON 1.0mg; SOD 354mg; CALC 68mg

BAKED SNAPPER WITH TOMATO-ORANGE SAUCE

prep: 12 minutes • cook: 40 minutes

Visit your local farmer's market for the best variety of fresh tomatoes. Then serve this dish with a side of couscous to capture the flavors of the rich tomato sauce.

3 cups chopped seeded red tomato
   (about 2 pounds)
2 cups chopped seeded yellow
   tomato (about 1½ pounds)
½ cup chopped onion
¼ cup dry white wine
1 teaspoon grated orange rind
¼ cup fresh orange juice
⅛ teaspoon ground turmeric
2 garlic cloves, minced
4 (6-ounce) red snapper, grouper,
   or other firm white fish fillets
1 teaspoon olive oil
¼ teaspoon salt
⅛ teaspoon pepper

1. Preheat oven to 400°.
2. Combine first 8 ingredients in an 11 x 7-inch baking dish. Bake at 400° for 20 minutes. Arrange fillets on top of tomato mixture. Drizzle with oil; sprinkle with salt and pepper. Cover with foil; bake 20 minutes or until fish flakes easily when tested with a fork. YIELD: 4 servings (serving size: 1 fillet and 1 cup sauce).

POINTS: 5; **EXCHANGES:** 1 Starch, 5 Very Lean Meat; **PER SERVING:** CAL 246 (15% from fat); PRO 37.3g; FAT 4.2g (sat 0.7g); CARB 14.9g; FIB 2.9; CHOL 63mg; IRON 1.5mg; SOD 278mg; CALC 77mg

PAN-FRIED TILAPIA WITH WHITE WINE AND CAPERS

prep: 8 minutes • cook: 8 minutes

Tilapia is a very mild-tasting fish that takes on the flavors of the ingredients it's cooked with. If you can't find tilapia, flounder or any other mild white fish is a good substitute.

¼ cup dry white wine
¼ cup chopped seeded tomato
2 tablespoons fresh lemon juice
2 tablespoons drained capers
1 garlic clove, minced
½ teaspoon dried basil
4 (6-ounce) tilapia fillets
½ teaspoon salt
¼ teaspoon freshly ground black pepper
¼ cup all-purpose flour
Cooking spray
1 tablespoon olive oil
2 tablespoons light butter
2 tablespoons chopped fresh parsley
Lemon wedges (optional)

1. Combine first 6 ingredients, stirring well with a whisk; set aside.
2. Sprinkle fillets with salt and pepper. Dredge fillets lightly in flour, and coat both sides of fillets with cooking spray.
3. Heat oil in a large nonstick skillet over medium-high heat. Add fillets; cook 3 minutes. Reduce heat to medium; turn fillets, and cook 3 minutes or until fish flakes easily when tested with a fork. Remove from pan.
4. Add wine mixture to pan; cook 30 seconds, stirring constantly. Remove from heat; stir in butter until melted. Spoon wine mixture over fillets; sprinkle with parsley.

Serve with lemon wedges, if desired.
YIELD: 4 servings (serving size: 1 fillet and 2 tablespoons sauce).

POINTS: 5; **EXCHANGES:** ½ Starch, 4 Very Lean Meat, 1 Fat; **PER SERVING:** CAL 229 (33% from fat); PRO 30.1g; FAT 8.4g (sat 2.9g); CARB 8.1g; FIB 0.7g; CHOL 90mg; IRON 1.2mg; SOD 580mg; CALC 34mg

GRILLED TUNA WITH HERBED MAYONNAISE

prep: 4 minutes • cook: 6 minutes

Be creative in the kitchen—experiment with a variety of fresh herbs to make up your own herbed mayonnaise.

¼ cup fat-free mayonnaise
¼ cup plain fat-free yogurt
1 teaspoon chopped fresh oregano
1 teaspoon chopped fresh tarragon
1 teaspoon lemon juice
¼ teaspoon salt
¼ teaspoon pepper
4 (6-ounce) tuna steaks (about 1 inch thick)
Cooking spray

1. Prepare grill.
2. Combine first 5 ingredients in a small bowl. Cover and chill.
3. Sprinkle salt and pepper over steaks. Place steaks on grill rack coated with cooking spray; grill 3 minutes on each side or until steaks are medium-rare or to desired degree of doneness. To serve, top steaks with mayonnaise mixture. YIELD: 4 servings (serving size: 1 tuna steak and 2 tablespoons mayonnaise mixture).

POINTS: 6; **EXCHANGES:** 5 Lean Meat; **PER SERVING:** CAL 267 (29% from fat); PRO 40.5g; FAT 8.5g (sat 2.2g); CARB 4.6g; FIB 0.1g; CHOL 65mg; IRON 8.6mg; SOD 414mg; CALC 288mg

QUICK SEARED TUNA STEAKS

prep: 5 minutes • cook: 10 minutes

It's amazing how a few simple ingredients can quickly transform fresh fish into a delicious entrée.

¼ cup dry sherry
2 tablespoons low-sodium soy sauce
1 tablespoon fresh lime juice
2 teaspoons olive oil
4 (6-ounce) tuna steaks (about 1 inch thick)
¼ teaspoon salt
½ teaspoon coarsely ground black pepper

1. Combine first 3 ingredients in a small bowl, stirring well with a whisk. Set aside.
2. Heat oil in a large nonstick skillet over medium-high heat. Sprinkle steaks with salt and pepper; add steaks to pan. Cook 4 minutes on each side until steaks are medium-rare or desired degree of doneness. Transfer steaks to a serving dish, and keep warm. Pour sherry mixture into pan. Cook 1 to 1½ minutes or until reduced to 2 tablespoons, stirring to deglaze pan; pour over steaks. YIELD: 4 servings (serving size: 1 tuna steak and ½ tablespoon sauce).

POINTS: 4; **EXCHANGES:** 5 Very Lean Meat; **PER SERVING:** CAL 203 (19% from fat); PRO 38.0g; FAT 4.0g (sat 0.9g); CARB 1.2g; FIB 0.1g; CHOL 80mg; IRON 2.2mg; SOD 512mg; CALC 52mg

LOUISIANA DEVILED CRAB CAKES WITH HOT PEPPERED SOUR CREAM

(pictured on back cover)
prep: 30 minutes • cook: 15 minutes

Ground red pepper adds the "devil" to these crab cakes. If you want a milder flavor, omit the pepper in both the crab cakes and the sour cream mixture.

Cooking spray
½ cup finely chopped red bell pepper
¼ cup finely chopped green onions
1 garlic clove, minced
¾ cup frozen whole-kernel corn, thawed and drained
2 tablespoons finely chopped fresh parsley
⅓ cup light mayonnaise
2 large egg whites
2 tablespoons fresh lemon juice
1 teaspoon Dijon mustard
¼ teaspoon salt
¼ teaspoon ground red pepper
¼ teaspoon freshly ground black pepper
1 pound lump crab meat, drained and shell pieces removed
1 cup dry breadcrumbs, divided
4 teaspoons vegetable oil, divided
Hot Peppered Sour Cream
Cilantro leaves (optional)

1. Heat a 12-inch nonstick skillet over medium-high heat; coat with cooking spray. Add red bell pepper and next 4 ingredients; cook 2 minutes. Remove from heat; cool slightly.
2. Combine mayonnaise and next 6 ingredients in a medium bowl, stirring with a whisk. Stir in red bell pepper mixture. Fold in crab and ½ cup breadcrumbs. Divide mixture into 10 equal portions, shaping each into a ¾-inch-thick patty. Dredge crab cakes in remaining ½ cup breadcrumbs.
3. Wipe pan with paper towels. Heat 2 teaspoons oil in pan over medium heat. Add 5 crab cakes; cook 3 minutes. Reduce heat to medium-low; coat tops of crab cakes with cooking spray. Turn crab cakes, and cook 3 minutes or until done. Keep warm. Wipe pan with paper towels. Repeat procedure with remaining oil and crab cakes. Serve immediately with Hot Peppered Sour Cream. Garnish with cilantro leaves, if desired. YIELD: 5 servings (serving size: 2 crab cakes and 2 tablespoons sour cream mixture).

POINTS: 7; **EXCHANGES:** 2 Starch, 3 Very Lean Meat, 2 Fat; **PER SERVING:** CAL 324 (37% from fat); PRO 23.4g; FAT 13.4g (sat 3.1g); CARB 27.4g; FIB 1.7g; CHOL 70mg; IRON 2.0mg; SOD 1,007mg; CALC 135mg

HOT PEPPERED SOUR CREAM
prep: 2 minutes

½ cup light sour cream
1 tablespoon fresh lemon juice
½ teaspoon salt
¼ teaspoon ground red pepper

1. Combine all ingredients, stirring well with a whisk. Cover and chill until ready to serve. YIELD: ½ cup (serving size: 1 tablespoon).

POINTS: 1; **EXCHANGE:** ½ Fat; **PER SERVING:** CAL 24 (69% from fat); PRO 0.7g; FAT 1.9g (sat 1.2g); CARB 1.2g; FIB 0g; CHOL 8mg; IRON 0mg; SOD 155mg; CALC 25mg

MUSSELS IN PIQUANT BROTH

prep: 11 minutes • cook: 42 minutes

For a spicier dish, substitute spicy hot vegetable juice for regular vegetable juice in this recipe.

1 tablespoon olive oil
1 small onion, finely chopped
2 large garlic cloves, minced
1 cup dry white wine
3 cups vegetable juice (such as V-8)
2 cups clam juice
3 tablespoons fresh lemon juice
½ teaspoon hot sauce
1 tablespoon dried Italian seasoning
2 bay leaves
½ teaspoon freshly ground black pepper
½ cup minced fresh cilantro
48 mussels, scrubbed and debearded

1. Heat oil in a large Dutch oven over medium-high heat. Add onion and garlic; sauté 2 minutes or until tender. Add wine; bring to a boil, and cook 5 minutes. Add vegetable juice and next 6 ingredients. Bring to a boil; reduce heat, and simmer, uncovered, 30 minutes. Stir in cilantro. Add mussels; bring to a boil. Cover, reduce heat, and simmer 5 minutes or until shells open.
2. Discard bay leaves and any unopened shells. Divide mussels evenly among 4 bowls. Ladle broth over mussels. YIELD: 4 servings (serving size: 12 mussels and 1¼ cups broth).

POINTS: 4; **EXCHANGES:** 1 Starch, 2 Lean Meat; **PER SERVING:** CAL 189 (29% from fat); PRO 16.7g; FAT 6.3g (sat 1.0g); CARB 17.4g; FIB 2.2g; CHOL 37mg; IRON 6.6mg; SOD 1,112mg; CALC 99mg

CURRIED SEA SCALLOPS

(pictured on page 70)

prep: 15 minutes • cook: 17 minutes

⅔ cup fat-free, less-sodium
    chicken broth
¼ cup fat-free half-and-half
1½ teaspoons fresh lemon juice
¾ teaspoon curry powder
½ teaspoon salt
¼ teaspoon pepper
1¼ pounds sea scallops
4 teaspoons all-purpose flour
Cooking spray
2 teaspoons olive oil, divided
2 tablespoons chopped fresh parsley
2 tablespoons thinly sliced green
    onions

1. Combine first 6 ingredients in a
bowl; stir well, and set aside.
2. Pat scallops dry with paper towels
to remove excess moisture; lightly
coat scallops with flour. Coat a large
nonstick skillet with cooking spray;
add 1 teaspoon oil. Place pan over
medium-high heat until hot. Add half
of scallops; cook 2 minutes on each
side. Remove scallops from pan; set
aside, and keep warm. Repeat procedure with remaining oil and scallops.
3. Return scallops to pan, and add
broth mixture; bring to a boil. Cook
3 minutes or until sauce is slightly
thickened. Sprinkle with parsley and
green onions. **YIELD:** 4 servings
(serving size: 5 ounces scallops and
2 tablespoons sauce).

POINTS: 4; **EXCHANGES:** ½ Starch, 3 Very Lean
Meat; **PER SERVING:** CAL 171 (19% from fat);
PRO 24.7g; FAT 3.4g (sat 0.4g); CARB 7.9g; FIB 0.4g;
CHOL 47mg; IRON 0.8mg; SOD 639mg; CALC 50mg

SCALLOP SENSE

**What's the difference between
bay scallops and sea scallops?**
Although there are many kinds,
scallops are generally classified as
bay or sea scallops. Bay scallops
are small and tender and usually
only ½ inch in diameter. Sea scallops are much larger, sometimes
as large as 2 inches in diameter,
and are often easier to find in grocery stores. The two kinds of scallops can be used interchangeably
in recipes, but cooking times will
vary slightly. We tested our
recipes with sea scallops, but if
you would like to substitute bay
scallops, just reduce the cooking
time by 2 to 3 minutes.

**What should I look for when
buying scallops?**
The best-quality scallops are
going to be found at a reputable
fish market. However, some grocery stores may also have a good
selection. When buying scallops,
make sure they have a shiny,
moist look and a slightly sweet
odor. Scallops should range in
color from pale beige to creamy
pink. Avoid those that are stark
white—they've been soaked in
water to increase their weight.

SCALLOPS WITH BASIL AND TOMATO

prep: 12 minutes • cook: 5 minutes

*The delicate flavor of sweet scallops
comes alive when they're tossed with
fresh tomatoes and olive oil.*

1 cup chopped seeded tomato
    (about 1 large)
2 tablespoons chopped fresh parsley
½ teaspoon dried basil leaves
1 garlic clove, minced
½ teaspoon salt
¼ teaspoon freshly ground black
    pepper
1 tablespoon olive oil
1 tablespoon light butter
1 pound sea scallops
Lemon wedges (optional)

1. Combine first 6 ingredients in a
small bowl. Set aside.
2. Heat oil and butter in a large
nonstick skillet over medium-high
heat. Add scallops, and cook 2 minutes on each side.
3. Add tomato mixture to pan, and
cook 1 minute, stirring gently, until
thoroughly heated. Serve immediately with lemon wedges, if desired.
YIELD: 4 servings (serving size: ½ cup
scallop mixture).

POINTS: 3; **EXCHANGES:** 3 Very Lean Meat, 1 Fat;
PER SERVING: CAL 154 (35% from fat); PRO 19.8g;
FAT 5.9g (sat 1.6g); CARB 5.3g; FIB 0.7g;
CHOL 42mg; IRON 0.7mg; SOD 496mg; CALC 37mg

PAN-SEARED SCALLOPS WITH CILANTRO

prep: 8 minutes • cook: 12 minutes

Two things are important when searing any food: use a very hot skillet, and cook the food in small batches. The high heat seals in the juices so that the food browns quickly.

    1 pound sea scallops
    1 teaspoon chili powder
    ½ teaspoon salt
    ¼ teaspoon black pepper
    1 tablespoon light butter, divided
Cooking spray
    ¼ cup water
    ½ jalapeño pepper, seeded and
        minced
    2 tablespoons lime juice
    2 tablespoons minced fresh
        cilantro

1. Sprinkle both sides of scallops with chili powder, salt, and black pepper.
2. Melt 1½ teaspoons butter in a large nonstick skillet coated with cooking spray over medium-high heat. Add half of scallops; cook 3 minutes on each side or until done. Remove scallops from pan; keep warm. Repeat procedure with remaining butter and scallops.
3. Add water, jalapeño pepper, and lime juice to pan; cook 1 minute, scraping bottom and sides of pan to loosen browned bits. Spoon sauce over scallops; sprinkle with cilantro. YIELD: 4 servings (serving size: 3 ounces scallops and about 2 tablespoons sauce).

POINTS: 3; **EXCHANGES:** 3 Very Lean Meat; **PER SERVING:** CAL 118 (19% from fat); PRO 19.5g; FAT 2.5g (sat 1.1g); CARB 4.1g; FIB 0.3g; CHOL 42mg; IRON 0.4mg; SOD 497mg; CALC 31mg

SAUTÉED SCALLOPS WITH WHITE WINE REDUCTION

prep: 5 minutes • cook: 5 minutes

As it evaporates and reduces, the wine combines with the flavorful browned bits in the pan to create a rich sauce.

    ⅓ cup dry white wine
    3 tablespoons water
    2 tablespoons minced fresh onion
    1 garlic clove, minced
    1 teaspoon Dijon mustard
    ½ teaspoon dried oregano
    1 pound sea scallops
    ½ teaspoon salt
    ¼ teaspoon freshly ground black
        pepper
    2 teaspoons olive oil
    2 tablespoons light butter
    2 tablespoons chopped fresh parsley

1. Combine first 6 ingredients; set aside.
2. Sprinkle scallops with salt and pepper. Heat oil in a large nonstick skillet over medium-high heat until hot. Add scallops; cook 2 minutes on each side or until done. Remove scallops from pan; keep warm.
3. Pour wine mixture into pan; cook over medium-high heat, scraping pan to loosen browned bits. Bring to a boil, and cook 1 minute or until reduced to ⅓ cup. Remove from heat; stir in butter. Spoon sauce over scallops; sprinkle scallops with parsley. YIELD: 4 servings (serving size: 3 ounces scallops and 2 tablespoons sauce).

POINTS: 4; **EXCHANGES:** 3 Very Lean Meat, 1 Fat; **PER SERVING:** CAL 152 (37% from fat); PRO 19.8g; FAT 6.3g (sat 2.4g); CARB 4.1g; FIB 0.3g; CHOL 47mg; IRON 0.7mg; SOD 543mg; CALC 39mg

SHRIMP-ANDOUILLE CREOLE

(pictured on page 70)
prep: 20 minutes • cook: 32 minutes

Cooking spray
    5 ounces andouille sausage, sliced
        into ¼-inch-thick slices
    ½ cup thinly sliced celery
    2 garlic cloves, minced
    1 (14.5-ounce) can diced
        tomatoes with green peppers
        and onions, undrained
    1 (5.5-ounce) can spicy tomato
        juice (such as V-8)
    8 ounces frozen peppers and
        onions, thawed
    1 cup frozen okra
    ½ teaspoon dried thyme
    1 bay leaf
    2 teaspoons Worcestershire sauce
    1 teaspoon hot sauce
    1¼ pounds medium shrimp, peeled
        and deveined
    2½ cups hot cooked rice
    2 tablespoons chopped fresh parsley

1. Heat a large Dutch oven coated with cooking spray over medium heat. Add sausage; cook 5 minutes or until lightly browned. Remove from pan. Add celery to drippings; cook 3 minutes. Add garlic; sauté 30 seconds.
2. Add sausage, tomatoes, and next 7 ingredients; bring to a boil. Cover, reduce heat, and simmer 10 minutes. Stir in shrimp; cover and simmer 10 minutes. Discard bay leaf. Serve over rice. Sprinkle with parsley. YIELD: 5 servings (serving size: 1 cup shrimp mixture and ½ cup rice).

POINTS: 5; **EXCHANGES:** 2 Starch, 1 Vegetable, 2 Lean Meat; **PER SERVING:** CAL 284 (20% from fat); PRO 22.9g; FAT 6.2g (sat 2.3g); CARB 33.8g; FIB 3.9g; CHOL 149mg; IRON 4.7mg; SOD 669mg; CALC 103mg

HOT-AND-SOUR SHRIMP WITH CHINESE CABBAGE

prep: 10 minutes • marinate: 1 hour
cook: 7 minutes

You can also grill these zesty shrimp.
Place the shrimp skewers on a
grill rack coated with cooking spray;
grill the shrimp 4 minutes on
each side or until done.

¼ cup orange marmalade
1 tablespoon olive oil
2 tablespoons fresh lime juice
2 tablespoons garlic chile sauce
   (such as House of Thai)
¼ teaspoon salt
1½ pounds jumbo shrimp (about
   20), peeled and deveined
Cooking spray
1 teaspoon vegetable oil
1 teaspoon dark sesame oil
6 cups shredded napa (Chinese)
   cabbage
¼ teaspoon salt

1. Combine first 5 ingredients in a
large heavy-duty zip-top plastic bag;
add shrimp. Seal; toss to coat. Marinate
in refrigerator 1 hour.
2. Preheat broiler.
3. Remove shrimp from marinade,
reserving marinade. Pour reserved
marinade into a small microwave-
safe bowl. Microwave at HIGH 30
seconds or until marinade boils; set
aside.
4. Thread shrimp onto 4 (8-inch)
skewers. Place skewers on a broiler
pan coated with cooking spray; broil
5 minutes or until done. Keep warm.
5. Heat vegetable and sesame oils in
a large nonstick skillet over high
heat; add cabbage. Cook 2 minutes
or until cabbage wilts; sprinkle with

salt. To serve, arrange shrimp on top
of cabbage; drizzle with marinade.
YIELD: 4 servings (serving size: 1 skewer, ½ cup cabbage, and 1½ tablespoons sauce).

POINTS: 5; **EXCHANGES:** 1 Starch, 3 Very Lean
Meat, 1 Fat; **PER SERVING:** CAL 219 (28% from fat);
PRO 23.4g; FAT 7.0g (sat 1.0g); CARB 16.6g;
FIB 1.1g; CHOL 202mg; IRON 4.2mg; SOD 602mg;
CALC 159mg

BAKED SHRIMP IN LEMONY GARLIC SAUCE

(pictured on page 69)
prep: 8 minutes • cook: 8 minutes

1¼ pounds large shrimp, peeled and
   deveined
Cooking spray
¼ cup fresh lemon juice
2 tablespoons light butter, melted
3 garlic cloves, minced
1 teaspoon Worcestershire sauce
¾ teaspoon lemon-pepper seasoning
¼ teaspoon ground red pepper
2 tablespoons chopped fresh parsley

1. Preheat oven to 425°.
2. Arrange shrimp in a single layer
in a 13 x 9-inch baking dish coated
with cooking spray. Combine lemon
juice and next 5 ingredients; pour
over shrimp.
3. Bake at 425° for 8 to 10 minutes
or until shrimp are done. Sprinkle
parsley over shrimp; serve immediately. **YIELD:** 4 servings (serving size:
3 ounces shrimp and 2 tablespoons
sauce).

POINTS: 3; **EXCHANGES:** 3 Very Lean Meat;
PER SERVING: CAL 117 (31% from fat); PRO 18.1g;
FAT 4.0g (sat 2.3g); CARB 2.6g; FIB 0.2g;
CHOL 171mg; IRON 2.8mg; SOD 322mg;
CALC 42mg

HOW TO PEEL AND DEVEIN SHRIMP

1. To peel shrimp, grasp the tail in one hand and the legs in the other.

2. In one motion, pull the legs off. Peel back the shell, and remove.

3. Use deveining tool to remove the shell and dark vein in one motion.

INDIAN CURRIED SHRIMP

prep: 15 minutes • cook: 12 minutes

¾ cup finely chopped onion
½ jalapeño pepper, seeded and
  minced
Cooking spray
1¼ pounds large shrimp, peeled and
  deveined
1 teaspoon ground ginger
½ to 1 teaspoon curry powder
1 cup light coconut milk
½ teaspoon salt
½ teaspoon sugar
½ cup frozen petite green peas
3 cups hot cooked long-grain rice

1. Heat a large nonstick skillet over
medium-high heat. Add onion and
jalapeño pepper. Coat vegetables
with cooking spray; sauté 4 minutes.
Add shrimp, ginger, and curry powder; sauté 3 minutes. Add coconut
milk and next 3 ingredients. Bring
to a boil; reduce heat, and simmer,
uncovered, 3 minutes or until
shrimp are done. Serve over rice.
YIELD: 4 servings (serving size: 1 cup
shrimp mixture and ¾ cup rice).

POINTS: 6; EXCHANGES: 3 Starch, 2 Lean Meat;
PER SERVING: CAL 302 (14% from fat); PRO 21.9g;
FAT 4.4g (sat 2.4g); CARB 41.8g; FIB 2.0g;
CHOL 161mg; IRON 4.8mg; SOD 514mg;
CALC 56mg

QUICK SHRIMP
Did you know that most grocery
stores sell raw shrimp that has been
peeled and deveined? You may
have to ask, but it will be well worth
the time you save. If you buy it
peeled and deveined, simply
decrease the amount called for in
the recipe by ¼ pound.

SHRIMP AND BOK CHOY STIR-FRY WITH GINGER AND CILANTRO

prep: 22 minutes • cook: 10 minutes

¼ cup low-sodium soy sauce
¼ cup minced fresh cilantro
2 tablespoons fresh lime juice
2 teaspoons grated peeled fresh
  ginger
4 garlic cloves, minced
1¼ pounds medium shrimp, peeled
  and deveined
¼ teaspoon ground red pepper
Cooking spray
2 teaspoons vegetable oil
2 cups sliced bok choy
1 cup sliced onion
1 cup fresh snow peas, trimmed
  (about 3 ounces)
2 cups hot cooked long-grain rice

1. Combine first 5 ingredients in a
bowl. Set aside.
2. Sprinkle shrimp with red pepper;
coat with cooking spray.
3. Heat a large nonstick skillet over
medium-high heat. Add shrimp, and
cook 4 minutes, stirring constantly.
Remove shrimp from pan, and
keep warm.
4. Heat oil in pan. Add bok choy,
onion, and snow peas. Cook 3 minutes, stirring constantly. Add shrimp
and reserved soy sauce mixture;
cook 1½ minutes or until bubbly,
stirring constantly. Serve over rice.
Yield: 3 servings (serving size: 1 cup
shrimp mixture and ⅔ cup rice).

POINTS: 6; EXCHANGES: 2 Starch, 1 Vegetable,
3 Very Lean Meat; **PER SERVING:** CAL 309
(14% from fat); PRO 30.2g; FAT 4.8g (sat 0.7g);
CARB 35.3g; FIB 3.0g; CHOL 215mg; IRON 5.9mg;
SOD 957mg; CALC 141mg

SHRIMP FRIED RICE

prep: 21 minutes • cook: 14 minutes

This is a great way to use leftover rice.

Cooking spray
1 pound shrimp, peeled and
  deveined
2 teaspoons vegetable oil
1 cup chopped celery
3 cups thinly sliced bok choy
1 cup (1-inch) diagonally cut
  snow pea pods
½ cup (1-inch) sliced green onions
2½ cups cooked long-grain rice,
  chilled
1 (8-ounce) can sliced water
  chestnuts, drained
1 teaspoon grated peeled fresh
  ginger
¼ cup low-sodium soy sauce
1 teaspoon toasted sesame oil
⅛ teaspoon pepper

1. Heat a large nonstick skillet coated
with cooking spray over medium-high
heat until hot. Add shrimp, and cook 3
to 4 minutes or until shrimp are done,
stirring occasionally. Remove shrimp.
2. Heat oil in pan over medium-
high heat. Add celery; cook, stirring
constantly, 2 minutes. Add bok choy,
pea pods, and green onion; cook,
stirring constantly, 4 minutes or until
bok choy is just wilted. Add remaining ingredients and shrimp; cook,
stirring often, 3 to 4 minutes or
until thoroughly heated. YIELD: 4
servings (serving size: 2 cups).

POINTS: 5; EXCHANGES: 2 Starch, 2 Vegetable,
2 Lean Meat; **PER SERVING:** CAL 278 (16% from fat);
PRO 18.7g; FAT 4.7g (sat 0.6g); CARB 38.9g;
FIB 4.6g; CHOL 121mg; IRON 15.1mg; SOD 813mg;
CALC 116mg

GREEK PASTA WITH SHRIMP AND ARTICHOKES

prep: 15 minutes • cook: 9 minutes
chill: 10 minutes

This zesty dish is delicious served hot as an entrée or chilled as a salad.

  6 ounces uncooked orzo (rice-shaped pasta)
1¼ pounds medium shrimp, peeled and deveined
  1 (14-ounce) can artichoke hearts, drained and coarsely chopped
  1 cup grape tomatoes, halved
  ¼ cup chopped fresh parsley
  ¼ cup (2 ounces) crumbled feta cheese with basil and sun-dried tomatoes
  2 tablespoons lemon juice
  1 teaspoon dried oregano
  ¼ to ½ teaspoon coarsely ground black pepper
  ½ teaspoon salt
  ⅛ teaspoon ground red pepper

1. Cook pasta according to package directions 6 minutes, omitting salt and fat. Add shrimp, and cook 3 minutes or until shrimp are done. Drain well.
2. Combine artichokes and remaining ingredients in a large bowl. Add shrimp and pasta; toss gently. Cover and chill 10 to 15 minutes. YIELD: 4 servings (serving size: 1½ cups).

POINTS: 6; **EXCHANGES:** 2 Starch, 1 Vegetable, 5 Very Lean Meat; **PER SERVING:** CAL 316 (14% from fat); PRO 27.0g; FAT 4.8g (sat 2.5g); CARB 39.6g; FIB 1.8g; CHOL 174mg; IRON 5.8mg; SOD 812mg; CALC 124mg

HERBED SHRIMP AND PASTA WITH FETA

prep: 10 minutes • cook: 15 minutes

Simply seasoned pasta and shrimp make a show-stopping dinner when paired with a glass of wine and gourmet salad greens.

  4 ounces uncooked vermicelli
  2 teaspoons extra-virgin olive oil
Cooking spray
  ¼ pound shrimp, peeled and deveined
  2 garlic cloves, minced
  1 tablespoon dried basil
  ½ teaspoon crushed red pepper
  1 (14.5-ounce) can diced tomatoes with green peppers and onions
  ¼ cup (2 ounces) crumbled feta cheese with basil and sun-dried tomatoes

1. Cook pasta according to package directions, omitting salt and fat; drain and toss with olive oil. Keep warm.
2. Heat a large nonstick skillet over medium-high heat. Coat pan with cooking spray; add shrimp, garlic, basil, and crushed red pepper. Sauté, 2 minutes, or just until shrimp begin to turn pink. Add tomatoes, and bring to a boil over medium-high heat; reduce heat, and simmer, uncovered, 2 minutes, stirring occasionally.
3. Serve tomato mixture over pasta, and top with feta cheese. YIELD: 4 servings (serving size: 1 cup tomato mixture, ½ cup vermicelli, and 1 tablespoon cheese).

POINTS: 6; **EXCHANGES:** 2 Starch, 3 Lean Meat; **PER SERVING:** CAL 288 (22% from fat); PRO 24.2g; FAT 6.8g (sat 2.7g); CARB 31.2g; FIB 3.3g; CHOL 174mg; IRON 4.4mg; SOD 737mg; CALC 143mg

CAJUN SHRIMP AND PASTA

prep: 4 minutes • cook: 12 minutes

Inspired by the piquant flavors of the Louisiana bayou, this no-fuss entrée makes entertaining easy.

  4 ounces uncooked vermicelli
  2 tablespoons light butter
  ¾ cup finely chopped Vidalia or other sweet onion
  ¼ pound large shrimp, peeled and deveined
1¾ teaspoons Cajun seasoning
  ¼ teaspoon salt
  ¼ cup water

1. Cook pasta according to package directions, omitting salt and fat; drain.
2. Heat butter in a large nonstick skillet over medium-high heat, stirring until butter melts. Add onion, and cook, stirring constantly, 3 minutes. Add shrimp, Cajun seasoning, and salt; cook 3 minutes or until shrimp are done, stirring constantly.
3. Remove from heat. Serve shrimp mixture over pasta. Add water to pan drippings, and cook over high heat 30 seconds; pour evenly over each serving. YIELD: 4 servings (serving size: ¾ cup shrimp mixture and ½ cup vermicelli).

POINTS: 5; **EXCHANGES:** 1½ Starch, 3 Very Lean Meat; **PER SERVING:** CAL 232 (18% from fat); PRO 22.0g; FAT 4.5g (sat 2.3g); CARB 25.4g; FIB 2.0g; CHOL 171mg; IRON 3.7mg; SOD 575mg; CALC 44mg

Baked Shrimp in
Lemony Garlic Sauce,
page 66

Curried Sea Scallops,
page 64

Shrimp-Andouille
Creole, page 65

Honey-Glazed
Salmon, page 61

Lemon Fettuccine with
Artichokes and Pine Nuts,
page 78

Frittata with Spaghetti
and Tomatoes,
page 76

Pizza with Tomatoes,
Asparagus, and Basil,
page 75

Meatless Main Dishes

ARTICHOKE-BASIL PITA PIZZAS

prep: 19 minutes • cook: 8 minutes

Don't let these simple pizzas fool you—they're covered with tasty toppings. And you get a whole pizza for only 5 POINTS.

2 (6-inch) white or whole wheat pita rounds
4 garlic cloves, minced
2 teaspoons olive oil
1 (14-ounce) can quartered artichoke hearts, drained and coarsely chopped
¼ cup thinly sliced red onion
¾ cup grape tomatoes, quartered
1 tablespoon chopped fresh basil or 1 teaspoon dried basil
¼ teaspoon crushed red pepper
1 cup (4 ounces) preshredded part-skim mozzarella cheese

1. Preheat oven to 425°.
2. Split pita rounds in half horizontally, forming pizza crust. Place pita halves, cut sides up, on an ungreased baking sheet; sprinkle with garlic.
3. Drizzle ½ teaspoon oil over each pita half; top evenly with artichokes and remaining ingredients.
4. Bake at 425° for 8 minutes or until cheese melts and edges are lightly browned. YIELD: 4 servings (serving size: 1 pita pizza).

POINTS: 5; EXCHANGES: 1 Starch, 1 Vegetable, 1 High-Fat Meat; PER SERVING: CAL 217 (33% from fat); PRO 12.7g; FAT 7.8g (sat 4.4g); CARB 23.5g; FIB 1.2g; CHOL 15mg; IRON 1.7mg; SOD 499mg; CALC 238mg

INDIVIDUAL FLATBREAD PIZZAS

prep: 18 minutes • cook: 15 minutes

Flatbread is thin, crackerlike bread. Creating pizzas on these crispy crackers makes the fresh ingredients and rich goat cheese stand out.

1 (10-ounce) package fresh spinach
2 teaspoons balsamic vinegar
2 (9-inch) flatbread rounds (such as Toufayan)
1 garlic clove, halved
½ (3.5-ounce) package goat cheese with garlic and herbs
2 plum tomatoes, thinly sliced
2 tablespoons chopped fresh basil
¼ teaspoon salt
¼ teaspoon freshly ground black pepper

1. Preheat oven to 400°.
2. Place spinach in a microwave-safe bowl; cover and microwave at HIGH 2 to 3 minutes or until wilted; drain well. Combine spinach and vinegar; toss well.
3. Place flatbread rounds on an ungreased baking sheet. Rub cut sides of garlic over top of each flatbread round. Spread goat cheese evenly over rounds. Top with spinach and tomato. Sprinkle with basil, salt, and pepper.
4. Bake at 400° for 10 to 12 minutes or until pizza is lightly browned and thoroughly heated. Cut into quarters, and serve immediately. YIELD: 2 servings (serving size: 1 flatbread round).

POINTS: 5; EXCHANGES: 2 Starch, 1½ Vegetable, 1 Medium-Fat Meat; PER SERVING: CAL 258 (20% from fat); PRO 15.4g; FAT 6.0g (sat 3.7g); CARB 39.6g; FIB 10.7g; CHOL 11mg; IRON 6.6mg; SOD 576mg; CALC 228mg

CARAMELIZED ONION, MUSHROOM, AND CHEESE PIZZA

prep: 15 minutes • cook: 45 minutes

Fontina is a creamy, mild cheese whose mellow flavor blends well with the sweet caramelized onions. If you prefer, mozzarella can be substituted for fontina.

Olive oil-flavored cooking spray
1 teaspoon olive oil
3 cups thinly sliced sweet onion (about 2)
1 (8-ounce) package presliced mushrooms
1 teaspoon minced fresh rosemary
½ teaspoon salt
¼ teaspoon pepper
1 (10-ounce) thin Italian cheese-flavored pizza crust (such as Boboli)
⅔ cup (2.6 ounces) shredded fontina cheese

1. Heat oil in a nonstick skillet coated with cooking spray over medium heat. Add onion; sauté 20 minutes or until golden. Add mushrooms and rosemary; sauté 10 minutes. Sprinkle with salt and pepper; stir well.
2. Preheat oven to 450°.
3. Place pizza crust on a large ungreased baking sheet. Lightly coat crust with cooking spray. Spread onion mixture evenly over crust; sprinkle with cheese.
4. Bake at 450° for 15 minutes or until cheese is bubbly. Cut into 8 slices. YIELD: 4 servings (serving size: 2 slices).

POINTS: 7; EXCHANGES: 2½ Starch, 1 High-Fat Meat; PER SERVING: CAL 315 (31% from fat); PRO 14.7g; FAT 10.8g (sat 4.9g); CARB 40.0g; FIB 2.9g; CHOL 21mg; IRON 2.7mg; SOD 815mg; CALC 307mg

PIZZA WITH TOMATOES, ASPARAGUS, AND BASIL

(pictured on page 72)
prep: 8 minutes • cook: 17 minutes

1 cup (1½-inch) diagonally cut
  asparagus (about ½ pound)
1 (10-ounce) thin Italian cheese-
  flavored pizza crust (such as
  Boboli)
Cooking spray
2 tablespoons commercial pesto
  (such as Classico)
6 plum tomatoes, cut into
  ¼-inch-thick slices (about ¾
  pound)
1 cup (4 ounces) preshredded
  part-skim mozzarella cheese
¼ cup thinly sliced fresh basil

1. Preheat oven to 450°.
2. Steam asparagus, covered, 2 minutes or until crisp-tender. Rinse
under cold running water; drain
well, and pat dry with paper towels.
3. Place pizza crust on an ungreased
pizza pan or baking sheet. Lightly
coat pizza crust with cooking spray.
Spread pesto evenly over crust.
Arrange tomatoes and asparagus over
pesto. Sprinkle with cheese. Bake at
450° for 15 minutes or until cheese
melts and pizza is thoroughly heated.
Remove from oven, and sprinkle
with basil.
4. Cut into 8 slices, and serve immediately. YIELD: 4 servings (serving size:
2 slices).

POINTS: 7; **EXCHANGES:** 2 Starch, 1 Vegetable,
1½ Medium-Fat Meat, 1 Fat; **PER SERVING:** CAL 342
(36% from fat); PRO 18.3g; FAT 13.6g (sat 6.2g);
CARB 36.4g; FIB 2.5g; CHOL 23mg; IRON 2.7mg;
SOD 651mg; CALC 506mg

PIZZA POINTER
Lightly coat the pizza crust with
cooking spray before adding
sauce or toppings. This makes
spreading sauce over a dry crust
much easier.

PIZZA WITH MUSHROOMS AND LEEKS

prep: 64 minutes • cook: 29 minutes

*We've given you the steps to make a
homemade crust, but a commercial thin
crust will work just as well—just start
with step 5.*

1½ teaspoons dry yeast
½ cup plus 1 tablespoon warm
  water (100° to 110°)
1⅓ cups all-purpose flour
¼ teaspoon salt
Cooking spray
2 teaspoons yellow cornmeal
1½ teaspoons olive oil
2 cups sliced fresh mushrooms
1 cup thinly sliced leek (about 1)
¼ teaspoon dried thyme
⅛ teaspoon pepper
1 cup tomato and basil pasta sauce
1 cup (4 ounces) preshredded part-
  skim mozzarella cheese

1. Dissolve yeast in warm water in a
medium bowl; let stand 5 minutes.
Lightly spoon flour into dry measuring cups; level with a knife. Add
flour and salt to yeast mixture; stir
until mixture forms a soft dough.
2. Turn dough out onto a lightly
floured surface; knead until smooth
and elastic (about 5 minutes). Place
dough in a medium bowl coated
with cooking spray, turning to coat
top. Cover and let rise in a warm
place (85°), free from drafts, 35 minutes or until doubled in size. (Press 2
fingers into dough. If indentation
remains, dough has risen enough.)
Punch dough down; cover and let
rest 10 minutes.
3. Preheat oven to 450°.
4. Roll dough into a 12-inch circle
on a lightly floured surface. Place on
a 12-inch pizza pan or baking sheet
coated with cooking spray and
sprinkled with cornmeal. Bake at
450° for 7 minutes.
5. Heat oil in a large nonstick skillet
over medium-high heat until hot.
Add mushrooms and leek; sauté 6
minutes or until mushrooms are
golden brown and leek is tender.
Sprinkle with thyme and pepper; stir
well. Remove from heat.
6. Spoon pasta sauce over pizza
crust. Top with mushroom mixture,
and sprinkle with cheese. Bake at
450° for 14 to 16 minutes or until
cheese melts and crust is browned.
Cut into 8 slices. YIELD: 4 servings
(serving size: 2 slices).

POINTS: 6; **EXCHANGES:** 2½ Starch, 1 Vegetable,
1 Medium-Fat Meat; **PER SERVING:** CAL 292
(23% from fat); PRO 13.3g; FAT 7.4g (sat 3.3g);
CARB 43.2g; FIB 3.4g; CHOL 15mg; IRON 3.5mg;
SOD 505mg; CALC 251mg

POTATO AND YELLOW SQUASH FRITTATA

prep: 17 minutes • cook: 16 minutes

2½ cups chopped potato (about ¾ pound)
2 teaspoons light butter, divided
2½ cups chopped yellow squash (about ¾ pound)
4 large eggs
2 large egg whites
⅓ cup 1% low-fat milk
1 teaspoon finely chopped fresh tarragon or chives
¾ teaspoon salt
¼ teaspoon pepper
⅔ cup (2.6 ounces) preshredded reduced-fat Cheddar cheese

1. Place potato in a large saucepan; cover with water. Bring to a boil; reduce heat, and simmer 8 minutes or just until tender. Drain well.
2. Melt 1 teaspoon butter in a large ovenproof nonstick skillet over medium-high heat. Add squash; sauté 5 minutes. Cool slightly.
3. Whisk together eggs and next 5 ingredients in a large bowl. Add potato and squash.
4. Preheat broiler.
5. Melt remaining butter in pan over low heat; add egg mixture (do not stir). Cook, uncovered, 12 minutes or until top is almost set. Sprinkle with cheese.
6. Wrap handle of pan with foil. Broil 4 minutes or until set. Cut into 8 wedges. Serve immediately. YIELD: 4 servings (serving size: 2 wedges).

POINTS: 5; **EXCHANGES:** 1 Starch, 1 Vegetable, 2 Medium-Fat Meat; **PER SERVING:** CAL 252 (38% from fat); PRO 16.1g; FAT 10.5g (sat 5.1g); CARB 23.0g; FIB 3.3g; CHOL 230mg; IRON 2.1mg; SOD 716mg; CALC 209mg

FRITTATA WITH SPAGHETTI AND TOMATOES

(pictured on page 72)

prep: 12 minutes • cook: 18 minutes

4 ounces uncooked spaghetti
4 large eggs
2 large egg whites
⅓ cup 1% low-fat milk
½ teaspoon salt
¼ teaspoon pepper
1½ cups chopped seeded plum tomato (about ½ pound)
1 large garlic clove, minced
¼ cup chopped fresh basil
Cooking spray
2 teaspoons butter
½ cup (2 ounces) preshredded fresh Parmesan cheese

1. Cook spaghetti according to package directions, omitting salt and fat. Drain well.
2. Combine eggs and next 4 ingredients in a large bowl; beat well with a whisk. Add spaghetti, tomato, garlic, and basil; stir well.
3. Preheat broiler.
4. Coat a large ovenproof nonstick skillet with cooking spray; melt butter in pan over medium heat. Add egg mixture. Cook, uncovered, 13 minutes or until top is almost set. Sprinkle with cheese.
5. Wrap handle of pan with foil; broil 4 to 5 minutes or until set. Cut into wedges. YIELD: 4 servings (serving size: 1 wedge).

POINTS: 6; **EXCHANGES:** 2 Starch, 2 Medium-Fat Meat; **PER SERVING:** CAL 293 (36% from fat); PRO 18.4g; FAT 11.7g (sat 5.4g); CARB 28.1g; FIB 2.2g; CHOL 228mg; IRON 2.4mg; SOD 651mg; CALC 238mg

OMELET WITH ZUCCHINI AND ONION

prep: 8 minutes • cook: 12 minutes

No matter if it's breakfast, brunch, lunch, or dinner, this 3-POINT omelet makes a filling meal anytime.

Cooking spray
1 teaspoon olive oil
1 cup finely chopped zucchini (about 1 large)
3 tablespoons chopped onion
2 large eggs
2 large egg whites
1 tablespoon preshredded fresh Parmesan cheese
⅛ teaspoon dried oregano
¼ teaspoon salt
⅛ teaspoon pepper

1. Coat an 8-inch nonstick skillet with cooking spray. Add oil; place over medium heat. Add zucchini and onion; sauté 7 minutes or until tender. Set aside, and let cool.
2. Combine eggs and remaining 5 ingredients in a medium bowl, stirring with a whisk until well blended. Stir in zucchini and onion.
3. Coat pan with cooking spray; return to medium heat. Add egg mixture; cook 4 to 5 minutes or until center is set (do not stir). Loosen omelet with spatula; fold in half. Slide omelet onto a plate. YIELD: 2 servings (serving size: ½ omelet).

POINTS: 3; **EXCHANGES:** 1 Vegetable, 1½ Medium-Fat Meat; **PER SERVING:** CAL 144 (53% from fat); PRO 11.9g; FAT 8.4g (sat 2.5g); CARB 5.0g; FIB 1.4g; CHOL 215mg; IRON 1.1mg; SOD 471mg; CALC 86mg

SALSA OMELET WITH ROASTED PEPPERS AND CHEESE

prep: 7 minutes • cook: 6 minutes

Substitute one (2-ounce) jar of sliced pimiento if you don't have roasted red peppers.

2 large eggs
2 large egg whites
2 tablespoons 1% low-fat milk
¼ teaspoon salt
⅛ teaspoon black pepper
2 tablespoons chopped bottled roasted red bell pepper
1 teaspoon butter
¼ cup (1 ounce) preshredded reduced-fat Cheddar cheese
2 tablespoons salsa
½ teaspoon finely chopped fresh cilantro

1. Combine first 5 ingredients in a bowl, stirring with a whisk. Stir in roasted red pepper.
2. Melt butter in an 8-inch nonstick skillet over medium heat. Add egg mixture, and cook 3 to 5 minutes or until set (do not stir). Sprinkle with cheese. Loosen omelet with spatula; fold in half. Slide omelet onto a plate.
3. Top with salsa, and sprinkle with cilantro. YIELD: 2 servings (serving size: ½ omelet).

POINTS: 4; EXCHANGES: 2 Medium-Fat Meat; PER SERVING: CAL 166 (57% from fat); PRO 14.1g; FAT 10.2g (sat 4.9g); CARB 3.0g; FIB 0.3g; CHOL 228mg; IRON 1.0mg; SOD 641mg; CALC 152mg

NOODLE GRATIN WITH CHEESE, CORN, AND ROASTED PEPPER

prep: 10 minutes • cook: 20 minutes

This "grown-up" mac and cheese has the creamy sauce we loved as kids but with a few adult additions.

2½ cups 1% low-fat milk, divided
2½ tablespoons all-purpose flour
1¼ cups (5 ounces) preshredded reduced-fat Cheddar cheese
½ teaspoon salt
¼ teaspoon black pepper
⅛ teaspoon ground nutmeg
1 cup frozen corn, thawed
⅓ cup chopped bottled roasted red bell pepper
5 cups cooked wide egg noodles (about 4 cups uncooked)
Cooking spray
1 (1-ounce) slice white bread
1 tablespoon light butter, melted

1. Preheat oven to 450°.
2. Pour 1½ cups milk into a saucepan; cook over medium heat 1 minute or until warm. Whisk remaining 1 cup milk and flour in a bowl until flour dissolves. Add to pan; cook, stirring constantly, 8 minutes or until bubbly. Reduce heat to low; add cheese, salt, black pepper, and nutmeg. Stir until cheese melts.
3. Add corn, roasted red bell pepper, and cheese sauce to noodles. Spoon mixture into an 11 x 7-inch baking dish coated with cooking spray.
4. Place bread in a food processor; pulse 5 times or until coarse crumbs measure ½ cup. Combine breadcrumbs and melted butter; sprinkle over noodle mixture.

5. Bake at 450° for 10 minutes or until golden brown and bubbly. YIELD: 4 servings (serving size: about 1 cup).

POINTS: 8; EXCHANGES: 3 Starch, 2 Medium-Fat Meat, ½ Fat; PER SERVING: CAL 384 (30% from fat); PRO 20.7g; FAT 12.7g (sat 7.5g); CARB 45.7g; FIB 2.3g; CHOL 65mg; IRON 2.2mg; SOD 797mg; CALC 459mg

MACARONI AND CHEESE

prep: 14 minutes • cook: 40 minutes

2½ cups 1% low-fat milk, divided
2 tablespoons all-purpose flour
1 tablespoon light butter
1½ cups (6 ounces) preshredded reduced-fat Cheddar cheese
2 tablespoons grated fresh Parmesan cheese
½ teaspoon salt
¼ teaspoon pepper
3 cups hot cooked elbow macaroni
Cooking spray
¼ cup dry breadcrumbs

1. Preheat oven to 375°.
2. Whisk together 1 cup milk and flour in a saucepan; add remaining 1½ cups milk, stirring well. Cook, stirring constantly, over medium heat 8 minutes or until bubbly. Reduce heat to low; add butter and next 4 ingredients. Cook, stirring constantly, 2 minutes. Stir in pasta; spoon into a 2-quart casserole coated with cooking spray. Sprinkle with breadcrumbs.
3. Bake at 375° for 30 minutes or until bubbly. YIELD: 5 servings (serving size: 1 cup).

POINTS: 8; EXCHANGES: 3 Starch, 2 Medium-Fat Meat; PER SERVING: CAL 377 (29% from fat); PRO 20.0g; FAT 11.5g (sat 7.1g); CARB 45.2g; FIB 1.7g; CHOL 35mg; IRON 2.1mg; SOD 692mg; CALC 446mg

LEMON FETTUCCINE WITH ARTICHOKES AND PINE NUTS

(pictured on page 71)
prep: 10 minutes • cook: 10 minutes

Cooking spray
1 teaspoon olive oil
½ cup minced fresh onion
2 garlic cloves, minced
1 (14.5-ounce) can no-salt-added diced tomatoes, drained
½ cup vegetable broth
½ cup dry white wine
2 zucchini, grated
2 (14-ounce) cans quartered artichoke hearts, drained
1 teaspoon grated lemon rind
2 teaspoons fresh lemon juice
½ teaspoon salt
¼ teaspoon pepper
3 cups hot cooked fettuccine
¼ cup thinly sliced fresh basil
½ cup (2 ounces) grated fresh Parmesan cheese
¼ cup toasted pine nuts

1. Heat oil in a large nonstick skillet coated with cooking spray over medium-high heat. Add onion and garlic; sauté 2 minutes. Reduce heat to medium; add tomatoes, broth, and wine. Bring to a boil. Add zucchini and next 5 ingredients; simmer 3 to 4 minutes. Add pasta and basil to sauce mixture, tossing well. Sprinkle with cheese and pine nuts. YIELD: 6 servings (serving size: 1½ cups pasta mixture, 2 tablespoons cheese, and 2 teaspoons nuts).

POINTS: 5; EXCHANGES: 2 Starch, 1 Vegetable, 1 Medium-Fat Meat, ½ Fat; **PER SERVING:** CAL 280 (26% from fat); PRO 14.8g; FAT 8.0g (sat 3.0g); CARB 37.6g; FIB 3.9g; CHOL 10mg; IRON 3.8mg; SOD 807mg; CALC 209mg

SPINACH MANICOTTI

prep: 7 minutes • cook: 30 minutes

A combination of three cheeses makes this filling extra creamy and flavorful.

8 manicotti shells, uncooked
1½ cups part-skim ricotta cheese
1 cup (4 ounces) preshredded part-skim mozzarella cheese
⅓ cup (1.3 ounces) grated fresh Parmesan cheese
¼ teaspoon salt
¼ teaspoon pepper
1 teaspoon dried Italian seasoning
1 (10-ounce) package frozen chopped spinach, thawed, drained, and squeezed dry
1 large egg, lightly beaten
1 large egg white
Olive oil-flavored cooking spray
2½ cups low-fat roasted garlic pasta sauce

1. Preheat oven to 350°.
2. Cook pasta according to package directions, omitting salt and fat. Drain and rinse.
3. Combine ricotta cheese and next 8 ingredients in a medium bowl, stirring well. Spoon mixture evenly into pasta shells. Place shells in an 11 x 7-inch baking dish coated with cooking spray. Spoon pasta sauce evenly over shells. Cover and bake at 350° for 20 minutes or until thoroughly heated. Serve warm. YIELD: 8 servings (serving size: 1 shell and about ½ cup sauce).

POINTS: 4; EXCHANGES: 1 Starch, 2 Medium-Fat Meat; **PER SERVING:** CAL 221 (40% from fat); PRO 15.4g; FAT 9.8g (sat 5.1g); CARB 17.7g; FIB 5.7g; CHOL 54mg; IRON 1.6mg; SOD 654mg; CALC 358mg

BAKED EGGPLANT AND PASTA

prep: 8 minutes • cook: 50 minutes

Since the flesh of an eggplant discolors rapidly, the eggplant should be cut just before it's baked.

4 cups cubed peeled eggplant (about 1 small)
Cooking spray
2¼ cups (6 ounces) uncooked rotini (corkscrew-shaped pasta)
2 cups low-fat pasta sauce
¾ cup 1% low-fat cottage cheese
¾ cup (3 ounces) preshredded part-skim mozzarella cheese

1. Preheat oven to 425°.
2. Place eggplant in a single layer on a baking sheet coated with cooking spray. Bake at 425° for 15 minutes or until tender, stirring once. Remove eggplant from oven, and reduce oven temperature to 400°.
3. Cook pasta according to package directions, omitting salt and fat; drain.
4. Spread ¼ cup pasta sauce in an 11 x 7-inch baking dish coated with cooking spray. (Layer will be thin.) Arrange pasta over sauce. Top with eggplant and spoonfuls of cottage cheese. Spoon remaining pasta sauce over top. Cover loosely with foil, and bake at 400° for 20 minutes. Uncover, sprinkle with mozzarella cheese, and bake an additional 15 minutes or until lightly browned. YIELD: 4 servings (serving size: about 1½ cups).

POINTS: 6; EXCHANGES: 2 Starch, 2 Vegetable, 1 Medium-Fat Meat; **PER SERVING:** CAL 297 (18% from fat); PRO 18.5g; FAT 5.9g (sat 2.7g); CARB 42.8g; FIB 5.0g; CHOL 13mg; IRON 2.4mg; SOD 677mg; CALC 273mg

PASTA WITH ZUCCHINI, PARSLEY, AND FETA

prep: 15 minutes • cook: 22 minutes

Zucchini and fresh parsley pair up as a refreshing duo in this summertime pasta.

2¼ cups (6 ounces) uncooked rotini (corkscrew-shaped pasta)
Olive oil-flavored cooking spray
2 teaspoons olive oil
1½ pounds zucchini (about 3), cut into ½-inch pieces
¼ teaspoon salt
½ cup (2 ounces) crumbled feta cheese
¼ cup finely chopped fresh parsley
2 teaspoons lemon juice
½ teaspoon salt
¼ teaspoon pepper

1. Cook rotini according to package directions, omitting salt and fat. Drain, reserving ¼ cup cooking liquid.
2. Coat a nonstick skillet with cooking spray. Add oil, and place over medium-high heat. Add zucchini; sauté 13 minutes or until tender. Sprinkle with ¼ teaspoon salt.
3. Combine hot pasta, reserved cooking liquid, zucchini, feta cheese, and remaining ingredients in a large bowl. Toss well. YIELD: 4 servings (serving size: 1¼ cups).

POINTS: 5; EXCHANGES: 2 Starch, 1 Vegetable, 1 Fat; PER SERVING: CAL 247 (26% from fat); PRO 9.7g; FAT 7.3g (sat 3.3g); CARB 36.5g; FIB 3.4g; CHOL 17mg; IRON 2.6mg; SOD 657mg; CALC 129mg

BAKED TORTELLINI WITH ZUCCHINI AND CARROTS

prep: 22 minutes • cook: 30 minutes

Cooking spray
1 teaspoon olive oil
1 pound zucchini (about 2), cut into ½-inch cubes
¾ cup chopped carrot
1 (9-ounce) refrigerated package 3-cheese tortellini
2 cups tomato and basil pasta sauce
1 cup (4 ounces) preshredded part-skim mozzarella cheese

1. Preheat oven to 375°.
2. Heat oil in a large nonstick skillet coated with cooking spray over medium-high heat. Add zucchini and carrot: cook, stirring occasionally, 13 minutes or until lightly browned. Remove from heat.
3. Cook tortellini according to package directions, omitting salt and fat. Drain, reserving ½ cup cooking liquid. Add pasta sauce and reserved ½ cup cooking liquid to zucchini mixture; stir well. Spread ½ cup pasta sauce mixture in bottom of an 11 x 7-inch baking dish coated with cooking spray. Spoon tortellini over top, and cover with remaining pasta sauce mixture. Cover and bake at 375° for 15 minutes. Uncover and sprinkle with cheese. Bake, uncovered, an additional 15 minutes or until bubbly and browned. YIELD: 4 servings (serving size: ¼ casserole).

POINTS: 7; EXCHANGES: 2½ Starch, 1 Vegetable, 1 Medium-Fat Meat, 1 Fat; PER SERVING: CAL 349 (29% from fat); PRO 18.2g; FAT 11.0g (sat 5.6g); CARB 43.9g; FIB 4.7g; CHOL 37mg; IRON 2.1mg; SOD 723mg; CALC 426mg

GEMELLI WITH WHITE BEANS AND ARTICHOKES

prep: 12 minutes • cook: 16 minutes

1 tablespoon olive oil
3 cups thinly sliced onion (about 2)
1 garlic clove, minced
1 (14-ounce) can artichoke hearts, drained and cut into ¼-inch slices
1 (15.5-ounce) can Great Northern beans, rinsed and drained
1½ cups (6 ounces) uncooked gemelli or other pasta twists
½ teaspoon salt
¼ teaspoon freshly ground black pepper
¼ cup finely chopped fresh basil
3 tablespoons preshredded fresh Parmesan cheese

1. Heat oil in a large nonstick skillet over medium-high heat. Add onion and cook, stirring occasionally, 12 minutes or until golden brown. Add garlic, sliced artichoke, and beans; toss gently. Cover, reduce heat, and simmer 4 minutes or until thoroughly heated.
2. Cook pasta according to package directions, omitting salt and fat. Drain, reserving ⅓ cup cooking liquid.
3. Combine pasta, onion mixture, reserved cooking liquid, and remaining ingredients in a large bowl. Toss well. YIELD: 4 servings (serving size: 1½ cups).

POINTS: 7; EXCHANGES: 4 Starch, 1 Medium-Fat Meat; PER SERVING: CAL 368 (15% from fat); PRO 17.3g; FAT 6.2g (sat 1.7g); CARB 62.2g; FIB 7.5g; CHOL 4mg; IRON 4.1mg; SOD 597mg; CALC 144mg

TORTIGLIONI WITH BLACK BEANS AND TOMATOES

prep: 12 minutes • cook: 27 minutes

Who needs meat when pasta, black beans, and fresh Parmesan come together in this quick skillet supper?

2¼ cups (about 6 ounces) uncooked tortiglioni (elbow springs)
1 tablespoon olive oil
1 (8-ounce) package presliced mushrooms
1 (14.5-ounce) can diced tomatoes, undrained
1 cup canned black beans, rinsed and drained
1 garlic clove, minced
½ teaspoon dried oregano
½ teaspoon salt
¼ teaspoon pepper
¼ cup (1 ounce) grated fresh Parmesan cheese

1. Cook pasta according to package directions, omitting salt and fat. Drain and set aside.
2. Heat oil in a nonstick skillet over medium-high heat. Add mushrooms; cook 4 minutes or until lightly browned, stirring frequently. Add tomatoes and next 5 ingredients. Bring to a boil; cover, reduce heat, and simmer 15 minutes, stirring occasionally. Serve over pasta. Sprinkle with Parmesan cheese. YIELD: 4 servings (serving size: 1⅔ cups pasta mixture and 1 tablespoon Parmesan cheese).

POINTS: 5; EXCHANGES: 3 Starch, 1 Fat; PER SERVING: CAL 284 (19% from fat); PRO 12.7g; FAT 6.3g (sat 1.8g); CARB 47.0g; FIB 6.7g; CHOL 5mg; IRON 3.4mg; SOD 673mg; CALC 136mg

RICE GRATIN WITH SPINACH AND LEEKS

prep: 11 minutes • cook: 30 minutes
stand: 5 minutes

½ (1-ounce) slice white bread
1 tablespoon light butter
1¼ cups thinly sliced leeks (about 2)
2 teaspoons all-purpose flour
1⅔ cups 1% low-fat milk
¾ cup (3 ounces) shredded reduced-fat Swiss cheese, divided
½ teaspoon dried basil
½ teaspoon salt
¼ teaspoon pepper
2 cups cooked long-grain brown rice
1 (10-ounce) package frozen chopped spinach, thawed, drained, and squeezed dry
2 large eggs, lightly beaten
Cooking spray

1. Preheat oven to 375°.
2. Place bread in a food processor; pulse 10 times or until coarse crumbs measure ¼ cup. Set aside.
3. Melt butter in a large nonstick skillet over medium heat. Add leek; cook, stirring frequently, 6 minutes or until lightly browned. Sprinkle with flour; stir well. Add milk; increase heat to medium-high, and cook, stirring constantly, until mixture comes to a simmer. Reduce heat, and simmer 1 minute, stirring constantly. Remove from heat; add ½ cup cheese and next 6 ingredients. Stir well. Spoon mixture into a 10-inch quiche dish or 9-inch pie plate coated with cooking spray. Combine remaining cheese and breadcrumbs; sprinkle over gratin. Bake at 375° for 30 minutes or until

set. Cool in dish 5 minutes on a wire rack. YIELD: 6 servings (serving size: 1 wedge).

POINTS: 4; EXCHANGES: 1½ Starch, 1 Vegetable, 1 High-Fat Meat; PER SERVING: CAL 215 (30% from fat); PRO 12.2g; FAT 7.3g (sat 3.8g); CARB 25.9g; FIB 3.1g; CHOL 87mg; IRON 2.3mg; SOD 335mg; CALC 294mg

SUMMER VEGETABLE RICE

prep: 20 minutes • cook: 36 minutes

Cooking spray
¾ cup chopped onion
1 red bell pepper, chopped
1 yellow bell pepper, chopped
1 (14.5-ounce) can diced tomatoes with basil, oregano, and garlic
1 (14.5-ounce) can vegetable broth
¼ teaspoon salt
⅛ teaspoon black pepper
¼ teaspoon hot sauce
1 zucchini, sliced
1 yellow squash, sliced
1 cup uncooked long-grain rice
¼ cup chopped fresh cilantro
½ cup (2 ounces) preshredded reduced-fat Cheddar cheese

1. Place a Dutch oven coated with cooking spray over medium-high heat. Add onion and peppers; sauté 6 minutes or until tender. Add tomatoes and next 4 ingredients; bring to a boil. Add zucchini, squash, and rice; return to a boil. Cover, reduce heat, and simmer 25 minutes. Remove from heat; stir in cilantro, and sprinkle evenly with cheese. YIELD: 5 servings (serving size: 1½ cups).

POINTS: 5; EXCHANGES: 2½ Starch, 2 Vegetable; PER SERVING: CAL 257 (10% from fat); PRO 9.5g; FAT 3.3g (sat 1.7g); CARB 47.7g; FIB 3.5g; CHOL 8mg; IRON 3.2mg; SOD 998mg; CALC 166mg

BARLEY WITH PINTO BEANS, TOMATOES, AND MUSHROOMS

prep: 5 minutes • cook: 25 minutes

Cooking spray
  2 teaspoons olive oil
  ½ cup finely chopped onion
  1 (6-ounce) package presliced
     portobello mushrooms, coarsely
     chopped
  1 (15.5-ounce) can pinto beans,
     rinsed and drained
  1 (14.5-ounce) can diced tomatoes
     with mild green chiles
  1 cup vegetable broth
  2 garlic cloves, minced
  1 tablespoon tomato paste
  ¾ teaspoon dried oregano
  ¼ teaspoon salt
  ⅛ teaspoon pepper
  2 cups hot cooked barley
  4 teaspoons minced fresh cilantro
  ¼ cup (1 ounce) preshredded
     Monterey Jack cheese

1. Heat oil in a large nonstick skillet coated with cooking spray over medium heat. Add onion and mushrooms; sauté 6 minutes. Add beans, tomatoes, and next 6 ingredients; stir well. Bring to a boil. Cover, reduce heat, and simmer 10 minutes, stirring occasionally. Serve tomato mixture over barley, and sprinkle evenly with cilantro and cheese. YIELD: 4 servings (serving size: 1 cup tomato mixture and ½ cup barley).

POINTS: 4; **EXCHANGES:** 2 Starch, 1 Vegetable, 1 Fat; **PER SERVING:** CAL 235 (22% from fat); PRO 10.3g; FAT 5.9g (sat 1.9g); CARB 36.5g; FIB 8.1g; CHOL 6mg; IRON 2.3mg; SOD 837mg; CALC 128mg

BLACK BEAN, SPINACH, AND CHEESE QUESADILLAS

prep: 5 minutes • cook: 13 minutes

*Top these cheesy quesadillas with sour cream and salsa depending on the number of **POINTS** you have for the day.*

Butter-flavored cooking spray
  1 cup chopped onion
  3 cups torn spinach
  4 (8-inch) low-fat flour tortillas
  1 cup canned black beans
  1 cup (4 ounces) preshredded
     reduced-fat Cheddar cheese

1. Coat a large nonstick skillet with cooking spray; place over medium-high heat until hot. Add onion; sauté 4 minutes. Add spinach; sauté 1 minute or until spinach is wilted. Remove from pan. Wipe pan with a paper towel.
2. Coat pan with cooking spray; place over medium heat until hot. Place one tortilla in pan. Cook 1 minute or until bottom of tortilla is golden. Sprinkle one-fourth each of spinach mixture, beans, and cheese over one side of tortilla. Fold tortilla in half. Cook tortilla 1 minute on each side or until golden and cheese melts. Repeat procedure with remaining tortillas, spinach mixture, beans, and cheese. YIELD: 4 servings (serving size: 1 quesadilla).

POINTS: 5; **EXCHANGES:** 2 Starch, 1 Vegetable, 1 Medium-Fat Meat; **PER SERVING:** CAL 266 (23% from fat); PRO 15.2g; FAT 6.9g (sat 4.1g); CARB 36.7g; FIB 5.8g; CHOL 20mg; IRON 3.2mg; SOD 852mg; CALC 283mg

REFRIED BEAN AND MUSHROOM BURRITOS

prep: 10 minutes • cook: 8 minutes

  4 (8-inch) low-fat flour tortillas
Cooking spray
  1 teaspoon vegetable oil
  1 (8-ounce) package presliced
     mushrooms
  ¼ teaspoon salt
  ¼ teaspoon hot sauce
  1 cup canned fat-free refried
     beans
  ½ cup (2 ounces) preshredded
     reduced-fat Cheddar cheese
  3 cups thinly sliced iceberg lettuce
  1 cup chopped seeded tomato
     (about 1 large)
  ½ cup salsa
  ¼ cup fat-free sour cream

1. Warm tortillas according to package directions.
2. Heat oil in a large nonstick skillet coated with cooking spray over medium-high heat. Add mushrooms; sauté 8 minutes or until lightly browned. Sprinkle with salt and hot sauce.
3. Spoon ¼ cup refried beans down center of each tortilla. Top each with ¼ cup mushrooms and 2 tablespoons cheese. Roll up tortilla. Serve over lettuce. Top with tomato, salsa, and sour cream. YIELD: 4 servings (serving size: 1 burrito, ¾ cup lettuce, ¼ cup tomato, 2 tablespoons salsa, and 1 tablespoon sour cream).

POINTS: 6; **EXCHANGES:** 2½ Starch, 1 Vegetable, ½ Medium-Fat Meat, 1 Fat; **PER SERVING:** CAL 298 (24% from fat); PRO 13.9g; FAT 7.8g (sat 2.9g); CARB 43.1g; FIB 5.0g; CHOL 11mg; IRON 3.0mg; SOD 923mg; CALC 262mg

BLACK BEANS AND VEGETABLES OVER RICE

prep: 35 minutes • cook: 55 minutes

Cooking spray
1 teaspoon olive oil
¾ cup chopped onion
¾ cup thinly sliced celery
3 cups chopped peeled sweet
  potato (about 2 large)
1½ cups chopped zucchini (about 2)
1½ cups sliced fresh green beans
1 (15.5-ounce) can black beans,
  rinsed and drained
1 (14.5-ounce) can diced
  tomatoes, undrained
1 (14.5-ounce) can vegetable broth
1 tablespoon dark brown sugar
¾ teaspoon dried rubbed sage
½ teaspoon salt
¼ teaspoon pepper
3 cups hot cooked rice
¾ cup (3 ounces) preshredded
  reduced-fat Cheddar cheese

1. Heat oil in a large nonstick skillet coated with cooking spray over medium-high heat. Add onion and celery; sauté 5 minutes or until tender. Add sweet potato and next 9 ingredients; stir well. Bring to a boil. Cover, reduce heat, and simmer 45 minutes or until vegetables are tender. Serve over rice. Sprinkle evenly with cheese. YIELD: 4 servings (serving size: 1⅓ cups bean mixture and ½ cup rice).

POINTS: 6; **EXCHANGES:** 3 Starch, 2 Vegetable, 1 Fat; **PER SERVING:** CAL 326 (14% from fat); PRO 12.3g; FAT 5.1g (sat 2.2g); CARB 57.8g; FIB 7.1g; CHOL 10mg; IRON 3.3mg; SOD 841mg; CALC 179mg

TAMALE PIE

prep: 20 minutes • cook: 48 minutes
stand: 10 minutes

1 teaspoon olive oil
½ cup finely chopped onion
½ cup chopped green bell pepper
⅓ cup finely chopped celery
1 cup frozen whole-kernel corn
3 tablespoons canned chopped
  mild green chiles
1½ teaspoons chili powder
½ teaspoon ground cumin
1 (15-ounce) can red kidney
  beans, rinsed and drained
1 cup low-fat pasta sauce
1½ cups 1% low-fat milk
1½ cups water
½ teaspoon salt
¾ cup yellow cornmeal
Cooking spray
¾ cup (3 ounces) preshredded
  reduced-fat Cheddar cheese

1. Heat oil in a nonstick skillet over medium-high heat. Add onion, pepper, and celery; sauté 5 minutes. Add corn and next 5 ingredients. Sauté 3 minutes; set aside.
2. Preheat oven to 350°.
3. Combine milk, water, and salt in a saucepan; bring to a boil over high heat. Add cornmeal, reduce heat, and simmer 10 minutes, stirring constantly.
4. Spoon vegetable mixture into an 11 x 7-inch baking dish coated with cooking spray. Top with cornmeal mixture; sprinkle with cheese. Bake at 350° for 30 minutes or until bubbly. Let stand 10 minutes. YIELD: 6 servings (serving size: 1½ cups).

POINTS: 5; **EXCHANGES:** 2½ Starch, 1 Medium-Fat Meat; **PER SERVING:** CAL 251 (18% from fat); PRO 11.6g; FAT 5.0g (sat 2.6g); CARB 39.5g; FIB 6.2g; CHOL 12mg; IRON 2.2mg; SOD 612mg; CALC 214mg

BAKED LENTILS WITH MUSHROOMS

prep: 12 minutes • cook: 56 minutes

1 cup uncooked brown basmati
  rice
2¼ cups water
6 cups water
1 cup lentils
Cooking spray
2 teaspoons olive oil
1½ cups diagonally sliced carrot
1 (8-ounce) package presliced
  mushrooms
1 (14.5-ounce) can diced
  tomatoes, undrained
1 tablespoon balsamic vinegar
½ teaspoon dried thyme
1 bay leaf
½ teaspoon salt
¼ teaspoon pepper
⅓ cup (1.3 ounces) crumbled feta
  cheese

1. Combine rice and 2¼ cups water in a saucepan; bring to a boil. Cover, reduce heat, and simmer 45 minutes or until liquid is absorbed. Let stand 10 minutes.
2. Combine 6 cups water and lentils in a large saucepan; bring to a boil. Cover, reduce heat, and simmer 20 minutes or until tender. Drain, reserving 1 cup cooking liquid.
3. Preheat oven to 400°.
4. Heat oil in a nonstick skillet coated with cooking spray over medium-high heat. Add carrot and mushrooms; sauté 6 minutes or until mushrooms are lightly browned.
5. Combine lentils, reserved cooking liquid, mushroom mixture, tomatoes, and next 5 ingredients. Spoon mixture into a 2-quart baking dish coated with cooking spray. Cover and

bake at 400° for 30 minutes or until bubbly. Remove bay leaf. Spoon lentil mixture over rice; sprinkle with cheese. YIELD: 6 servings (serving size: 1 cup lentil mixture, ½ cup rice, and 1 tablespoon feta cheese).

POINTS: 5; **EXCHANGES:** 3 Starch, 1 Vegetable, 1 Fat; **PER SERVING:** CAL 285 (16% from fat); PRO 12.9g; FAT 5.2g (sat 2.0g); CARB 50.2g; FIB 10.5g; CHOL 8mg; IRON 3.9mg; SOD 402mg; CALC 88mg

VEGETARIAN CHILI DOGS

prep: 5 minutes • cook: 5 minutes

Cooking spray
4 frozen low-fat vegetarian hot dogs, thawed
1 (15-ounce) can 99%-fat-free vegetarian chili with beans
4 teaspoons spicy brown mustard
4 lite wheat hot dog buns, toasted
¼ cup finely chopped onion
½ cup (2 ounces) preshredded reduced-fat sharp Cheddar cheese

1. Place a large nonstick skillet coated with cooking spray over medium heat. Add hot dogs, and cook until evenly browned, turning frequently.
2. Pour chili into a small saucepan; cook over medium heat until bubbly.
3. Spread 1 teaspoon mustard over inside of each hot dog bun. Place hot dogs in buns; spoon chili evenly over each hot dog. Sprinkle 1 tablespoon onion and 2 tablespoons cheese over each hot dog. YIELD: 4 servings (serving size: 1 chili dog).

POINTS: 6; **EXCHANGES:** 3 Starch, 2 Lean Meat; **PER SERVING:** CAL 300 (13% from fat); PRO 24.0g; FAT 4.5g (sat 2.1g); CARB 43.6g; FIB 10.6g; CHOL 10mg; IRON 3.1mg; SOD 1,324mg; CALC 188mg

MEATLESS STROGANOFF

prep: 6 minutes • cook: 15 minutes

Meatless crumbles are a vegetarian substitute for meat. They cook and crumble just like ground beef.

2 teaspoons butter
1 cup chopped onion (about 1)
2 teaspoons minced garlic (about 2 cloves)
2 (8-ounce) packages presliced mushrooms
1 (12-ounce) package burger-style recipe crumbles
¼ cup vegetable broth
½ teaspoon Worcestershire sauce
¼ teaspoon freshly ground black pepper
1 (10¾-ounce) can condensed reduced-fat, reduced-sodium cream of mushroom soup, undiluted
1 (8-ounce) carton fat-free sour cream
2½ cups hot cooked egg noodles

1. Melt butter in a large nonstick skillet over medium heat. Add onion, garlic, and mushrooms; cook, stirring frequently, 7 minutes or until mushrooms are tender. Stir in crumbles, broth, Worcestershire sauce, and pepper; cook 2 minutes. Reduce heat to medium-low; stir in soup. Fold in sour cream, and cook until thoroughly heated (do not boil). Serve immediately over hot noodles. YIELD: 5 servings (serving size: ½ cup noodles and 1 cup stroganoff).

POINTS: 8; **EXCHANGES:** 2 Starch, 2 Vegetable, 2 Medium-Fat Meat, ½ Fat; **PER SERVING:** CAL 377 (30% from fat); PRO 23.4g; FAT 12.9g (sat 4.1g); CARB 42.8g; FIB 5.7g; CHOL 40mg; IRON 6.4mg; SOD 645mg; CALC 186mg

SANTA FE SKILLET CASSEROLE

prep: 5 minutes • cook: 10 minutes

Substituting Mexican-seasoned burger-style crumbles for plain crumbles adds an extra kick to this one-dish meal.

1 (12-ounce) package burger-style recipe crumbles
1 cup chopped onion (about 1)
1 cup chopped green bell pepper (about 1)
1½ cups uncooked instant rice (such as Uncle Ben's 5-Minute Rice)
1½ cups vegetable broth
¼ teaspoon salt
¼ teaspoon black pepper
1 (14.5-ounce) can Mexican-style stewed tomatoes, undrained
¾ cup (3 ounces) preshredded reduced-fat sharp Cheddar cheese

1. Combine first 3 ingredients in a large nonstick skillet; cook over medium-high heat until crumbles are browned and vegetables are tender.
2. Add rice and next 4 ingredients. Cover, reduce heat, and simmer 5 minutes or until rice is tender and liquid is absorbed. Sprinkle with cheese; serve immediately. YIELD: 6 servings (serving size: ⅙ of casserole).

POINTS: 6; **EXCHANGES:** 2 Starch, 2 Medium-Fat Meat; **PER SERVING:** CAL 287 (32% from fat); PRO 18.3g; FAT 10.2g (sat 3.8g); CARB 31.0g; FIB 5.1g; CHOL 10mg; IRON 4.2mg; SOD 935mg; CALC 168mg

MEXICAN TOFU BURRITOS

prep: 8 minutes • cook: 9 minutes

1 (10.5-ounce) package extra-firm
   light tofu, drained and cut into
   ½-inch cubes
1 teaspoon ground cumin
1 teaspoon chili powder
2 teaspoons cider vinegar
2 teaspoons vegetable oil
1 cup sliced onion (about 1)
1 cup chopped red or green bell
   pepper (about 1)
1 cup chopped zucchini (about 1)
½ cup chunky salsa with cilantro
¼ teaspoon salt
4 (8-inch) low-fat flour tortillas
¼ cup sliced green onions
¼ cup low-fat sour cream
½ cup (2 ounces) preshredded
   reduced-fat Monterey Jack
   cheese

1. Sprinkle tofu with cumin, chili
powder, and vinegar. Toss gently to
coat; set aside.
2. Heat oil in a large nonstick skillet
over medium heat. Add 1 cup onion;
sauté 2 minutes. Add bell pepper and
zucchini; sauté 4 minutes. Stir in tofu
mixture, salsa, and salt; cook 2 minutes, stirring occasionally. Remove
from heat.
3. Warm tortillas according to package directions. Spoon about ¾ cup
tofu mixture down center of each
tortilla. Top with 1 tablespoon each
of green onions and sour cream, and
2 tablespoons cheese; roll up. **YIELD:** 4
servings (serving size: 1 burrito).

POINTS: 6; **EXCHANGES:** 2 Starch, 1 Vegetable,
1 Medium-Fat Meat, 1 Fat; **PER SERVING:** CAL 295
(30% from fat); PRO 16.4g; FAT 9.8g (sat 3.5g);
CARB 37.1g; FIB 2.8g; CHOL 15mg; IRON 2.6mg;
SOD 700mg; CALC 296mg

THAI-SEARED TOFU

prep: 10 minutes • cook: 9 minutes
marinate: 2 hours

*Two hours of marinating gives the
tofu time to soak up the fresh herbs,
ginger, and soy sauce.*

½ cup chopped fresh basil
½ cup chopped fresh cilantro
⅓ cup low-sodium soy sauce
½ cup fresh lime juice
¼ cup chopped fresh mint
2 tablespoons honey
1 tablespoon minced peeled fresh
   ginger
2 teaspoons sesame oil
2 teaspoons curry powder
½ teaspoon crushed red pepper
4 garlic cloves, minced
2 (10.5-ounce) packages firm light
   tofu, drained
Cooking spray
3 cups hot cooked spaghetti
   (about 6 ounces uncooked pasta)

1. Combine first 11 ingredients in a
small bowl; stir with a whisk until
blended. Cut each tofu cake crosswise into 4 slices. Place tofu slices in
a shallow dish. Pour soy sauce mixture over tofu; cover and marinate in
refrigerator at least 2 hours.
2. Coat a large nonstick skillet with
cooking spray; place over medium-
high heat until hot. Remove tofu
slices from marinade, reserving marinade. Add tofu slices to pan; cook 2
minutes on each side or until
browned. Remove from pan. Set
aside, and keep warm.
3. Add reserved marinade to pan;
bring to a simmer over medium-
high heat. Spoon pasta onto plates;
top with tofu slices. Drizzle warm

marinade over tofu and pasta. **YIELD:** 4
servings (serving size: ¾ cups pasta, 2
tofu slices, and ½ cup sauce).

POINTS: 6; **EXCHANGES:** 3 Starch, 1 Medium-Fat
Meat; **PER SERVING:** CAL 296 (14% from fat);
PRO 17.1g; FAT 4.5g (sat 0.7g); CARB 48.2g;
FIB 2.8g; CHOL 0mg; IRON 3.4mg; SOD 805mg;
CALC 94mg

ORANGE-GINGER-TOFU STIR-FRY

prep: 10 minutes • cook: 9 minutes

*Orange juice concentrate is an easy
way to get the fresh citrus flavor of
oranges without having to do any
peeling or squeezing.*

3 tablespoons thawed orange juice
   concentrate
1 tablespoon dry sherry
1½ teaspoons cornstarch
1 teaspoon brown sugar
2 teaspoons dark sesame oil
½ teaspoon salt
2 teaspoons vegetable oil
1 tablespoon minced peeled fresh
   ginger
3 garlic cloves, crushed
1 (8-ounce) package presliced
   mushrooms
¾ pound asparagus, cut into 1-inch
   pieces
1½ cups thinly sliced leek (about 2
   large)
1 (10.5-ounce) package firm light
   tofu, drained and cubed
3 cups hot cooked brown rice

1. Combine first 6 ingredients in a
small bowl, and set cornstarch mixture aside.
2. Heat 2 teaspoons vegetable oil in
a stir-fry pan or wok over medium

heat. Add ginger and garlic; stir-fry 30 seconds. Add mushrooms, asparagus, and leek; stir-fry 3 minutes. Add cubed tofu; stir-fry 4 minutes. Stir in cornstarch mixture. Bring to a boil; cook 1 minute. Serve over rice. YIELD: 4 servings (serving size: 1 cup tofu mixture and ¾ cup rice).

POINTS: 5; EXCHANGES: 2 Starch, 2 Vegetable, 1 Fat; PER SERVING: CAL 264 (49% from fat); PRO 11.9g; FAT 6.6g (sat 0.9g); CARB 41.7g; FIB 4.5g; CHOL 0mg; IRON 3.0mg; SOD 378mg; CALC 85mg

VEGETABLE LO MEIN WITH TOFU

prep: 10 minutes • cook: 19 minutes

Tofu's greatest asset is its versatility. Not only does it absorb the flavors of the sauce it's cooked in, but it pairs well with any vegetable combination. So if you don't have the vegetables listed in this recipe, use those you have on hand.

6 ounces uncooked linguine, broken in half
2 teaspoons dark sesame oil
1½ teaspoons cornstarch
1½ teaspoons water
¼ cup low-sodium soy sauce
1 tablespoon rice vinegar
1½ teaspoons sugar
1 cup vegetable broth
1 garlic clove, minced
½ pound extra-firm light tofu, drained
2 teaspoons vegetable oil
Cooking spray
1 cup matchstick-cut carrots
1 cup diagonally sliced snow peas
1 cup fresh bean sprouts
¼ cup thinly sliced green onions

1. Cook linguine in a Dutch oven according to package directions, omitting salt and fat; drain. Run under cold water to cool immediately; drain well. Transfer to a large bowl; add sesame oil, tossing to coat.
2. Combine cornstarch and water in a medium bowl; stir with a whisk. Add soy sauce and next 4 ingredients, stirring with a whisk.
3. Cut tofu into ½-inch cubes, and pat dry with paper towels.
4. Heat 2 teaspoons vegetable oil in a large nonstick skillet coated with cooking spray over high heat. Add tofu, and cook, shaking or turning occasionally, 5 minutes or until golden. Remove tofu, and keep warm.
5. Add vegetable broth mixture, pasta, carrot, snow peas, bean sprouts, and green onions to pan, stirring constantly, 3 minutes or until slightly thickened. Gently stir in tofu. YIELD: 4 servings (serving size: about 1½ cups).

POINTS: 5; EXCHANGES: 3 Starch, 1 Fat; PER SERVING: CAL 276 (19% from fat); PRO 12.5g; FAT 6.0g (sat 0.7g); CARB 43.8g; FIB 3.4g; CHOL 0mg; IRON 3.3mg; SOD 856mg; CALC 58mg

THE TRUTH ABOUT TOFU

Tofu is made from soybean milk in a method similar to that of making cheese from cow's milk. The amount of whey drained off during processing will determine the texture of the tofu. Almost any cooking method can be used when preparing tofu, depending on tofu's texture. Listed below are descriptions and cooking recommendations for different tofu textures.

Extra-firm/Firm Tofu: These tofus are more substantial and absorb marinades well. They're packaged in water and must be refrigerated. They're ideal for slicing, dicing, frying, grilling and broiling. Firm or extra-firm tofu can be used as a meat alternative because it maintains its shape during cooking. When frozen, extra-firm tofu develops a chewy texture and can be used in the same manner as ground beef.

Soft Tofu: Soft tofu is much less dense than the firmer textures. It's ideal for blending into salad dressings and sauces.

Silken Tofu: This tofu has the texture of custard. Silken tofu can be eaten raw or pureed and used as a dairy alternative or fat replacement in smoothies, dips, and desserts, such as cheesecakes. If using as a dairy alternative, remember that tofu is not as rich a source of calcium as most dairy products.

How to Drain Tofu: No matter what texture you use, most tofus need to be drained before cooking with them. To drain, place tofu on a plate layered with paper towels. Set another plate on top of the tofu, and weigh the plate down with cans or a heavy bowl. Allow tofu to drain 15-30 minutes.

How to Store Tofu: Any leftover tofu should be rinsed, covered with water, and refrigerated; it can be kept up to one week if the water is changed daily.

Meats

SMOTHERED SIRLOIN PATTIES WITH VEGGIES AND HORSERADISH SOUR CREAM

prep: 10 minutes • **cook:** 18 minutes

To make this dish more kid-friendly, skip the horseradish sour cream.

½ cup fat-free sour cream
1 tablespoon prepared horseradish
½ teaspoon salt, divided
1 pound ground sirloin
1 teaspoon Cajun seasoning, divided
Cooking spray
¾ cup green bell pepper strips (about ½ medium, cut into ¼-inch strips)
1 small onion, cut into eighths
2 (4-ounce) yellow squash, quartered lengthwise
¼ cup water

1. Combine sour cream, horseradish, and ¼ teaspoon salt; stir well with a whisk. Set aside.
2. Divide meat into 4 equal portions, shaping each into a ½-inch-thick patty.
3. Place patties in a nonstick skillet over medium-high heat. Sprinkle with ½ teaspoon Cajun seasoning. Cook 5 minutes; turn, sprinkle with ½ teaspoon Cajun seasoning, and cook 4 minutes. Remove patties from pan, and keep warm.
4. Coat pan with cooking spray, and place over medium-high heat. Add bell pepper, ¼ teaspoon salt, onion, and squash. Cover, reduce heat to medium-low, and cook 6 minutes or until squash is crisp-tender, stirring occasionally.
5. Return patties to pan; add water.

Cover and cook over medium heat 3 minutes or until done. Serve with sour cream mixture. YIELD: 4 servings (serving size: 1 patty, ¼ of vegetables, and about 2 tablespoons sour cream mixture).

POINTS: 5; **EXCHANGES:** ½ Starch, 4 Lean Meat; **PER SERVING:** CAL 233 (32% from fat); PRO 28.7g; FAT 8.2g (sat 3.4g); CARB 10.0g; FIB 1.6g; CHOL 81mg; IRON 3.3mg; SOD 496mg; CALC 77mg

SANTA FE MEAT LOAF

prep: 8 minutes • **cook:** 1 hour

1 large egg, lightly beaten
3 tablespoons grated fresh onion
1 (10-ounce) can diced tomatoes with green chiles, undrained
1 (1.1-ounce) package fiesta ranch-style dip mix (such as Hidden Valley)
1 (8.75-ounce) can whole-kernel corn, drained
½ teaspoon pepper
1 teaspoon Worcestershire sauce
1½ pounds ground sirloin
¼ cup Italian-seasoned breadcrumbs
Cooking spray

1. Preheat oven to 350°.
2. Combine first 7 ingredients in a large bowl; crumble beef over vegetable mixture. Add breadcrumbs, and stir until well blended.
3. Shape beef mixture into an 8 x 4-inch loaf on a broiler pan coated with cooking spray. Bake at 350° for 1 hour or until a thermometer registers 160°. Cool 5 minutes. YIELD: 6 servings (serving size: ⅙ of loaf).

POINTS: 6; **EXCHANGES:** 1 Starch, 3 Lean Meat; **PER SERVING:** CAL 268 (39% from fat); PRO 26.1g; FAT 11.5g (sat 4.4g); CARB 13.8g; FIB 1.5g; CHOL 77mg; IRON 3.2mg; SOD 1,147mg; CALC 31mg

MARINATED FLANK STEAK WITH LIME-CHIPOTLE GLAZE

prep: 8 minutes • **marinate:** 4 hours **cook:** 15 minutes

¼ cup fresh lime juice
2 drained canned chipotle chiles in adobo sauce
2 tablespoons adobo sauce (reserved from drained chiles)
2 tablespoons honey
1 garlic clove, peeled
1 teaspoon ground cumin
½ teaspoon salt
1 (1-pound) flank steak, trimmed
Cooking spray

1. Combine first 7 ingredients in a blender or food processor; process until smooth. Pour into a heavy-duty zip-top plastic bag; add steak. Seal and marinate in refrigerator at least 4 hours, turning bag occasionally.
2. Prepare grill.
3. Remove steak from bag, reserving marinade. Pour marinade into a 2-cup glass measure; microwave at HIGH 1½ minutes or until marinade boils, stirring every 30 seconds.
4. Place steak on grill rack coated with cooking spray; cover and grill 7 minutes on each side or to desired degree of doneness, basting frequently with reserved marinade. Cut steak diagonally across grain into thin slices. YIELD: 4 servings (serving size: 3 ounces steak).

POINTS: 5; **EXCHANGES:** ½ Starch, 3 Lean Meat; **PER SERVING:** CAL 231 (37% from fat); PRO 23.9g; FAT 9.3g (sat 3.8g); CARB 11.9g; FIB 1.0g; CHOL 59mg; IRON 2.7mg; SOD 463mg; CALC 14mg

FLANK STEAK WITH TOMATO-AVOCADO SALSA

(pictured on page 90)
prep: 15 minutes • marinate: 8 hours
cook: 12 minutes • stand: 5 minutes

*The habanero chile pepper is
extremely hot and is used in many
Caribbean dishes.*

½ cup minced green onions
2 tablespoons cider vinegar
2 garlic cloves, minced
1 habanero chile pepper, seeded
  and minced
1 tablespoon minced peeled fresh
  ginger
4 teaspoons Jamaican jerk seasoning
1 (1¾-pound) flank steak, trimmed
Cooking spray
Tomato-Avocado Salsa
Cilantro sprigs (optional)

1. Combine first 6 ingredients in a
small bowl. Score a diamond pattern
on steak. Place steak in a shallow dish.
Spread green onion mixture on steak.
Cover and marinate in refrigerator at
least 8 hours.
2. Prepare grill.
3. Place steak on grill rack coated
with cooking spray; grill 6 minutes on
each side or to desired degree of
doneness. Let stand 5 minutes. Cut
steak diagonally across grain into thin
slices. Serve with Tomato-Avocado
Salsa. Garnish with cilantro sprigs, if
desired. YIELD: 6 servings (serving size:
3 ounces steak and ⅓ cup salsa).

POINTS: 6; **EXCHANGES:** 1 Vegetable, 3 Medium-
Fat Meat; **PER SERVING:** CAL 246 (47% from fat);
PRO 24.9g; FAT 12.9g (sat 4.4g); CARB 7.6g;
FIB 2.3g; CHOL 59mg; IRON 2.9mg; SOD 330mg;
CALC 19mg

TOMATO-AVOCADO SALSA
prep: 10 minutes

*Serve leftover salsa with baked
tortilla chips or as a topping for fajitas,
burritos, and quesadillas.*

1 teaspoon grated lime rind
2 tablespoons fresh lime juice
3 plum tomatoes, seeded and
  diced
⅓ cup chopped onion
¼ cup chopped fresh cilantro
1 garlic clove, minced
⅛ teaspoon salt
⅛ teaspoon pepper
1 ripe peeled avocado, seeded and
  diced

1. Combine all ingredients in a bowl;
toss well, and chill. YIELD: 2 cups (serving size: 1 tablespoon).

POINTS: 0; **EXCHANGES:** free up to ¼ cup;
PER TABLESPOON: CAL 10 (47% from fat); PRO 0.2g;
FAT 0.8g (sat 0.1g); CARB 2.0g; FIB 0.4g; CHOL 0mg;
IRON 0.1mg; SOD 11mg; CALC 2mg

HOW TO SCORE MEAT

Scoring before marinating helps
tenderize the meat and allows it
to absorb more flavors. To score
a flank steak, use a sharp knife to
make diagonal cuts across the
grain of the meat about 1 inch
apart and ⅛ inch deep on both
sides of the meat.

BEEF FAJITA PIZZA

prep: 10 minutes • stand: 5 minutes
cook: 13 minutes

2 teaspoons chili powder
¼ teaspoon garlic powder
½ pound lean, boneless sirloin
  steak, trimmed
1 (10-ounce) thin Italian cheese-
  flavored pizza crust (such as
  Boboli)
Cooking spray
½ cup chunky salsa
1 medium green bell pepper, cut
  into strips
1 medium red onion, thinly sliced
  and separated into rings
¾ cup (3 ounces) preshredded
  light Mexican cheese blend

1. Preheat oven to 450°.
2. Place a nonstick skillet over
medium-high heat until hot. While
pan heats, combine chili powder and
garlic powder; sprinkle over both
sides of steak. Add steak to pan; cook
4 minutes on each side. Remove
steak from pan; let stand 5 minutes.
Slice steak diagonally across grain
into ¼-inch slices.
3. Lightly coat pizza crust with
cooking spray; spread salsa evenly
over crust. Arrange pepper and
onion evenly over salsa. Top with
steak strips; sprinkle with cheese.
Bake at 450° for 8 to 10 minutes.
Cut into 8 slices. YIELD: 4 servings
(serving size: 2 slices).

POINTS: 7; **EXCHANGES:** 2 Starch, 1 Vegetable,
3 Medium-Fat Meat; **PER SERVING:** CAL 349
(25% from fat); PRO 27.2g; FAT 9.9g (sat 4.4g);
CARB 37.5g; FIB 2.5g; CHOL 42mg; IRON 3.7mg;
SOD 800mg; CALC 352mg

Committed To Success

KIRK GEBICKE • **HEIGHT** 6'3" • **BEFORE** 329.8 LBS. • **AFTER** 229.8 LBS.

KATHY GEBICKE • **HEIGHT** 5'3" • **BEFORE** 228.4 LBS. • **AFTER** 126.4 LBS.

Advice: Never underestimate the importance of exercise in your search for weight-loss success.

It's 5 a.m., and husband and wife team Kathy and Kirk Gebicke have walking shoes on, laces tied, and are ready to hit the pavement. It's part of their commitment to weight loss, to weight maintenance, and to each other.

For most of their lives both Kathy and Kirk were overweight. They had each tried different diet plans over the years, but finally found Weight Watchers to be the right fit for both of them.

In January 2001 the dynamic duo joined Weight Watchers and set a goal of losing more than 100 pounds each. With the winning **POINTS** plan, their daily walking ritual, and each other's support, the two were well on their way to achieving their goal.

> *"The time walking with Kathy is very enjoyable, and has become quality time that we cannot live without."*

From the very beginning, the couple found success. "The weight came off fast for both of us," Kathy says. "And it was a long time before we had any "ups" in weight. The exercise and the **POINTS** have really been the key for us."

In addition to eating a bigger percentage of fruits and vegetables, cutting back on the amount of cheese they cook with, and reducing the overall fat in their meals, Kirk and Kathy made a commitment to focus on exercise.

"Exercise is probably the reason we have succeeded so well," Kirk explains. And Kathy agrees. "We lost a lot, and we lost it quickly," she says. "I definitely think that's because of the walking."

The couple begins their day— every day—with an early morning walk. What started out as a 1 mile a day adventure has increased over the past 2 years to an average of 4 miles a day—rain or shine, hot or cold. "The time walking with Kathy is very enjoyable, and has become quality time that we cannot live without," Kirk says.

Though their weight loss is physically and dramatically noticeable, that by no means has been the only benefit. Their overall health and fitness has improved drastically, and they've been able to cut back on their blood pressure and thyroid medications.

It's now been about a year and a half since the Gebickes first began their quest for weight loss. And they're happy to report that they've each lost 100 pounds.

Flank Steak with
Tomato-Avocado Salsa,
page 88

Grilled Pork Tenderloin
with Black Bean Salad,
page 98

Lamb, Goat Cheese,
and Roasted Pepper
Calzones, page 94

Spiced Pork Chops
with Pineapple Salsa,
page 96

Skillet Ham with
Ginger-Peach Glaze,
page 98

CITRUS-BEEF STIR-FRY WITH CARROTS

prep: 9 minutes • marinate: 15 minutes
cook: 16 minutes

1 pound boneless sirloin steak, cut
   into thin strips
¼ cup low-sodium soy sauce,
   divided
½ cup fresh orange juice
3 tablespoons light brown sugar
1 tablespoon cider vinegar
1 tablespoon grated orange rind
½ teaspoon crushed red pepper
2 teaspoons sesame oil
2 cups matchstick-cut carrots
1 onion, cut into 8 wedges and
   separated

1. Place beef in a shallow dish; pour
2 tablespoons soy sauce over beef.
Turn to coat completely. Let marinate 15 minutes in refrigerator.
2. Combine orange juice, sugar, 2
tablespoons soy sauce, vinegar,
orange rind, and red pepper in a
small bowl. Stir with a whisk.
3. Heat oil in a large nonstick skillet
over high heat. Add beef, and cook 6
minutes. Remove from heat, and
place on a serving platter; keep warm.
4. Reduce heat to medium-high;
add carrot and onion. Cook 7 minutes or until carrot is lightly
browned and crisp-tender, stirring
frequently. Increase heat to high; add
beef and its juices, and orange juice
mixture. Cook 3 minutes or until
slightly thickened. YIELD: 4 servings
(serving size: 1 cup).

POINTS: 6; EXCHANGES: 1½ Starch, 3 Lean
Meat; **PER SERVING:** CAL 298 (29% from fat);
PRO 28.8g; FAT 9.5g (sat 3.0g); CARB 24.0g; FIB 2.3g;
CHOL 77mg; IRON 3.6mg; SOD 587mg;
CALC 48mg

SIRLOIN STEAK WITH SHERRY-SOY SAUCE

prep: 3 minutes • cook: 7 minutes

*If you don't have sherry on hand,
beef broth is a good substitute.*

⅓ cup dry sherry
2 tablespoons low-sodium soy
   sauce
2 tablespoons red wine vinegar
1 tablespoon sugar
2 garlic cloves, minced
¼ teaspoon crushed red pepper
1 pound boneless sirloin steak
   (about ½ inch thick)
¼ teaspoon salt
¼ teaspoon black pepper
Cooking spray

1. Combine sherry and next 5
ingredients in a small bowl; set aside.
2. Sprinkle both sides of steak with
salt and pepper.
3. Place a large nonstick skillet over
high heat. Coat pan with cooking
spray; add steak, and cook 3 minutes.
Reduce heat to medium-high; turn
steak, and cook 3 minutes or until
desired degree of doneness. Remove
steak, and set aside.
4. Add sherry mixture, scraping bottom and sides of pan; cook over
medium heat 1 minute, stirring constantly. Slice steak, and serve with
sauce. YIELD: 4 servings (serving size:
3 ounces beef and 2 tablespoons sauce).

POINTS: 5; Exchanges: 3 1/2 Lean Meat;
Per Serving: CAL 207 (31% from fat); PRO 26.8g; FAT
6.9g (sat 2.7g); CARB 4.8g; FIB 0.2g; CHOL 77mg;
IRON 3.3mg; SOD 473mg; CALC 16mg

SEARED ROSEMARY BEEF TENDERLOIN

(pictured on page 2)
prep: 5 minutes • cook: 20 minutes

*Serve these tasty beef medallions
with lots of crusty French bread
so you can sop up every drop
of the rosemary sauce.*

4 (4-ounce) beef tenderloin
   steaks, trimmed (about 1 inch
   thick)
¼ teaspoon salt
¼ teaspoon freshly ground black
   pepper
1 teaspoon olive oil
1 tablespoon chopped fresh rosemary
2 tablespoons minced shallot
2 garlic cloves, minced
¼ cup Madeira wine
1 (14-ounce) can low-salt beef
   broth
1 tablespoon light butter

1. Sprinkle steaks with salt and
pepper. Heat oil in a large nonstick
skillet over medium-high heat. Add
steaks; cook 8 minutes, turning every
2 minutes. Transfer beef to a serving
platter; cover and keep warm.
2. Reduce heat to medium-low; add
rosemary, shallot, and garlic to pan.
Cook, stirring constantly, 30 seconds.
Add wine and broth; bring to a boil
over high heat. Cook, stirring often,
10 minutes or until reduced to ⅓
cup. Remove from heat; stir in butter. YIELD: 4 servings (serving size: 1
steak and 2 tablespoons sauce).

POINTS: 5; EXCHANGES: 3 Lean Meat;
PER SERVING: CAL 224 (44% from fat); PRO 23.8g;
FAT 10.8g (sat 4.2g); CARB 2.8g; FIB 0.1g;
CHOL 68mg; IRON 3.0mg; SOD 245mg; CALC 15mg

CUBAN BRISKET

prep: 10 minutes • marinate: 8 hours
cook: 3 hours and 15 minutes

Serve this sweet-and-spicy brisket over noodles or with black beans and rice.

1¾ pounds beef brisket, trimmed
¼ cup fresh lime juice
¼ cup molasses
3 tablespoons Worcestershire sauce
2 teaspoons dried oregano
1 garlic clove, minced
1 teaspoon salt
½ teaspoon pepper
1½ teaspoons ground cumin
2 teaspoons paprika
2 teaspoons dried coriander
½ teaspoon ground allspice
2 teaspoons vegetable oil
1½ cups chopped onion
1 cup chopped celery
1 (14-ounce) can beef broth
1 (14.5-ounce) can diced tomatoes
    with green peppers and onion
1 bay leaf

1. Cut several ¼-inch-deep slits into brisket. Combine lime juice and next 10 ingredients in a large heavy-duty zip-top plastic bag; add brisket. Seal and marinate in refrigerator 8 hours, turning bag occasionally.
2. Preheat oven to 325°.
3. Remove brisket from bag, reserving marinade. Heat oil in a large oven-proof Dutch oven over medium-high heat. Add brisket; cook 4 minutes on each side or until browned. Remove brisket from pan. Reduce heat to medium; add onion and celery to pan. Cook 3 minutes or until tender. Add broth, tomatoes, bay leaf, reserved marinade, and brisket; bring to a boil. Remove from heat.

4. Cover and bake at 325° for 3 hours. Remove and discard bay leaf. Remove brisket from pan; shred with 2 forks. Add meat to sauce.
YIELD: 6 servings (serving size: 1 cup).

POINTS: 6; EXCHANGES: 1 Starch, 3 Lean Meat; PER SERVING: CAL 285 (33% from fat); PRO 25.7g; FAT 10.5g (sat 3.2g); CARB 21.5g; FIB 3.0g; CHOL 70mg; IRON 4.4mg; SOD 1,063mg; CALC 99mg

LAMB, GOAT CHEESE, AND ROASTED PEPPER CALZONES

(pictured on page 91)
prep: 15 minutes • cook: 23 minutes

½ pound ground lamb
¾ cup chopped onion
½ teaspoon minced garlic
½ teaspoon dried Italian seasoning
¼ teaspoon salt
⅛ teaspoon black pepper
1 (10-ounce) package refrigerated
    pizza crust
½ (3.5-ounce) package goat
    cheese, crumbled
½ cup bottled roasted red bell
    peppers, cut into thin strips
1⅓ cups fat-free marinara sauce
    (such as Colavita), warmed

1. Preheat oven to 425°.
2. Cook lamb, onion, and garlic in a nonstick skillet over medium-high heat until lamb is browned, stirring to crumble. Drain. Return lamb mixture to pan. Stir in Italian seasoning, salt, and black pepper.
3. Unroll pizza crust onto an ungreased baking sheet. Cut dough into 4 quarters, using a sharp knife or pizza cutter. Pat each quarter into a 6 x 5-inch rectangle.

4. Spoon lamb mixture evenly in center of each rectangle; sprinkle with cheese and red pepper. Bring opposite corners of rectangles together, pinching to seal. Pinch all seams together to completely enclose lamb mixture.
5. Bake at 425° for 13 minutes or until lightly browned. Serve with marinara sauce. YIELD: 4 servings (serving size: 1 calzone and ⅓ cup sauce).

POINTS: 7; EXCHANGES: 2½ Starch, 1 Vegetable, 2 Medium-Fat Meat; PER SERVING: CAL 352 (27% from fat); PRO 19.2g; FAT 10.7g (sat 5.0g); CARB 42.5g; FIB 3.9g; CHOL 43mg; IRON 3.3mg; SOD 1,027mg; CALC 59mg

HOW TO MAKE CALZONES

1. Unroll pizza crust onto an ungreased baking sheet; cut into 4 quarters. Pat each quarter into a 6 x 5-inch rectangle.

2. Spoon lamb mixture evenly in center of each rectangle; sprinkle with cheese and red pepper.

3. Bring opposite corners of rectangle together, pinching to seal. Pinch all seams together to completely enclose lamb mixture.

DIJON PORK CUTLETS

prep: 4 minutes • stand: 15 minutes
cook: 8 minutes

*Pounding the chops to ¼-inch
thickness cuts the cooking time.*

　8 (2-ounce) boneless center-cut
　　loin pork chops
　3 tablespoons Dijon mustard
　3 tablespoons sugar
1½ teaspoons cider vinegar
　¼ teaspoon crushed red pepper
Cooking spray
　¼ cup water

1. Place pork between 2 sheets of
heavy-duty plastic wrap; pound each
piece to a ¼-inch thickness, using a
meat mallet or rolling pin.
2. Combine mustard and next 3
ingredients in a small bowl. Place
pork in a shallow dish; spoon 2
tablespoons mustard mixture over
pork, turning to coat. Let stand 15
minutes.
3. Heat a large nonstick skillet coated
with cooking spray over medium-
high heat. Add pork, and cook 4
minutes on 1 side; turn pork, and
spoon reserved mustard mixture over
pork. Cook pork 2 minutes or just
until done.
4. Add water, stirring slightly; cook
2 minutes or until slightly thickened.
Turn pork to coat, and place on a
serving platter. Pour pan juices over
pork. YIELD: 4 servings (serving size: 2
cutlets).

POINTS: 5; EXCHANGES: ½ Starch, 3½ Lean
Meat; **PER SERVING:** CAL 225 (33% from fat);
PRO 26.4g; FAT 8.2g (sat 2.7g); CARB 10.8g; FIB
0.2g; CHOL 73mg; IRON 1.3mg; SOD 338mg;
CALC 36mg

QUICK PORK WITH SWEET BOURBON SAUCE

prep: 6 minutes • cook: 17 minutes

½ cup diet cola
¼ cup bourbon
　3 tablespoons balsamic vinegar
　2 tablespoons low-sodium soy
　　sauce
　3 tablespoons dark brown sugar
　¼ teaspoon dried red pepper flakes
　4 (6-ounce) bone-in center-cut
　　loin pork chops (about ½ inch
　　thick)
　¼ teaspoon black pepper
Cooking spray

1. Combine first 6 ingredients in a
small bowl; set aside.
2. Sprinkle both sides of pork with
black pepper. Place a large nonstick
skillet over medium-high heat until
hot. Coat pan with cooking spray;
add pork, and cook 4 minutes on
each side. Remove pork from pan,
and keep warm.
3. Add cola mixture to pan; scrape
pan to loosen browned bits. Bring to
a boil; reduce heat to medium, and
cook about 5 minutes or until mixture is reduced to about ½ cup.
4. Return pork to pan, and simmer
2 minutes. Turn pork, and cook 2
minutes or until pork is no longer
pink and mixture is reduced to
⅓ cup. YIELD: 4 servings (serving size:
1 pork chop and about 1½ tablespoons sauce).

POINTS: 5; EXCHANGES: 1 Starch, 3 Very Lean
Meat; **PER SERVING:** CAL 213 (25% from fat);
PRO 21.8g; FAT 5.8g (sat 2.1g); CARB 12.6g;
FIB 0.1g; CHOL 58mg; IRON 1.1mg; SOD 318mg;
CALC 40mg

PORK WITH DRIED PLUMS AND ONIONS

prep: 8 minutes • cook: 24 minutes

　1 cup apple cider
　2 tablespoons low-sodium soy
　　sauce
1½ teaspoons Worcestershire sauce
　¼ teaspoon ground red pepper
　4 (4-ounce) boneless center-cut
　　loin pork chops, trimmed
　¼ teaspoon salt
　¼ teaspoon black pepper
Cooking spray
　1 onion, thinly sliced
　1 cup bite-sized dried plums
　　(about 20)

1. Combine first 4 ingredients in a
small bowl; set aside.
2. Sprinkle both sides of pork with
salt and pepper. Place a large nonstick skillet over medium-high heat
until hot. Coat skillet with cooking
spray; add pork, and cook 4 minutes
on each side. Remove pork from
pan, and keep warm.
3. Add cider mixture to pan, scraping
pan to loosen browned bits. Bring to
a boil; add onion, and cook 2 minutes. Reduce heat to medium, and
add plums; cook 2 minutes. Add pork,
and simmer 6 minutes. Turn pork;
cook 6 minutes or until pork is no
longer pink and onion mixture is
reduced to 1 cup. Serve onion mixture over pork. YIELD: 4 servings (serving size: 1 pork chop and ¼ cup
onion mixture).

POINTS: 6; EXCHANGES: 2 Fruit, 3½ Lean Meat;
PER SERVING: CAL 318 (27% from fat); PRO 25.9g;
FAT 9.3g (sat 3.4g); CARB 31.6g; FIB 3.2g;
CHOL 60mg; IRON 1.3mg; SOD 480mg; CALC 47mg

SPICED PORK CHOPS WITH PINEAPPLE SALSA

(pictured on page 92)
prep: 15 minutes • chill: 30 minutes
stand: 10 minutes • cook: 14 minutes

1 cup chopped fresh pineapple
8 dried apricots, chopped
2 tablespoons finely chopped red onion
½ of 1 jalapeño pepper, seeded and finely chopped (about 2 teaspoons)
¼ teaspoon grated lime rind
2 tablespoons fresh lime juice
2 tablespoons chopped fresh cilantro
¼ teaspoon salt
¼ teaspoon black pepper
¼ teaspoon ground allspice
¼ teaspoon ground red pepper
4 (4-ounce) boneless center-cut loin pork chops, trimmed
Cooking spray

1. Combine first 7 ingredients in a bowl; cover and chill 30 minutes.
2. While salsa chills, combine salt and next 3 ingredients. Sprinkle both sides of pork with salt mixture; let stand 10 minutes.
3. Prepare grill.
4. Place pork on grill rack coated with cooking spray; cover and grill 6 to 7 minutes on each side or until pork is no longer pink. Serve with salsa. YIELD: 4 servings (serving size: 1 pork chop and about ⅓ cup salsa).

POINTS: 6; **EXCHANGES:** 1 Fruit, 1 Vegetable, 3 Lean Meat; **PER SERVING:** CAL 267 (38% from fat); PRO 22.3g; FAT 11.2g (sat 4.1g); CARB 19.6g; FIB 1.8g; CHOL 59mg; IRON 1.7mg; SOD 578mg; CALC 33mg

PORK CHOPS WITH SWEET POTATOES AND APPLES

prep: 17 minutes • stand: 15 minutes
cook: 28 minutes

½ teaspoon paprika
¼ teaspoon ground allspice
⅛ teaspoon dried thyme
¼ teaspoon pepper
¼ teaspoon salt
4 (4-ounce) boneless center-cut loin pork chops, trimmed
Cooking spray
2 teaspoons vegetable oil
1 cup thinly sliced onion
1 small sweet potato, peeled and thinly sliced (about ½ pound)
1 cup orange juice, divided
¼ teaspoon ground cinnamon
¼ teaspoon salt
1½ teaspoons sugar
½ teaspoon Worcestershire sauce
1 apple, cut into wedges

1. Combine first 5 ingredients in a small bowl; rub evenly over both sides of pork. Let pork stand 15 minutes in refrigerator.
2. Heat a large nonstick skillet coated with cooking spray over medium-high heat. Add pork; cook 3 minutes on each side. Remove pork from pan.
3. Add oil to pan; reduce heat to medium. Add onion and sweet potato; sauté 7 minutes. Add ¼ cup orange juice; cook until liquid evaporates, scraping pan to loosen browned bits. Add remaining orange juice, cinnamon, and next 3 ingredients; stir well.
4. Add reserved pork to pan; spoon onion mixture over pork. Top with apple. Simmer, uncovered, 7 minutes or until done, turning pork once. Serve immediately. YIELD: 4 servings

(serving size: 1 pork chop, ¼ cup vegetables, and 3 tablespoons sauce).

POINTS: 6; **EXCHANGES:** 1 Starch, 3½ Lean Meat; **PER SERVING:** CAL 272 (32% from fat); PRO 26.9g; FAT 9.7g (sat 2.8g); CARB 19.1g; FIB 2.0g; CHOL 73mg; IRON 1.5mg; SOD 651mg; CALC 43mg

SPEEDY PORK TOSTADAS

prep: 10 minutes • cook: 7 minutes

4 (6.5-inch) low-fat flour tortillas
Cooking spray
½ pound pork tenderloin, cut into short, thin strips
1 teaspoon minced garlic
1 teaspoon ground cumin
1 (15.5-ounce) can black beans, rinsed and drained
½ cup chunky salsa
2 cups shredded romaine lettuce
½ cup (2 ounces) preshredded reduced-fat Cheddar cheese
1 cup chopped tomato (about 1)
¼ cup fat-free sour cream

1. Preheat oven to 375°.
2. Lightly coat both sides of tortillas with cooking spray. Bake at 375° for 7 to 8 minutes or until golden.
3. Place a large nonstick skillet coated with cooking spray over medium-high heat until hot. Add pork, garlic, and cumin; sauté 3 minutes or until pork is browned. Add beans and salsa; simmer 4 minutes or until pork is tender.
4. Top tortillas evenly with lettuce, pork mixture, cheese, tomato, and sour cream. YIELD: 4 servings (serving size: 1 tostada).

POINTS: 6; **EXCHANGES:** 2½ Starch, 1 Vegetable, 3 Lean Meat; **PER SERVING:** CAL 327 (18% from fat); PRO 25.7g; FAT 6.4g (sat 2.9g); CARB 43.9g; FIB 7.3g; CHOL 45mg; IRON 4.3mg; SOD 815mg; CALC 210mg

PORK WITH CURRIED FRUIT

prep: 11 minutes • cook: 18 minutes

2 tablespoons all-purpose flour
2 teaspoons curry powder
¼ teaspoon ground ginger
¾ teaspoon salt
¼ teaspoon pepper
2 teaspoons olive oil
1 pound pork tenderloin, trimmed
   and cut into 1-inch cubes
¾ cup finely chopped onion
½ cup chopped celery
1 large garlic clove, minced
1 (8-ounce) package dried mixed
   fruit blend, chopped
1 (14-ounce) can fat-free,
   less-sodium chicken broth
1 (5-ounce) can fat-free evaporated
   milk
1 teaspoon honey
2 teaspoons chopped fresh rosemary
3 cups hot cooked egg noodles
   (about 2 cups uncooked)

1. Combine first 5 ingredients in a
bowl; stir well with a whisk.
2. Heat oil in a large nonstick skillet
over medium-high heat; add pork.
Cook 4 minutes or until browned.
Remove pork from pan. Add onion,
celery, and garlic to pan; sauté 2 minutes. Stir in mixed fruit; cook 2 minutes. Reduce heat to medium-low.
Slowly stir in flour mixture, broth,
and milk; add honey and rosemary.
Return pork to pan; cook 10 minutes,
stirring frequently. Serve over noodles.
YIELD: 6 servings (serving size: ¾ cup
pork mixture and ½ cup noodles).

POINTS: 7; **EXCHANGES:** 2 Starch, 1½ Fruit, 3
Lean Meat; **PER SERVING:** CAL 356 (15% from fat);
PRO 24.2g; FAT 6.1g (sat 1.7g); CARB 53.0g;
FIB 4.6g; CHOL 78mg; IRON 3.7mg; SOD 407mg;
CALC 121mg

PORK MARSALA

prep: 5 minutes • cook: 9 minutes

¼ cup all-purpose flour
¼ teaspoon salt
1 pound pork tenderloin, trimmed
   and cut into ½-inch-thick slices
1 tablespoon light butter
Cooking spray
¾ cup Marsala or other red wine
1 large garlic clove, minced
1 teaspoon beef-flavored bouillon
   granules
½ teaspoon freshly ground black
   pepper

1. Combine flour and salt in a
heavy-duty, zip-top plastic bag. Add
pork; seal bag, and shake until pork is
coated.
2. Melt butter in a large nonstick
skillet coated with cooking spray
over medium heat. Add pork; cook
until browned, turning once.
Remove from pan. Add wine, garlic,
bouillon granules, and pepper to pan;
bring to a boil. Reduce heat, and
simmer, uncovered, 2 minutes.
Return pork to pan; cover and simmer 2 minutes or until sauce thickens. Serve over pasta, if desired. YIELD: 4
servings (serving size: ¾ cup pork
mixture).

POINTS: 4; **EXCHANGES:** ½ Starch, 3 Lean Meat;
PER SERVING: CAL 180 (28% from fat); PRO 24.0g;
FAT 5.5g (sat 2.4g); CARB 7.3g; FIB 0.3g;
CHOL 69mg; IRON 1.8mg; SOD 402mg;
CALC 12mg

PORK TENDERLOIN WITH GINGERED CRANBERRIES

prep: 10 minutes • cook: 35 minutes
stand: 5 minutes

*Dried cranberries, sweetened and
unsweetened, are now readily
available in most supermarkets.
We preferred the sweetened
cranberries for this recipe.*

1 (1-pound) pork tenderloin,
   trimmed
Cooking spray
2 teaspoons Worcestershire sauce
½ teaspoon cracked black pepper
¼ teaspoon salt
½ cup dry red wine
½ cup orange juice
½ cup dried cranberries
⅛ teaspoon ground cinnamon
½ teaspoon minced peeled fresh
   ginger

1. Preheat oven to 425°.
2. Place pork in a 13 x 9-inch baking
pan coated with cooking spray.
Drizzle with Worcestershire sauce;
sprinkle with pepper and salt. Bake at
425° for 25 to 30 minutes or until a
meat thermometer inserted into
thickest portion of pork registers
160°. Let stand 5 minutes.
3. Combine red wine and next 3
ingredients in a small saucepan; bring
to a boil. Boil, uncovered, 5 minutes,
stirring frequently. Remove from heat;
stir in ginger. Spoon sauce over pork.
YIELD: 4 servings (3 ounces pork and
about 2 tablespoons sauce).

POINTS: 4; **EXCHANGES:** 1 Fruit, 3½ Very Lean
Meat; **PER SERVING:** CAL 220 (17% from fat);
PRO 24.1g; FAT 4.0g (sat 1.4g); CARB 15.2g; FIB 1.3g;
CHOL 74mg; IRON 1.8mg; SOD 233mg; CALC 17mg

GRILLED PORK TENDERLOIN WITH BLACK BEAN SALAD

(pictured on page 90)
prep: 10 minutes • marinate: 30 minutes
cook: 20 minutes • stand: 10 minutes

2 (¾-pound) pork tenderloins,
   trimmed
1 tablespoon olive oil
2 tablespoons fresh lime juice
2 tablespoons minced shallot
2 teaspoons minced garlic
½ teaspoon salt
½ teaspoon freshly ground black
   pepper
½ teaspoon ground cumin
Cooking spray
Black Bean Salad

1. Place pork in a heavy-duty zip-top plastic bag. Combine olive oil and next 6 ingredients, stirring well with a whisk; pour over pork. Seal bag; marinate in refrigerator 30 minutes. Remove pork from bag, reserving marinade.
2. Prepare grill.
3. Place pork on grill rack coated with cooking spray. Insert meat thermometer into thickest part of pork. Brush with reserved marinade. Cover and grill 20 minutes or until thermometer registers 160° (slightly pink), turning pork occasionally. Remove pork from grill; let stand 10 minutes. Serve with Black Bean Salad. YIELD: 6 servings (serving size: 3 ounces pork and ½ cup salad).

POINTS: 5; EXCHANGES: 1 Starch, 4 Lean Meat; PER SERVING: CAL 264 (36% from fat); PRO 27.7g; FAT 11.1g (sat 2.4g); CARB 15.7g; FIB 4.5g; CHOL 67mg; IRON 2.9mg; SOD 861mg; CALC 41mg

BLACK BEAN SALAD

prep: 13 minutes • stand: 1 hour

To allow all the flavors of the Black Bean Salad to develop, make it ahead of time.

1 (15-ounce) can black beans,
   rinsed and drained
1½ cups chopped seeded tomato
   (about 2 large)
¼ cup fresh lime juice
2 tablespoons olive oil
⅓ cup chopped fresh cilantro
2 tablespoons minced shallot
1 teaspoon minced garlic
½ teaspoon salt
½ teaspoon black pepper
¼ teaspoon crushed red pepper

1. Combine all ingredients, stirring well. Cover and let stand 1 hour. YIELD: 3 cups (serving size: 1 tablespoon).

POINTS: 0; EXCHANGES: free up to ¼ cup; PER TABLESPOON: CAL 12 (38% from fat); PRO 0.5g; FAT 0.6g (sat 0.1g); CARB 1.7g; FIB 0.5g; CHOL 0mg; IRON 0.2mg; SOD 50mg; CALC 4mg

LIGHT AND LEAN PORK

Today's pork offers more nutrient value for fewer calories than ever before. An average 3-ounce serving of lean pork contains 200 calories or less and has only 80 milligrams of cholesterol. And less than one-third of the fat in pork is saturated.

SKILLET HAM WITH GINGER-PEACH GLAZE

(pictured on page 92)
prep: 6 minutes • cook: 7 minutes

Fresh ginger is available in the produce section. Look for pieces that are firm with a smooth skin.

¼ cup peach spread
1 tablespoon water
1 tablespoon grated peeled fresh
   ginger
1 tablespoon dark brown sugar
2 teaspoons whole grain Dijon
   mustard
4 (3-ounce) slices 33%-less-sodium
   lean ham
Cooking spray

1. Combine first 5 ingredients; set aside.
2. Coat both sides of ham slices with cooking spray. Place a large nonstick skillet over medium-high heat until hot. Add ham slices; cook 1½ to 2 minutes on each side or until lightly browned. Transfer ham to a platter.
3. Reduce heat to medium-low. Add peach spread mixture to pan; cook 30 seconds until peach spread melts. Add ham slices; cook 2 minutes, turning frequently to glaze. YIELD: 4 servings (serving size: 1 slice).

POINTS: 4; EXCHANGES: 1 Starch, 2 Lean Meat; PER SERVING: CAL 186 (24% from fat); PRO 18.0g; FAT 4.9g (sat 1.6g); CARB 18.0g; FIB 0.1g; CHOL 45mg; IRON 1.4mg; SOD 898mg; CALC 13mg

SAUSAGE AND RICE CASSEROLE

prep: 17 minutes • cook: 20 minutes
stand: 2 minutes

Cooking spray
½ pound 97%-fat-free breakfast
  sausage (such as Jimmy Dean)
1 cup chopped onion
1 medium red bell pepper,
  chopped
½ cup thinly sliced celery
4 garlic cloves, minced
¼ teaspoon crushed red pepper
1 (10.75-ounce) can condensed
  reduced-fat, reduced-sodium
  cream of celery soup, undiluted
1 (8-ounce) can sliced water
  chestnuts, drained
2 teaspoons Worcestershire sauce
2 tablespoons light soy sauce
½ cup frozen green peas
1 cup hot cooked long-grain
  brown rice

1. Coat a nonstick skillet with cooking spray; place over medium heat
until hot. Add sausage; cook until
meat is browned, stirring to crumble;
remove from pan.
2. Add onion, bell pepper, and celery
to sausage drippings; sauté 4 minutes
or until tender. Add garlic and
crushed red pepper; cook 30 seconds. Add sausage, soup, and next 4
ingredients; stir well. Bring just to a
simmer; cover, reduce heat, and simmer 10 minutes. Stir in rice; cover,
remove from heat, and let stand 2
minutes. YIELD: 4 servings (serving
size: about 1 cup).

POINTS: 3; **EXCHANGES:** 2 Starch, 1 Very Lean
Meat; **PER SERVING:** CAL 173 (10% from fat);
PRO 5.1g; FAT 2.0g (sat 0.5g); CARB 35.0g; FIB 5.4g;
CHOL 3mg; IRON 1.5mg; SOD 824mg; CALC 130mg

HAM AND VIDALIA ONION FRITTATA

prep: 20 minutes • cook: 21 minutes

1 (16-ounce) carton egg substitute
⅓ cup thinly sliced green onions
¼ teaspoon dried thyme
¼ teaspoon ground red pepper
¼ teaspoon black pepper
¼ teaspoon salt
¾ cup (3 ounces) preshredded
  reduced-fat sharp Cheddar
  cheese, divided
Cooking spray
¼ pound lean deli ham, chopped
1 teaspoon vegetable oil
1½ cups thinly sliced Vidalia onion

1. Combine first 6 ingredients and
¼ cup cheese in a bowl; set aside.
2. Place a 12-inch ovenproof nonstick skillet over medium heat until
hot; coat pan with cooking spray.
Add ham, and cook 2 minutes or
until lightly browned; remove from
pan, and set aside.
3. Heat oil in pan over medium
heat. Add onion, and cook 5 minutes
or until tender. Reduce heat to
medium-low; add ham. Pour egg
mixture evenly over onion mixture.
Cook 10 minutes or until set around
edges (middle will be soft). Sprinkle
with remaining ½ cup cheese.
Remove from heat.
4. Preheat broiler.
5. Wrap handle of pan with foil.
Broil 4 minutes or until center is set
and cheese melts. Slide gently onto a
platter, and cut into 4 wedges. YIELD:
4 servings (serving size: 1 wedge).

POINTS: 5; **EXCHANGES:** 1 Vegetable, 3½ Lean
Meat; **PER SERVING:** CAL 209 (38% from fat);
PRO 26.2g; FAT 8.4g (sat 2.4g); CARB 4.9g; FIB 1.6g;
CHOL 21mg; IRON 3.3mg; SOD 847mg; CALC 159mg

VENISON KEBABS

prep: 18 minutes • cook: 8 minutes

*Grill the kebabs, covered,
8 to 10 minutes over medium-hot
coals (350° to 400°), if desired.
Serve with basmati rice and
baked apples.*

1 pound lean venison, cut into
  1½-inch cubes
1 small red onion, cut into
  1-inch pieces
1 medium red bell pepper, cut
  into 1-inch pieces
1 medium green bell pepper,
  cut into 1-inch pieces
½ cup mango or other fruit chutney
⅓ cup fat-free honey mustard
1 tablespoon water
1 teaspoon minced garlic
Cooking spray

1. Preheat broiler.
2. Thread venison cubes, onion
pieces, and pepper pieces alternately
onto 4 (15-inch) metal skewers.
3. Combine chutney and next 3
ingredients in a small bowl; stir well.
Brush mixture evenly on kebabs.
4. Coat rack of a broiler pan with
cooking spray. Place kebabs on rack;
broil 8 to 10 minutes or to desired
degree of doneness, turning occasionally. YIELD: 4 servings.

POINTS: 4; **EXCHANGES:** 1 Starch, 1 Vegetable, 3
Very Lean Meat; **PER SERVING:** CAL 218 (12% from
fat); PRO 26.9g; FAT 2.9g (sat 1.1g); CARB 19.8g;
FIB 1.4g; CHOL 96mg; IRON 4.4mg; SOD 352mg;
CALC 17mg

Poultry

CHICKEN, SPINACH, AND FETA PIZZA

prep: 8 minutes • cook: 12 minutes

Creamy alfredo sauce makes a perfect base for juicy roasted chicken and sharp feta cheese.

1 (10-ounce) Italian cheese-flavored thin pizza crust (such as Boboli)
⅓ cup refrigerated reduced-fat Alfredo sauce (such as Contadina)
1 (10-ounce) package frozen chopped spinach, thawed, drained, and squeezed dry
1½ cups shredded roasted chicken breast
½ (4-ounce) package crumbled feta cheese with basil and sun-dried tomatoes

1. Preheat oven to 450°.
2. Place pizza crust on an ungreased baking sheet or pizza pan. Combine Alfredo sauce and spinach; spoon over pizza crust. Sprinkle chicken and feta cheese over spinach.
3. Bake at 450° for 10 to 12 minutes or until golden. Cut into 8 slices. YIELD: 4 servings (serving size: 2 slices).

POINTS: 8; **EXCHANGES:** 2½ Starch, 3 Lean Meat; **PER SERVING:** CAL 377 (27% from fat); PRO 30.0g; FAT 11.2g (sat 5.1g); CARB 38.5g; FIB 2.8g; CHOL 60mg; IRON 3.8mg; SOD 852mg; CALC 349mg

ROASTED CHICKEN AND CORN RISOTTO

prep: 18 minutes • cook: 50 minutes

2 cups fresh corn kernels (about 3 large ears)
Cooking spray
5 cups fat-free, low-sodium chicken broth
2 teaspoons olive oil
½ cup minced shallots
2 garlic cloves, minced
1¼ cups Arborio rice or other short-grain rice
½ cup dry vermouth or vodka
4 cups chopped roasted chicken breast
⅓ cup fat-free half-and-half
¼ cup thinly sliced green onions
¼ teaspoon freshly ground black pepper
½ cup (2 ounces) grated fresh Asiago cheese
3 slices 40%-less-fat bacon, cooked and crumbled

1. Preheat broiler.
2. Place corn on a baking sheet coated with cooking spray. Broil 7 minutes or until lightly browned. Remove from baking sheet, and set aside.
3. Bring broth to a simmer in a medium saucepan (do not boil). Keep warm over low heat.
4. Heat oil in a large Dutch oven over medium-high heat. Add shallots and garlic; sauté 2 minutes or until tender. Reduce heat to medium. Add rice; cook 1 minute, stirring constantly. Add vermouth; cook 1 minute or until liquid is nearly absorbed, stirring constantly.
5. Reduce heat to medium-low. Add broth, ½ cup at a time, stirring constantly until each portion of broth is absorbed before adding the next (about 25 to 30 minutes total).
6. Gently stir in chicken and corn. Add half-and-half, green onions, and black pepper. Cook until thoroughly heated (do not boil). Sprinkle each serving evenly with cheese and bacon. Serve immediately. YIELD: 8 servings (serving size: about 1 cup).

POINTS: 7; **EXCHANGES:** 2½ Starch, 4 Lean Meat; **PER SERVING:** CAL 363 (17% from fat); PRO 30.6g; FAT 6.6g (sat 2.4g); CARB 40.4g; FIB 1.9g; CHOL 68mg; IRON 1.4mg; SOD 531mg; CALC 104mg

---

WHERE TO GET COOKED CHICKEN

Have you ever started to prepare a recipe only to see that the main ingredient is cooked chicken? If you're in a hurry, you probably don't have time to cook the chicken. Luckily, cooked chicken is available in most supermarkets. Look for:

• **Rotisserie chickens**—Prepared daily at delis in some grocery stores, these chickens have a great roasted flavor and aroma. Be sure to remove the skin!

• **Frozen diced chicken breast** (such as Tyson)—Defrost the chicken in the microwave, and you've got cooked chicken ready to be seasoned.

• **Refrigerated chicken breast strips** (such as Louis Rich)—This product comes in a variety of tasty flavors such as grilled, teriyaki, Southwestern, and Italian.

CHICKEN AND SAUSAGE RAGOÛT

(pictured on page 112)
prep: 10 minutes • cook: 22 minutes
stand: 5 minutes

Cooking spray
¾ pound skinless, boneless chicken breast halves, cut into bite-sized pieces
4 ounces low-fat smoked turkey sausage, thinly sliced
1 large onion, chopped
1 large green bell pepper, chopped
1½ cups quartered fresh mushrooms
4 garlic cloves, minced
1 (14.5-ounce) can Cajun stewed tomatoes
2 tablespoons dry red wine
1 teaspoon dried basil
½ teaspoon dried oregano
1 teaspoon sugar
2 tablespoons chopped fresh parsley
¼ teaspoon salt
2 cups hot cooked long-grain rice

1. Coat a Dutch oven with cooking spray; place over medium-high heat. Add chicken, and cook 2 minutes, stirring frequently. Add sausage and onion; sauté 1 minute. Add bell pepper, mushrooms, and garlic; cook 4 minutes, stirring frequently. Add tomatoes and next 4 ingredients; cook 15 minutes or until bell pepper is very tender. Remove from heat, and stir in parsley and salt. Let stand, uncovered, 5 minutes before serving. Serve over rice. YIELD: 4 servings (serving size: 1 cup ragoût and ½ cup rice).

POINTS: 5; **EXCHANGES:** 2 Starch, 2 Vegetable, 4 Very Lean Meat; **PER SERVING:** CAL 296 (7% from fat); PRO 27.8g; FAT 2.3g (sat 0.6g); CARB 40.5g; FIB 3.4g; CHOL 59.5mg; IRON 3.1mg; SOD 824mg; CALC 70mg

MARINATED GREEK KEBABS

prep: 16 minutes • marinate: 3 hours
cook: 15 minutes

1 (8-ounce) carton plain fat-free yogurt
⅓ cup (1.3 ounces) crumbled feta cheese with basil and sun-dried tomatoes
½ teaspoon grated lemon rind
2 tablespoons fresh lemon juice
2 teaspoons dried oregano
½ teaspoon salt
¼ teaspoon black pepper
¼ teaspoon dried rosemary, crushed
1 pound skinless, boneless chicken breast halves, cut into 1-inch pieces
1 large red onion, cut into 8 wedges
1 large green bell pepper, cut into 1½-inch pieces
Cooking spray

1. Combine first 8 ingredients in a medium bowl, stirring well with a whisk. Add chicken, tossing to coat; cover and marinate in refrigerator 3 hours.
2. Prepare grill.
3. Cut onion wedges in half crosswise. Remove chicken from yogurt mixture, discarding yogurt mixture. Thread chicken, onion chunks, and bell pepper pieces evenly on 4 (12-inch) skewers, alternating chicken and vegetables.
4. Place skewers on grill rack coated with cooking spray. Grill 15 minutes or until done, turning twice. YIELD: 4 servings (serving size: 1 skewer).

POINTS: 4; **EXCHANGES:** 2 Vegetable, 4 Very Lean Meat; **PER SERVING:** CAL 185 (13% from fat); PRO 29.1g; FAT 2.7g (sat 1.2g); CARB 10.5g; FIB 2.0g; CHOL 71mg; IRON 1.4mg; SOD 266mg; CALC 91mg

SPICY GINGER CHICKEN

prep: 12 minutes • cook: 7 minutes

½ cup water
¼ cup low-sodium soy sauce
¼ cup dry sherry
2 tablespoons dark brown sugar
1½ tablespoons cornstarch
1 tablespoon grated peeled fresh ginger
2 garlic cloves, minced
½ teaspoon chicken-flavored bouillon granules
¼ teaspoon crushed red pepper
Cooking spray
¾ pound skinless, boneless chicken breast halves, cut into thin strips
2 teaspoons sesame oil
1 cup thinly sliced onion
1 red bell pepper, cut into thin strips
1¼ cups quartered fresh mushrooms
2 cups broccoli florets

1. Combine first 9 ingredients; stir well with a whisk. Set aside.
2. Place a 12-inch nonstick skillet over medium-high heat. Coat pan with cooking spray; add chicken, and cook 2 minutes or until chicken is done. Remove from pan; set aside.
3. Add oil to pan. Add onion and bell pepper; cook 3 minutes, stirring frequently. Add mushrooms and broccoli; cook 3 minutes. Add cooked chicken and soy sauce mixture. Bring to a boil; reduce heat, and simmer, uncovered, 1 minute or until slightly thickened, stirring constantly. YIELD: 4 servings (serving size: 1 cup).

POINTS: 5; **EXCHANGES:** ½ Starch, 2 Vegetable, 3 Lean Meat; **PER SERVING:** CAL 246 (30% from fat); PRO 23.3g; FAT 8.3g (sat 1.3g); CARB 17.9g; FIB 2.9g; CHOL 49.3mg; IRON 2.2mg; SOD 648mg; CALC 49mg

CHICKEN TOPPED WITH FETA AND GREEN ONIONS

prep: 5 minutes • cook: 25 minutes

Hot pepper sauce is made with green tabasco peppers and vinegar. Don't confuse this product with hot sauce, which is red and fiery hot.

½ cup (2 ounces) feta cheese with basil and sun-dried tomatoes
2 tablespoons minced green onions
½ teaspoon dried basil
1 teaspoon extra-virgin olive oil
1 tablespoon country-style Dijon mustard
½ teaspoon hot pepper sauce
4 (4-ounce) skinless, boneless chicken breast halves
Cooking spray
⅛ teaspoon freshly ground black pepper

1. Preheat oven to 350°.
2. Combine first 4 ingredients in a small bowl; toss gently. Set aside.
3. Combine mustard and hot pepper sauce; stir well.
4. Place chicken on a broiler pan coated with cooking spray. Spread mustard mixture evenly over chicken. Bake at 350° for 20 minutes. Sprinkle cheese mixture evenly on chicken. Bake an additional 5 minutes or until cheese is slightly melted. Sprinkle with pepper. YIELD: 4 servings (serving size: 1 chicken breast half).

POINTS: 4; **EXCHANGES:** 4 Very Lean Meat; **PER SERVING:** CAL 178 (30% from fat); PRO 28.3g; FAT 5.6g (sat 2.6g); CARB 1.0g; FIB 0.2g; CHOL 78mg; IRON 1.0mg; SOD 338mg; CALC 85mg

FRESH SALSA CHICKEN

prep: 15 minutes • cook: 10 minutes

Make this salsa ahead of time; its flavor develops as it chills.

6 ounces cherry tomatoes, quartered
½ cup finely chopped yellow bell pepper
2 tablespoons capers, drained
1 tablespoon cider vinegar
1 garlic clove, minced
¾ teaspoon dried basil
⅛ teaspoon crushed red pepper
1½ teaspoons extra-virgin olive oil
4 (4-ounce) skinless, boneless chicken breast halves
Cooking spray
¼ teaspoon salt
¼ teaspoon black pepper

1. Preheat broiler.
2. Combine first 8 ingredients in a bowl; cover and chill until ready to serve.
3. Place chicken on a broiler pan coated with cooking spray; sprinkle with salt and black pepper. Broil 5 minutes on each side or until done. Serve tomato mixture over chicken. YIELD: 4 servings (serving size: 1 chicken breast half and 1 cup salsa).

POINTS: 3; **EXCHANGES:** 4 Very Lean Meat; **PER SERVING:** CAL 157 (19% from fat); PRO 26.9g; FAT 3.3g (sat 0.6g); CARB 4.0g; FIB 0.9g; CHOL 66mg; IRON 1.3mg; SOD 352mg; CALC 24mg

SWEET TEQUILA-LIME CHICKEN

prep: 7 minutes • cook: 18 minutes

Create a quick Mexican fiesta with this chicken, tortillas, and fresh lime margaritas.

3 garlic cloves, minced
¼ cup tequila
1 teaspoon grated lime rind
¼ cup fresh lime juice
2 tablespoons light brown sugar
¼ teaspoon salt
⅛ to ¼ teaspoon ground red pepper
Cooking spray
4 (4-ounce) skinless, boneless chicken breast halves

1. Combine first 7 ingredients in a bowl; stir well. Set aside.
2. Coat a nonstick skillet with cooking spray; place over medium-high heat until hot. Add chicken; cook 4 minutes on each side or until browned.
3. Add tequila mixture; bring to a boil. Cover, reduce heat, and simmer 8 minutes. Uncover, turn chicken, and simmer 2 minutes or until chicken is done and sauce is thickened. YIELD: 4 servings (serving size: 1 chicken breast half and 1 tablespoon sauce).

POINTS: 4; **EXCHANGES:** ½ Starch, 4 Very Lean Meat; **PER SERVING:** CAL 186 (7% from fat); PRO 26.4g; FAT 1.5g (sat 0.4g); CARB 6.7g; FIB 0.2g; CHOL 66mg; IRON 1.0mg; SOD 223mg; CALC 23mg

CHICKEN PUTTANESCA

prep: 12 minutes • cook: 25 minutes

Puttanesca is a traditional Italian sauce made of tomatoes, olives, capers, and garlic. The powerful ingredients in the sauce give chicken a new look and zesty flavor.

1 (14.5-ounce) can diced tomatoes
2 garlic cloves, minced
6 kalamata olives, pitted and coarsely chopped
2 tablespoons tomato paste
2 tablespoons red wine vinegar
1 tablespoon capers, rinsed and drained
½ teaspoon dried oregano
¼ teaspoon salt
¼ teaspoon pepper
4 (4-ounce) skinless, boneless chicken breast halves
1½ tablespoons Italian-seasoned breadcrumbs
Cooking spray
1 tablespoon olive oil

1. Combine first 9 ingredients in a medium bowl; stir well.
2. Coat chicken with breadcrumbs (coating will be light). Heat oil in a large nonstick skillet coated with cooking spray over medium-high heat until hot. Add chicken, and cook 5 minutes on each side or until golden brown. Pour tomato mixture over chicken; cover, reduce heat, and simmer 15 minutes or until chicken is done. YIELD: 4 servings (serving size: 1 chicken breast half and ⅓ cup sauce).

POINTS: 4; EXCHANGES: 1 Vegetable, 4 Very Lean Meat; PER SERVING: CAL 201 (24% from fat); PRO 27.9g; FAT 5.4g (sat 0.9g); CARB 9.6g; FIB 2.4g; CHOL 66mg; IRON 1.8mg; SOD 592mg; CALC 46mg

HOISIN CHICKEN

prep: 10 minutes • cook: 17 minutes

¾ cup fat-free, less-sodium chicken broth
2 tablespoons hoisin sauce
1 teaspoon cornstarch
½ teaspoon sugar
½ teaspoon grated peeled fresh ginger
½ teaspoon dark sesame oil
1 garlic clove, crushed
¼ teaspoon salt
⅛ teaspoon pepper
1½ tablespoons dry breadcrumbs
4 (4-ounce) skinless, boneless chicken breast halves
1½ teaspoons vegetable oil
2 teaspoons finely chopped fresh cilantro

1. Combine first 9 ingredients in a bowl, stirring well with a whisk.
2. Sprinkle breadcrumbs on both sides of chicken.
3. Heat a large nonstick skillet over medium-high heat; add vegetable oil. Add chicken, and cook 3 minutes. Turn chicken. Reduce heat to medium-low; cover and cook 12 minutes or until chicken is done. Remove chicken from pan; keep warm.
4. Add broth mixture to pan. Bring to a boil; reduce heat, and simmer 2 minutes or until slightly thickened, stirring constantly. Spoon sauce evenly over chicken. Sprinkle with cilantro. YIELD: 4 servings (serving size: 1 chicken breast half and about 2½ tablespoons sauce).

POINTS: 4; EXCHANGES: ½ Starch, 4 Very Lean Meat; PER SERVING: CAL 181 (21% from fat); PRO 27.4g; FAT 4.1g (sat 0.7g); CARB 7.0g; FIB 0.3g; CHOL 66mg; IRON 1.1mg; SOD 487mg; CALC 23mg

CHICKEN WITH GREEN ONION SAUCE

(pictured on page 113)
prep: 6 minutes • cook: 27 minutes

1 (14-ounce) can fat-free, less-sodium chicken broth
2 tablespoons all-purpose flour
2 garlic cloves, minced
¼ teaspoon dried thyme
Cooking spray
4 (4-ounce) skinless, boneless chicken breast halves
⅓ cup finely chopped green onions, divided
⅛ teaspoon salt
⅛ teaspoon pepper

1. Combine ¼ cup broth and flour in a small bowl, stirring with a whisk until smooth. Add remaining broth, garlic, and thyme; set aside.
2. Place a large nonstick skillet coated with cooking spray over medium-high heat until hot. Add chicken, and cook 4 to 5 minutes or until lightly browned. Turn chicken; add 2 tablespoons green onions. Pour broth mixture over chicken; sprinkle with salt and pepper. Reduce heat, and simmer, uncovered, 15 to 20 minutes or until chicken is done, basting often.
3. Remove chicken from pan; keep warm. Bring sauce to a boil over medium-high heat. Scrape bottom and sides of pan, using a rubber spatula. Cook 2 minutes or until sauce is reduced to ¾ cup. Pour sauce evenly over chicken, and top with remaining green onions. YIELD: 4 servings (serving size: 1 chicken breast half).

POINTS: 3; EXCHANGES: 4 Very Lean Meat; PER SERVING: CAL 155 (13% from fat); PRO 28.0g; FAT 2.1g (sat 0.7g); CARB 4.3g; FIB 0.2g; CHOL 67mg; IRON 1.1mg; SOD 195mg; CALC 24mg

CHICKEN WITH CREAMY TARRAGON-MUSTARD SAUCE

prep: 7 minutes • cook: 15 minutes

Be sure to remove the skillet from the heat before making the sauce. There will be enough heat left in the pan to warm the sauce.

2 tablespoons Dijon mustard
2 tablespoons light mayonnaise
1½ teaspoons lime juice
¼ teaspoon dried tarragon
2 teaspoons olive oil
4 (4-ounce) skinless, boneless chicken breast halves
2 tablespoons finely chopped green onions

1. Combine first 4 ingredients in a small bowl, stirring well with a whisk.
2. Heat oil in a large nonstick skillet over medium-high heat. Add chicken, and cook 3 minutes; turn and reduce heat to medium-low. Cover and cook 12 minutes or until chicken is done. Remove chicken; keep warm.
3. Remove pan from heat. Add mustard mixture to drippings in pan; stir well. Spoon mustard sauce over chicken; top with green onions. YIELD: 4 servings (serving size: 1 chicken breast half and about 1½ tablespoons sauce).

POINTS: 4; **EXCHANGES:** 3 Very Lean Meat, 1 Fat; **PER SERVING:** CAL 181 (35% from fat); PRO 26.8g; FAT 6.8g (sat 1.1g); CARB 2.0g; FIB 0.2g; CHOL 68mg; IRON 1.1mg; SOD 324mg; CALC 25mg

ORANGE-BRAISED CHICKEN WITH VEGETABLES

prep: 9 minutes • cook: 28 minutes

1 cup fat-free, less-sodium chicken broth
2 tablespoons tomato paste
1½ teaspoons grated orange rind
1 teaspoon sugar
¾ teaspoon dried basil
¼ teaspoon salt
¼ teaspoon pepper
4 (4-ounce) skinless, boneless chicken breast halves
1½ tablespoons Italian-seasoned breadcrumbs
1 tablespoon olive oil
Cooking spray
1 cup matchstick-cut carrots
1 cup thinly sliced leeks
½ cup chopped celery
2 tablespoons dry vermouth or vodka

1. Combine first 7 ingredients in a bowl; stir with a whisk. Set aside. Coat chicken with breadcrumbs.
2. Heat oil in a large nonstick skillet coated with cooking spray over medium-high heat. Add chicken; cook 5 minutes on each side or until golden brown. Remove chicken.
3. Add carrot, leeks, celery, and vermouth to pan. Sauté 3 minutes or until leeks are soft. Return chicken to pan. Pour broth mixture over chicken; cover, reduce heat, and simmer 15 minutes or until chicken is done. YIELD: 4 servings (serving size: 1 chicken breast half and ½ cup sauce).

POINTS: 5; **EXCHANGES:** 2 Vegetable, 4 Very Lean Meat; **PER SERVING:** CAL 230 (22% from fat); PRO 30.2g; FAT 5.7g (sat 1.1g); CARB 11.7g; FIB 2.1g; CHOL 66mg; IRON 2.1mg; SOD 732mg; CALC 53mg

PAN-FRIED CORNMEAL CHICKEN WITH CORN AND ONIONS

(pictured on page 111)
prep: 7 minutes • cook: 18 minutes

¼ cup stone-ground cornmeal
1½ teaspoons Cajun seasoning
4 (4-ounce) skinless, boneless chicken breast halves
1 tablespoon light butter
Cooking spray
½ cup chopped onion
½ cup chopped green bell pepper
1 cup frozen whole-kernel corn, thawed
¼ teaspoon salt
⅛ teaspoon black pepper
⅓ cup fat-free, less-sodium chicken broth
1 teaspoon cornstarch

1. Place cornmeal and seasoning in a zip-top plastic bag; add chicken. Seal and shake well to coat.
2. Melt butter in a large skillet over medium-high heat. Add chicken, and cook 6 minutes on each side or until done. Remove chicken from pan.
3. Coat pan with cooking spray. Add onion, bell pepper, and corn to pan; sauté 2 minutes over medium heat. Add salt and black pepper.
4. Combine chicken broth and cornstarch, stirring well; add to chicken, and cook until slightly thickened and bubbly. Serve corn mixture over chicken. YIELD: 4 servings (serving size: 1 chicken breast half and ¼ cup corn mixture).

POINTS: 5; **EXCHANGES:** 1½ Starch, 4 Very Lean Meat; **PER SERVING:** CAL 242 (13% from fat); PRO 29.1g; FAT 3.3g (sat 1.4g); CARB 20.6g; FIB 2.0g; CHOL 76mg; IRON 1.5mg; SOD 486mg; CALC 20mg

CHEESE-STUFFED ITALIAN CHICKEN

prep: 10 minutes • cook: 15 minutes
stand: 5 minutes

You'll never believe that this tender chicken oozing with gooey cheese is only 5 POINTS.

4 (4-ounce) skinless, boneless
  chicken breast halves
⅛ teaspoon salt
¾ teaspoon dried basil, divided
¼ teaspoon crushed red pepper
¼ cup minced green bell pepper
4 (¾-ounce) part-skim mozzarella
  cheese sticks
2 tablespoons fat-free Italian
  dressing
⅛ teaspoon paprika
¼ cup dry breadcrumbs
Cooking spray

1. Preheat oven to 400°.
2. Place each chicken breast half between 2 sheets of heavy-duty plastic wrap; pound to ¼-inch thickness using a meat mallet or rolling pin.
3. Sprinkle chicken evenly with salt, ¼ teaspoon basil, and crushed red pepper.
4. Sprinkle each chicken breast half with 1 tablespoon minced bell pepper. Place 1 cheese stick lengthwise down center. Roll up jelly roll fashion. Brush rolls evenly with Italian dressing.
5. Combine paprika and breadcrumbs; dredge chicken breast rolls in breadcrumb mixture, turning to coat. Place on a baking sheet coated with cooking spray seam side down. Lightly coat chicken rolls with cooking spray. Sprinkle evenly with remaining basil.

6. Bake at 400° for 15 minutes or until done. Let stand 5 minutes before serving. YIELD: 4 servings (serving size: 1 chicken breast roll).

POINTS: 5; EXCHANGES: ½ Starch, 4½ Very Lean Meat; **PER SERVING:** CAL 221 (27% from fat); PRO 32.6g; FAT 6.5g (sat 3.2g); CARB 7.0g; FIB 0.5g; CHOL 81.2mg; IRON 1.4mg; SOD 495mg; CALC 150mg

HOW TO STUFF CHICKEN BREASTS

1. Gently pound each chicken breast half to a ¼-inch thickness using a meat mallet or rolling pin.

2. Place a cheese stick lengthwise in center of each chicken breast half. Then, roll chicken breast up jelly roll fashion.

SICILIAN CHICKEN

prep: 8 minutes • cook: 3 hours and 40 minutes

Add the spinach to the slow cooker quickly to keep too much heat from escaping.

1 small onion, chopped
1 cup matchstick-cut carrots
1 tablespoon bottled minced garlic
1 teaspoon chopped fresh rosemary
½ teaspoon crushed red pepper
4 (4-ounce) skinless, boneless
  chicken breast halves
3 tablespoons dried tomato
  sprinkles (such as L'Esprit)
½ teaspoon salt
½ teaspoon freshly ground black
  pepper
1 (14.5-ounce) can diced
  tomatoes with green pepper and
  onion (such as Delmonte)
½ cup dry red wine
6 cups fresh spinach
2 cups hot cooked pasta

1. Place first 11 ingredients in a 5-quart electric slow cooker in order listed. Cover with lid; cook on high-heat setting 3½ hours.
2. Add spinach (do not stir). Cover with lid; cook on high-heat setting 10 minutes. Uncover and stir until spinach wilts. Top pasta with chicken and vegetable mixture. YIELD: 4 servings (serving size: 1 chicken breast half, ½ cup pasta, and 1 cup vegetable mixture).

POINTS: 5; EXCHANGES: 2 Starch, 1 Vegetable, 3½ Very Lean Meat; **PER SERVING:** CAL 293 (8% from fat); PRO 33.6g; FAT 2.6g (sat 0.4g); CARB 35.2g; FIB 5.2g; CHOL 66mg; IRON 4.8mg; SOD 939mg; CALC 138mg

GRILLED LEMON-OREGANO CHICKEN

prep: 5 minutes • cook: 20 minutes

4 chicken drumsticks
    (about 1 pound), skinned
4 chicken thighs (about 1 pound),
    skinned
Cooking spray
⅓ cup fresh lemon juice
1 tablespoon extra-virgin olive oil
¼ teaspoon garlic powder
2 teaspoons dried oregano
¾ teaspoon salt
¼ teaspoon pepper

1. Prepare grill.
2. Place chicken on grill rack coated with cooking spray; cover and grill 10 minutes on each side or until done.
3. Combine lemon juice and next 5 ingredients. Pour over grilled chicken; toss gently. YIELD: 4 servings (serving size: 1 drumstick and 1 thigh).

POINTS: 4; EXCHANGES: 3 Very Lean Meat; PER SERVING: CAL 175 (41% from fat); PRO 22.9g; FAT 7.8g (sat 1.6g); CARB 2.4g; FIB 0.4g; CHOL 92mg; IRON 1.6mg; SOD 535mg; CALC 26mg

TANGY BALSAMIC CHICKEN DRUMSTICKS

(pictured on page 110)
prep: 5 minutes • cook: 40 minutes

2 tablespoons balsamic vinegar
1 tablespoon ketchup
1 teaspoon Dijon mustard
¼ teaspoon salt
Cooking spray
1 cup chopped onion
4 garlic cloves, minced
8 chicken drumsticks
    (about 2 pounds), skinned

1. Combine first 4 ingredients in a bowl; set aside.
2. Place a large nonstick skillet over medium-high heat. Coat pan with cooking spray; add onion, and sauté, 4 minutes or until tender. Add garlic; cook 30 seconds. Remove onion mixture from pan.
3. Recoat pan with cooking spray; add chicken, and brown well on all sides. Add onion mixture, and drizzle evenly with balsamic mixture. Cover, reduce heat, and simmer 15 minutes. Turn chicken; cover and simmer 15 minutes or until chicken is done. YIELD: 4 servings (serving size: 2 drumsticks).

POINTS: 4; EXCHANGES: 4 Very Lean Meat; PER SERVING: CAL 162 (25% from fat); PRO 25.9g; FAT 4.4g (sat 1.1g); CARB 3.3g; FIB 0.1g; CHOL 95mg; IRON 1.5mg; SOD 335mg; CALC 24mg

GARLIC-ROASTED CHICKEN AND ONIONS

prep: 12 minutes • cook: 60 minutes

12 garlic cloves
Cooking spray
4 chicken drumsticks
    (about 1 pound), skinned
4 chicken thighs (about ¾ pound),
    skinned
½ cup finely chopped onion
½ teaspoon dried oregano
¼ teaspoon dried thyme
¾ teaspoon salt, divided
¼ teaspoon pepper

1. Preheat oven to 425°.
2. Sprinkle garlic into a 13 x 9-inch baking dish coated with cooking spray. Arrange chicken over garlic; sprinkle onion, oregano, thyme, ½ teaspoon salt and pepper over chicken. Cover and bake at 425° for 30 minutes. Uncover; bake 30 minutes or until chicken is done. Remove chicken. Add ¼ teaspoon salt to drippings. Drizzle drippings over chicken. YIELD: 4 servings (serving size: 1 drumstick and 1 thigh).

POINTS: 4; EXCHANGES: 4 Very Lean Meat; PER SERVING: CAL 178 (26% from fat); PRO 27.2g; FAT 4.9g (sat 1.3g); CARB 5.0g; FIB 0.7g; CHOL 105mg; IRON 1.8mg; SOD 556mg; CALC 39mg

MAPLE-BARBECUED DRUMSTICKS

prep: 15 minutes • cook: 40 minutes

⅓ cup pure maple syrup
2 tablespoons cider vinegar
2 tablespoons Dijon mustard
2 teaspoons Worcestershire sauce
¼ teaspoon ground allspice
¼ teaspoon salt
⅛ teaspoon pepper
8 chicken drumsticks
    (about 2 pounds), skinned
Cooking spray

1. Combine first 7 ingredients in a saucepan over medium heat; simmer, uncovered, 6 minutes or until sauce measures ⅓ cup, stirring occasionally.
2. Prepare grill.
3. Place chicken on grill rack coated with cooking spray. Cover and grill 35 minutes or until done, turning every 10 minutes. Baste chicken with sauce, and grill, uncovered, 5 minutes. YIELD: 4 servings (serving size: 2 drumsticks).

POINTS: 5; EXCHANGES: 1 Starch, 4 Very Lean Meat; PER SERVING: CAL 230 (20% from fat); PRO 26.0g; FAT 5.0g (sat 1.1g); CARB 19.6g; FIB 0.2g; CHOL 95mg; IRON 2.0mg; SOD 402mg; CALC 47mg

ROAST CHICKEN WITH LEMON AND TARRAGON

prep: 5 minutes • cook: 75 minutes
stand: 10 minutes

The skin on the chicken locks in the natural juices of the chicken, keeping each bite moist and juicy. Be sure to remove the skin before serving.

1 (3½-pound) roasting chicken
2 teaspoons dried tarragon, crushed
½ to 1 teaspoon salt
¼ to ½ teaspoon pepper
1 lemon, cut in half
Cooking spray

1. Preheat oven to 350°.
2. Remove and discard giblets and neck from chicken. Rinse chicken with cold water, and pat dry. Trim excess fat.
3. Rub chicken with tarragon, salt, and pepper. Place lemon in body cavity. Secure lemon in cavity with skewers or wooden picks.
4. Place chicken, breast side up, on a broiler pan coated with cooking spray. Insert meat thermometer into meaty part of thigh, making sure not to touch bone. Bake at 350° for 75 to 90 minutes or until meat thermometer registers 180°. Remove chicken from oven; cover with foil, and let stand 10 minutes. Discard skin and lemon. YIELD: 4 servings (serving size: 3 ounces chicken).

POINTS: 3; **EXCHANGES:** 3 Very Lean Meat; **PER SERVING:** CAL 143 (23% from fat); PRO 24.8g; FAT 3.5g (sat 0.9g); CARB 1.8g; FIB 0.4g; CHOL 78mg; IRON 1.4mg; SOD 529mg; CALC 31mg

BARBECUED DUCK WITH MANGO SALSA

(pictured on page 110)
prep: 5 minutes • marinate: 4 hours
cook: 20 minutes

½ cup spicy barbecue sauce
¾ cup mango nectar
1 teaspoon ground ginger
4 (6-ounce) boneless duck breast halves, thawed and skinned
Cooking spray

1. Combine first 3 ingredients in a large heavy-duty zip-top plastic bag; add duck. Seal; marinate in refrigerator 4 hours.
2. Prepare grill.
3. Remove duck from marinade. Pour marinade into a 2-cup glass measure. Microwave at HIGH 3 minutes. Place duck on grill rack coated with cooking spray; grill 7 minutes on each side or until done. Drizzle with marinade; serve with Mango Salsa. YIELD: 6 servings (serving size: 3 ounces duck and ⅓ cup Mango Salsa).

POINTS: 5; **EXCHANGES:** 1 Fruit, 3 Lean Meat; **PER SERVING:** CAL 229 (28% from fat); PRO 22.1g; FAT 7.1g (sat 1.8g); CARB 18.8g; FIB 1.6g; CHOL 84mg; IRON 5.3mg; SOD 299mg; CALC 11mg

MANGO SALSA
prep: 15 minutes

1⅓ cups chopped ripe mango
1 cup chopped red bell pepper
¼ cup minced green onions
2 tablespoons chopped cilantro
1 tablespoon fresh lime juice
1 tablespoon olive oil

1. Combine all ingredients, stirring well. YIELD: 2 cups.

TURKEY TETRAZZINI

prep: 15 minutes • cook: 10 minutes

1 cup fat-free, less-sodium chicken broth
1 cup 1% low-fat milk
3 tablespoons all-purpose flour
¼ teaspoon salt
¼ teaspoon pepper
Cooking spray
2 teaspoons light butter
1 (8-ounce) package presliced mushrooms
½ cup chopped celery
1 tablespoon dry sherry
2½ cups hot cooked spaghetti (about 5 ounces uncooked)
2 cups cubed cooked turkey breast (about ½ pound)
¾ cup (3 ounces) preshredded reduced-fat sharp Cheddar cheese

1. Preheat oven to 450°.
2. Combine broth and next 4 ingredients in a bowl, stirring well.
3. Melt butter in a large nonstick skillet coated with cooking spray over medium-high heat. Add mushrooms and celery; sauté 5 minutes. Add broth mixture and sherry; cook 2 minutes or until thick, stirring constantly. Add cooked spaghetti and turkey. Cook until thoroughly heated. Spoon into an 11 x 7-inch baking dish coated with cooking spray. Top with cheese.
4. Bake at 450° for 10 minutes or until cheese melts. YIELD: 5 servings (serving size: about 1 cup).

POINTS: 6; **EXCHANGES:** 2 Starch, 3 Lean Meat; **PER SERVING:** CAL 276 (23% from fat); PRO 20.3g; FAT 7.3g (sat 4.2g); CARB 34.1g; FIB 2.2g; CHOL 41mg; IRON 1.9mg; SOD 846mg; CALC 194mg

Grandma's New Hobby

CINDY DYER • **HEIGHT** 5'5" • **BEFORE** 216.2 LBS. • **AFTER** 135 LBS.

Advice: Approach weight loss as a hobby. The attitude of making it fun instead of considering it a chore really makes all the difference.

Mother of six and grandmother of eight, Cindy Dyer will be the first to admit that she has always had a weight problem. Like many other women, Cindy fell into the yo-yo category. She'd gain, lose, and gain some more.

By October 2000 her weight was the highest it had ever been—216 pounds. "I had resigned myself to being an overweight grandma, just holding my grandkids on my lap and making them—and me—lots of cookies," she says. Cindy worked at home as the bookkeeper for her husband's business. So she didn't feel the need to shop for clothes since she didn't get out much.

"I had very few clothes, and I hated clothes shopping," she says. "Going into the big women stores was painful." Cindy recalls one shopping experience that was particularly tough. "A sales clerk told me one time not to tie the strings on the back of my dress in a bow because it made me look fatter than I already was."

Another problem with being overweight was the inconvenience it caused when vacationing at her beach home. "There were a few times that I couldn't even make it down the 50 steep steps to the beach," she says. "To be that close to the beach and not even be able to enjoy it was depressing. My knees hurt, and I was winded just thinking about moving around too much."

But all in all it was not being able to play with her grandchildren that was the toughest part about being overweight. "I just had to sit and watch them grow up without being able to participate in their activities. That was the hardest thing."

Cindy joined Weight Watchers with a friend. "It sure helped having a weight-loss buddy," Cindy says. "She would lift my spirits when I was struggling and was there to help me celebrate my successes." With her friend's encouragement and the information, education, and support she received from Weight Watchers, Cindy managed to reach her goal by losing 80 pounds in about a year.

> *"Making it (weight loss) fun instead of considering it a chore has really made all the difference."*

"Most importantly, I learned to make weight loss a hobby." Whether she was counting **POINTS,** grocery shopping, trying new recipes, journaling, or even clothes shopping, Cindy attacked it all with enthusiasm. "I've actually had fun doing it," she says. "When you start any new hobby, you are excited and motivated, and that's how I approached weight loss. Making it fun instead of considering it a chore has really made all the difference."

Now Cindy describes her life as busy, hectic, and rewarding. "I love every minute of it," she says. "And I know that I will be able to keep the weight off because I have learned how to eat right."

Tangy Balsamic
Chicken Drumsticks,
page 107

Barbecued Duck
with Mango Salsa,
page 108

Pan-Fried Cornmeal Chicken
with Corn and Onions,
page 105

Chicken and
Sausage Ragoût,
page 102

Chicken with Green
Onion Sauce,
page 104

Red-Orange Coleslaw
with Sweet Dijon
Dressing, page 120

Beet, Blue Cheese, and
Toasted Walnut Salad,
page 119

White Bean and
Tomato Salad,
page 124

Fruited Wild Rice Salad,
page 124

The Big Catch

JIM NAPPER • **HEIGHT** 5'11" • **BEFORE** 270.5 LBS. • **AFTER** 183 LBS.

Proudest Moment: Stepping off the airplane in Minneapolis where he was meeting his friends. Seeing their suprised looks was priceless.

Jim Napper had the usual incentives for wanting to lose weight: better health, fewer physical limitations, and improved physical appearance. But it was finalizing his plans for his lifetime dream—a fishing trip to Canada with some of his high school buddies from west Texas—that sealed the deal. "I visualized how much more enjoyable the 8 to 10 hours a day in a boat would be as a smaller me," he says. "It was the final incentive I needed to get me through the doors of Weight Watchers."

So in February 2001, with guidance from the Weight Watchers staff, Jim set a goal to lose 40 pounds before the fishing trip in August.

"I quickly identified my primary eating problem as fast food and snack food," Jim says. "My major sins were chips, Fritos, and popcorn. And I didn't realize how much of these things that I was eating until I started eliminating them!"

With fast food and snack food out of his diet, Jim began to concentrate on preparing a home-cooked meal each night and varying his breakfasts and lunches. Jim credits this habit along with the **POINTS** program as his key to weight-loss success.

"I never ate or drank anything without at least a mental calculation of the **POINTS**, or without questioning if it was worth the **POINTS**. I didn't eliminate eating out completely, but I did order smarter and brought my own low-**POINT** substitutions for salad dressings and butter."

By May 17, 2001, Jim had lost over 42 pounds—an average of 3½ pounds per week—and reset his goal to be as light as possible by trip time. As the trip rolled around Jim found himself a total of 76 pounds lighter.

Stepping off the airplane in Minneapolis where he was meeting up with his high school friends before heading to Canada was Jim's proudest moment. "Seeing their surprised looks was priceless," he says. "They just kept shaking their heads. They couldn't believe it was me."

To date, Jim has lost a total of 90 pounds and remains vigilant in his weight-loss management. "All I can do is enjoy what I have accomplished, and the only way I can do that is to keep the Weight Watchers program in mind at all times."

"My major sins were chips, Fritos, and popcorn."

"There have been two downsides, though," he says with a chuckle. "Purchasing new clothes was expensive, and, regrettably, the weight loss did not improve my golf game. But I'm not complaining! Thank you, Weight Watchers!"

Salads

CURRIED WALDORF SALAD

prep: 12 minutes

If you can't find crisp, juicy Red Delicious apples, you may substitute Gala apples.

¼ cup fat-free mayonnaise
¼ cup plain fat-free yogurt
2 teaspoons fresh lemon juice
½ teaspoon curry powder
¼ teaspoon salt
⅛ teaspoon pepper
2 medium Red Delicious apples, cored and cubed
¼ cup chopped celery
2 tablespoons raisins
2 tablespoons chopped toasted walnuts

1. Combine first 6 ingredients in a medium bowl; stir well with a whisk.
2. Add apple and remaining 3 ingredients, tossing to coat. YIELD: 6 servings (serving size: ½ cup).

POINTS: 1; EXCHANGES: ½ Starch, ½ Fruit; PER SERVING: CAL 65 (23% from fat); PRO 1.2g; FAT 1.8g (sat 0.2g); CARB 12.6g; FIB 1.4g; CHOL 0mg; IRON 0.3mg; SOD 181mg; CALC 29mg

WALDORF WISDOM

Did you know that Waldorf salad gets its name from the hotel where it was created—the Waldorf-Astoria in New York City? The first salad contained primarily apple, celery, and mayonnaise. Over the years, walnuts, raisins, and other ingredients, such as curry, have found their way into the traditional salad.

CREAMY FROZEN CRANBERRY SALAD

prep: 7 minutes • freeze: 8 hours stand: 10 minutes

Cranberries appear on many holiday menus. Here, they're in a sweet salad with cream cheese, pineapple, and whipped topping.

5 ounces ⅓-less-fat cream cheese
2 tablespoons light mayonnaise
1 tablespoon sugar
1 (16-ounce) can whole-berry cranberry sauce
1 (8-ounce) can crushed pineapple in juice, drained
½ (12-ounce) container frozen fat-free whipped topping, thawed
1 teaspoon vanilla extract
Cooking spray

1. Combine cream cheese and mayonnaise in a large bowl; beat with a mixer at medium speed until creamy. Gradually add sugar, beating well. Stir in cranberry sauce and pineapple. Fold in whipped topping and vanilla. Pour into an 8-inch square baking dish coated with cooking spray. Cover and freeze 8 hours. Let stand 10 minutes before cutting into squares. Yield: 12 servings (serving size: 1 square).

POINTS: 3; EXCHANGES: 1½ Starch, ½ Fat; PER SERVING: CAL 133 (25% from fat); PRO 1.3g; FAT 3.6g (sat 1.9g); CARB 23.4g; FIB 0.7g; CHOL 10mg; IRON 0.1mg; SOD 83mg; CALC 12mg

LEMON-GINGER MIXED MELONS

prep: 6 minutes • stand: 5 minutes

2 tablespoons sugar
3 tablespoons fresh lemon juice
2 teaspoons grated peeled fresh ginger
1 cup cubed cantaloupe
1 cup cubed watermelon
1 cup cubed honeydew melon

1. Combine first 3 ingredients in a small bowl; stir with a whisk (sugar does not have to dissolve).
2. Place fruit in a shallow bowl; pour lemon mixture over fruit. Toss gently to coat; let stand 5 minutes. YIELD: 4 servings (serving size: ¾ cup).

POINTS: 1; EXCHANGE: 1 Fruit; PER SERVING: CAL 71 (4% from fat); PRO 0.9g; FAT 0.4g (sat 0.1g); CARB 17.7g; FIB 1.0g; CHOL 0mg; IRON 0.4mg; SOD 11mg; CALC 12mg

TROPICAL GREENS WITH ORANGE VINAIGRETTE

prep: 6 minutes • cook: 4 minutes

¼ cup flaked sweetened coconut
¼ cup sliced almonds
¼ cup orange juice
3 tablespoons honey
2 tablespoons lemon juice
1 tablespoon cider vinegar
¼ teaspoon ground cumin
¼ teaspoon crushed red pepper
⅛ teaspoon salt
4 cups mixed salad greens
½ small red onion, thinly sliced
1 cup pineapple tidbits in juice, drained

1. Heat a large nonstick skillet over medium heat. Add coconut and almonds; cook 4 to 5 minutes or until golden, stirring constantly. Set aside.

2. Combine orange juice and next 6 ingredients in a small jar; cover and shake vigorously.

3. Combine mixed greens and onion, tossing gently. Arrange mixture on individual plates. Drizzle with orange juice mixture, and sprinkle with pineapple, almonds, and coconut. Serve immediately. YIELD: 4 servings (serving size: about 1⅓ cups salad, ¼ cup pineapple, 1 tablespoon coconut, 1 tablespoon almonds, and 3 tablespoons dressing).

POINTS: 3; EXCHANGES: 1½ Starch, 1 Vegetable, 1 Fat; PER SERVING: CAL 153 (27% from fat); PRO 3.1g; FAT 5.1g (sat 1.6g); CARB 27.2g; FIB 3.0g; CHOL 0mg; IRON 1.5mg; SOD 103mg; CALC 62mg

MESCLUN WITH RED GRAPEFRUIT AND FETA

prep: 5 minutes

Mesclun is an assortment of mixed baby salad greens.

1 (5-ounce) package gourmet salad greens (mesclun)
1 cup bottled refrigerated red grapefruit sections (such as Del Monte)
¼ cup crumbled feta cheese
2 tablespoons grapefruit juice
1 tablespoon white wine vinegar
1 teaspoon extra-virgin olive oil
1 teaspoon honey
¼ teaspoon salt
⅛ teaspoon freshly ground black pepper

1. Combine first 3 ingredients in a large bowl. Combine grapefruit juice and remaining 5 ingredients in a small bowl; stir well with a whisk. Pour over salad greens; toss gently. YIELD: 4 servings (serving size: 1½ cups).

POINTS: 1; EXCHANGES: 1 Vegetable, ½ Fat; PER SERVING: CAL 67 (41% from fat); PRO 2.2g; FAT 3.3g (sat 1.6g); CARB 8.2g; FIB 1.4g; CHOL 8mg; IRON 0.6mg; SOD 261mg; CALC 72mg

AVOCADO-CUCUMBER TOSS

prep: 11 minutes

This cool salad is a fun addition to Mexican food, and it's much healthier than refried beans covered in cheese.

1 tablespoon plus 1 teaspoon cider vinegar
1 tablespoon extra-virgin olive oil
½ teaspoon salt
¼ teaspoon pepper
1 cup cherry tomatoes, quartered (about 12 tomatoes)
1 diced peeled avocado (about 1 cup)
2 cups chopped cucumber

1. Combine first 4 ingredients in a jar; cover tightly, and shake vigorously. Place tomato, avocado, and cucumber in a bowl; add vinegar mixture, and toss gently to coat. Serve immediately. YIELD: 4 servings (serving size: 1 cup).

POINTS: 3; EXCHANGES: 2 Vegetable, 2 Fat; PER SERVING: CAL 129 (72% from fat); PRO 1.8g; FAT 11.3g (sat 1.7g); CARB 7.9g; FIB 3.5g; CHOL 0mg; IRON 1.0mg; SOD 304mg; CALC 17mg

BEET, BLUE CHEESE, AND TOASTED WALNUT SALAD

(pictured on page 114)
prep: 19 minutes • chill: 2 hours

If you're in a hurry, toss the orange juice and beet mixture with the lettuce before dividing it among individual plates.

¼ cup orange juice
3 tablespoons balsamic vinegar
1 tablespoon olive oil
1 teaspoon Dijon mustard
2 tablespoons chopped fresh chives
½ teaspoon salt
½ teaspoon freshly ground black pepper
1 (14.5-ounce) can sliced beets, drained (about 1½ cups)
4 cups torn red leaf lettuce
2 tablespoons crumbled blue cheese
¼ cup chopped walnuts, toasted

1. Combine first 7 ingredients in a small bowl; stir well with a whisk. Add beets; toss well. Cover and chill 2 hours.

2. Arrange lettuce evenly on individual plates. Spoon beet mixture evenly over lettuce, using a slotted spoon. Reserve remaining orange juice mixture.

3. Sprinkle blue cheese and walnuts evenly over beet mixture. Drizzle reserved orange juice mixture evenly over each salad. YIELD: 4 servings (serving size: 1 cup lettuce, about ⅓ cup beets, 1½ teaspoons cheese, and 2 tablespoons orange juice mixture).

POINTS: 2; EXCHANGES: 2 Vegetable, 1½ Fat; PER SERVING: CAL 114 (53% from fat); PRO 3.6g; FAT 7.2g (sat 1.4g); CARB 10.5g; FIB 2.6g; CHOL 3mg; IRON 2.2mg; SOD 522mg; CALC 74mg

CITRUSY BROCCOLI AND CAULIFLOWER SALAD

prep: 25 minutes • chill: 4 hours

Citrus fruits do double duty in this recipe. First, grate the orange and lemon rinds; then, cut the fruits in half and squeeze out the juice.

¼ cup light mayonnaise
2 teaspoons grated orange rind
2 tablespoons fresh orange juice
1 teaspoon grated lemon rind
1 tablespoon fresh lemon juice
2 teaspoons sugar
2 teaspoons Dijon mustard
¼ teaspoon salt
¼ teaspoon black pepper
3 cups small broccoli florets
3 cups small cauliflower florets
½ cup chopped red bell pepper
⅓ cup raisins
3 slices center-cut bacon, cooked and crumbled

1. Combine first 9 ingredients in a bowl; stir with a whisk until blended.
2. Combine broccoli and remaining 4 ingredients in a large bowl. Spoon mayonnaise mixture over broccoli mixture; toss gently to coat. Cover and chill 4 hours. YIELD: 8 servings (serving size: ¾ cup).

POINTS: 2; EXCHANGES: ½ Starch, 1 Vegetable, 1 Fat; PER SERVING: CAL 87 (38% from fat); PRO 2.7g; FAT 4.0g (sat 0.8g); CARB 11.8g; FIB 2.5g; CHOL 4.6mg; IRON 0.7mg; SOD 224mg; CALC 28mg

RED-ORANGE COLESLAW WITH SWEET DIJON DRESSING

(pictured on page 113)
prep: 10 minutes • stand: 5 minutes

2 tablespoons cider vinegar
1 tablespoon extra-virgin olive oil
1 tablespoon Dijon mustard
1 tablespoon sugar
½ teaspoon salt
3 cups finely shredded red cabbage
1 cup shredded carrot

1. Combine first 5 ingredients in a large bowl; stir with a whisk. Stir in cabbage and carrot. Let mixture stand 5 minutes. YIELD: 4 servings (serving size: 1 cup).

POINTS: 1; EXCHANGES: 2 Vegetable, 1 Fat; PER SERVING: CAL 74 (47% from fat); PRO 1.3g; FAT 3.9g (sat 0.5g); CARB 10.0g; FIB 1.9g; CHOL 0mg; IRON 0.6mg; SOD 401mg; CALC 40mg

FAMILY TIES

What do all three recipes on this page have in common? They all star cruciferous vegetables. Members of the cabbage family, these veggies get their name from their four-petaled flowers which resemble a crucifer, or cross. Common cruciferous vegetables include broccoli, cauliflower, cabbages, Brusselsprouts, turnips, and rutabagas.

These veggies have gotten a lot of attention lately for their possible cancer-preventing capabilities. The jury is still out on cancer prevention, but these 0-*POINT* vegetables are definitely a good source of fiber and Vitamin C.

CRUNCHY ASIAN SLAW

prep: 10 minutes • chill: 1 hour

Before opening the ramen noodles, gently crush them while they're still in the bag. Remove the seasoning packet before sprinkling the crushed noodles over the cabbage mixture.

8 cups thinly sliced Savoy cabbage (about 1 head)
1 cup julienne-cut carrot
¾ cup sliced green onions (about 4)
1 (3-ounce) package ramen noodles, uncooked and crumbled (omit seasoning packet)
1 tablespoon sliced almonds, toasted
1 tablespoon unsalted sunflower seeds, toasted
2 teaspoons sesame seeds, toasted
⅓ cup seasoned rice vinegar
3 tablespoons sugar
2 tablespoons vegetable oil
2 teaspoons dark sesame oil
½ teaspoon salt
½ teaspoon pepper

1. Combine first 3 ingredients in a large bowl; toss well. Sprinkle with noodles, almonds, sunflower seeds, and sesame seeds; toss gently.
2. Combine vinegar and remaining 5 ingredients in a small bowl; stir with a whisk. Pour vinegar mixture over cabbage mixture; toss well. Cover and chill 1 hour. Toss gently just before serving. YIELD: 8 servings (serving size: 1 cup).

POINTS: 3; EXCHANGES: 1 Starch, 1 Vegetable, 1 Fat; PER SERVING: CAL 140 (36% from fat); PRO 3.2g; FAT 5.7g (sat 0.8g); CARB 19.6g; FIB 3.3g; CHOL 0mg; IRON 1.8mg; SOD 232mg; CALC 39mg

GREEN BEAN SALAD WITH BLUE CHEESE DRESSING

prep: 13 minutes • cook: 14 minutes

Here's your salad and your side all in one dish. This blue cheese and green bean combo is delicious served with a juicy beef tenderloin.

¼ cup low-fat sour cream
1 tablespoon light mayonnaise
2 tablespoons low-fat buttermilk
2 tablespoons crumbled blue
  cheese
½ teaspoon fresh lemon juice
⅛ teaspoon salt
⅛ teaspoon pepper
2 cups trimmed and halved green
  beans (about 8 ounces)
⅓ cup finely chopped red onion
2 slices 40%-less-fat bacon (such
  as Gwaltney), cooked and
  crumbled

1. Combine first 7 ingredients in a small bowl; stir with a whisk.
2. Steam green beans, covered, 14 minutes or until crisp-tender. Rinse with cold water. Drain well, and pat dry with paper towels.
3. Combine beans and onion in a large bowl; add dressing, and stir gently. Sprinkle evenly with crumbled bacon. YIELD: 4 servings (serving size: ½ cup).

POINTS: 2; **EXCHANGES:** 1 Vegetable, 1 Fat; **PER SERVING:** CAL 89 (51% from fat); PRO 4.3g; FAT 5.2g (sat 2.5g); CARB 7.0g; FIB 2.2g; CHOL 15mg; IRON 0.7mg; SOD 256mg; CALC 79mg

THREE-BEAN SALAD

prep: 10 minutes • cook: 2 minutes
chill: 8 hours

1 (16-ounce) can green beans,
  drained
1 (14.5-ounce) can yellow wax
  beans, drained
1 (15.5-ounce) can dark red
  kidney beans, rinsed and drained
½ cup chopped red bell pepper
¼ cup minced red onion
¼ cup minced seeded jalapeño
  pepper
⅓ cup cider vinegar
⅔ cup unsweetened apple juice
2 tablespoons sugar
1 tablespoon olive oil
½ teaspoon black pepper
¼ teaspoon dry mustard

1. Combine first 5 ingredients in a medium bowl; toss gently.
2. Combine jalapeño pepper and remaining 6 ingredients in a small saucepan; stir well with a whisk. Bring to a boil; reduce heat, and simmer, uncovered, 2 minutes or until sugar dissolves, stirring often. Pour over bean mixture; toss gently to coat. Cover and chill at least 8 hours. Serve salad with a slotted spoon. YIELD: 10 servings (serving size: ½ cup).

POINTS: 1; **EXCHANGES:** 1 Starch, 1 Vegetable; **PER SERVING:** CAL 98 (15% from fat); PRO 4.0g; FAT 1.7g (sat 0.2g); CARB 18.1g; FIB 5.2g; CHOL 0mg; IRON 0.9mg; SOD 207mg; CALC 25mg

CHOPPED VEGETABLE SALAD WITH BUTTERMILK DRESSING

prep: 9 minutes

To make preparation even easier, try using an English cucumber; it's seedless.

¼ cup low-fat buttermilk
2 tablespoons grated Parmesan
  cheese
2 tablespoons fat-free sour cream
2 tablespoons fat-free mayonnaise
1 teaspoon fresh lemon juice
¼ teaspoon salt
¼ teaspoon freshly ground black
  pepper
3 cups coarsely chopped iceberg
  lettuce
1 cup chopped cucumber
1 cup chopped plum tomato
¼ cup chopped celery

1. Combine first 7 ingredients in a medium bowl; stir with a whisk. Combine lettuce and remaining 3 ingredients in a large bowl; add buttermilk dressing, and toss well. Serve immediately. YIELD: 4 servings (serving size: 1½ cups).

POINTS: 1; **EXCHANGE:** 1 Vegetable; **PER SERVING:** CAL 52 (23% from fat); PRO 3.2g; FAT 1.5g (sat 0.8g); CARB 7.4g; FIB 1.4g; CHOL 4mg; IRON 0.5mg; SOD 293mg; CALC 88mg

MARINATED MUSHROOM AND ARTICHOKE SALAD

prep: 17 minutes • chill: 8 hours

1 (8-ounce) package whole mushrooms
1 (14-ounce) can artichoke quarters, drained
¼ small red onion, vertically sliced
2 tablespoons chopped fresh basil
3 tablespoons light olive oil vinaigrette (such as Ken's Steak House)
1 tablespoon fresh lemon juice
¼ teaspoon pepper
⅛ teaspoon salt

1. Cook mushrooms in boiling water 2 minutes. Drain and plunge into ice water; drain. Place mushrooms in a bowl. Add remaining 7 ingredients, tossing to coat. Cover and chill 8 hours. YIELD: 6 servings (serving size: ½ cup).

POINTS: 1; EXCHANGES: 2 Vegetable, ½ Fat; PER SERVING: CAL 60 (27% from fat); PRO 3.5g; FAT 1.8g (sat 0.2g); CARB 10.3g; FIB 4.2g; CHOL 0mg; IRON 1.3mg; SOD 330mg; CALC 35mg

RED CURRY POTATO SALAD

prep: 12 minutes • cook: 15 minutes
chill: 8 hours

2 pounds small red potatoes, quartered
2 hard-cooked large egg whites, chopped
¼ cup light mayonnaise
2 tablespoons chopped fresh parsley
¼ cup chopped green onions
½ teaspoon salt
1 tablespoon red curry paste (such as A Taste of Thai)
1 tablespoon hot water

1. Place potato in a large saucepan, and cover with water; bring to a boil. Reduce heat, and simmer 15 minutes or until tender. Drain and plunge potato into ice water; drain. Place potato in a large bowl.
2. Combine egg whites, mayonnaise, parsley, green onions, and salt. Add curry paste and water to mayonnaise mixture; stir well. Pour over cooled potato; toss gently to coat. Cover and chill 8 hours. YIELD: 11 servings (serving size: ½ cup).

POINTS: 2; EXCHANGES: 1 Starch, ½ Fat; PER SERVING: CAL 95 (18% from fat); PRO 2.3g; FAT 2.0g (sat 0.3g); CARB 17.4g; FIB 1.6g; CHOL 2mg; IRON 0.3mg; SOD 169mg; CALC 6mg

ASIAN SNOW PEAS AND CARROTS

prep: 15 minutes • stand: 1 hour

2 teaspoons dark sesame oil
1½ teaspoons grated peeled fresh ginger
¼ teaspoon crushed red pepper
¼ teaspoon salt
1½ cups matchstick-cut carrots
1 red bell pepper, thinly sliced
1 cup snow peas, trimmed
1 (8-ounce) can water chestnuts, drained

1. Combine first 4 ingredients in a medium-size bowl; stir with a whisk. Stir in carrot and remaining 3 ingredients. Cover and let stand 1 hour. YIELD: 4 servings (serving size: 1 cup).

POINTS: 2; EXCHANGES: 1 Starch, 1 Vegetable, ½ Fat; PER SERVING: CAL 117 (19% from fat); PRO 2.2g; FAT 2.6g (sat 0.4g); CARB 22.8g; FIB 4.3g; CHOL 0mg; IRON 11.3mg; SOD 469mg; CALC 26mg

SPINACH SALAD WITH FRESH CHERRIES

prep: 12 minutes • chill: 1 hour

Substitute a drained 16.5-ounce can of Queen Anne cherries if fresh cherries aren't in season.

¼ cup red wine vinegar
2 tablespoons olive oil
2 tablespoons water
1 tablespoon sugar
1½ teaspoons whole-grain Dijon mustard
¼ teaspoon salt
¼ teaspoon freshly ground black pepper
2 cups pitted fresh Rainier cherries
1 (7-ounce) package baby spinach
⅓ cup (1.3 ounces) crumbled blue cheese
2 tablespoons nutlike cereal nuggets (such as Grape-Nuts)

1. Combine first 7 ingredients in a medium bowl; stir well with a whisk. Add cherries, tossing gently; cover and chill 1 hour.
2. Toss spinach and cheese together in a large bowl. Pour cherry mixture over spinach mixture. Toss gently. Divide salad among 6 individual salad plates. Sprinkle each serving with cereal. Serve immediately. YIELD: 6 servings (serving size: about 1 cup salad and 1 teaspoon cereal).

POINTS: 3; EXCHANGES: ½ Fruit, 1 Vegetable, 1½ Fat; PER SERVING: CAL 126 (50% from fat); PRO 3.5g; FAT 7.4g (sat 2.1g); CARB 13.5g; FIB 2.2g; CHOL 6mg; IRON 1.9mg; SOD 274mg; CALC 83mg

SPINACH WITH CRANBERRIES AND BLUE CHEESE CRUMBLES

prep: 15 minutes

The sweet-tangy fat-free dressing for this salad beats any low-fat raspberry vinaigrette you could buy!

¼ cup seedless raspberry spread (such as Polaner All Fruit)
3 tablespoons balsamic vinegar
2 tablespoons orange juice concentrate, thawed
1 tablespoon water
¼ teaspoon crushed red pepper
¼ teaspoon salt
4 cups spinach leaves
⅓ cup (1.3 ounces) crumbled blue cheese
¼ cup sweetened dried cranberries (such as Craisins)
¼ cup thinly sliced red onion
½ cup alfalfa sprouts

1. Combine first 6 ingredients in a small bowl; stir with a whisk until blended.
2. Pour dressing over spinach; toss well. Place spinach mixture on individual plates. Top evenly with cheese, cranberries, onion, and sprouts. Serve immediately. YIELD: 4 servings (serving size: about ¾ cup spinach mixture).

POINTS: 3; EXCHANGES: 1½ Starch, ½ Fat; PER SERVING: CAL 137 (22% from fat); PRO 3.9g; FAT 3.5g (sat 2.1g); CARB 23.2g; FIB 1.8g; CHOL 8mg; IRON 1.1mg; SOD 333mg; CALC 99mg

ROASTED VEGETABLE SALAD

(pictured on page 3)

prep: 18 minutes • cook: 20 minutes
cool: 10 minutes

2 small yellow squash, cut into 1-inch pieces (about 2½ cups)
1 green bell pepper, cut into ¼-inch strips
½ onion, cut into 6 wedges and separated
2 teaspoons extra-virgin olive oil, divided
Cooking spray
1 cup halved grape tomatoes
16 pitted kalamata olives, chopped
1 tablespoon balsamic vinegar
1 tablespoon chopped fresh basil
1½ teaspoons chopped fresh oregano
¼ teaspoon salt
¼ teaspoon freshly ground black pepper

1. Preheat oven to 450°.
2. Combine first 3 ingredients on a large jelly-roll pan. Drizzle with 1 teaspoon oil; toss well. Coat squash mixture with cooking spray; arrange in a single layer. Bake at 450° for 15 minutes. Add tomatoes; turn vegetables with a spatula. Bake 5 minutes or until lightly browned. Remove from oven; cool on a wire rack 10 minutes.
3. Combine squash mixture, 1 teaspoon oil, olives, and remaining 5 ingredients in a bowl; toss gently. Serve immediately. YIELD: 4 servings (serving size: ¾ cup).

POINTS: 2; EXCHANGES: 2½ Vegetable, 1 Fat; PER SERVING: CAL 116 (49% from fat); PRO 2.5g; FAT 6.8g (sat 0.9g); CARB 13.3g; FIB 3.5g; CHOL 0mg; IRON 0.9mg; SOD 397mg; CALC 40mg

TIPS FOR ROASTING VEGETABLES

Make sure the vegetables have enough room on the jelly-roll pan and are arranged in a single layer when roasting.

SLICED TOMATO SALAD WITH CAPERS AND BASIL

prep: 6 minutes

2 tomatoes (about ¾ pound)
1 teaspoon capers
2 tablespoons coarsely chopped fresh basil
1 tablespoon balsamic vinegar
1 tablespoon water
2 teaspoons extra-virgin olive oil
1 small garlic clove, minced
⅛ teaspoon salt
¼ teaspoon freshly ground black pepper

1. Cut each tomato vertically into 6 slices. Arrange on a serving plate; sprinkle with capers and basil.
2. Combine vinegar and remaining 5 ingredients in a small bowl; stir with a whisk. Pour vinegar mixture over tomato. YIELD: 4 servings (serving size: 3 tomato slices).

POINTS: 1; EXCHANGES: 1 Vegetable, ½ Fat; PER SERVING: CAL 37 (55% from fat); PRO 0.7g; FAT 2.5g (sat 0.3g); CARB 3.8g; FIB 0.9g; CHOL 0mg; IRON 0.4mg; SOD 106mg; CALC 8mg

WHITE BEAN-AND-TOMATO SALAD

(pictured on page 114)
prep: 12 minutes

1 (15.8-ounce) can Great Northern beans, rinsed and drained
3 cups chopped seeded tomato
3 tablespoons chopped celery
2 tablespoons sliced green onions
1 tablespoon extra-virgin olive oil
1 tablespoon fresh lemon juice
1½ teaspoons chopped fresh sage
¼ teaspoon salt
¼ teaspoon pepper

1. Combine all ingredients in a bowl; toss gently. Garnish with sage, if desired. YIELD: 4 servings (serving size: 1 cup).

POINTS: 3; **EXCHANGES:** 1½ Starch, 1 Vegetable, 1 Fat; **PER SERVING:** CAL 188 (20% from fat); PRO 9.5g; FAT 4.3g (sat 0.7g); CARB 30.4g; FIB 7.6g; CHOL 0mg; IRON 2.7mg; SOD 322mg; CALC 83mg

BULGUR SALAD WITH FETA

prep: 18 minutes • stand: 20 minutes

⅔ cup uncooked bulgur
⅔ cup boiling water
2 cups grape tomatoes, halved
1 (15-ounce) can garbanzo beans, drained
⅔ cup chopped seeded cucumber
½ cup chopped celery
⅓ cup chopped red onion
¼ cup finely chopped fresh parsley
3 tablespoons fresh lemon juice
1 tablespoon extra-virgin olive oil
½ teaspoon salt
¼ teaspoon pepper
⅓ cup (1.3 ounces) crumbled feta cheese

1. Combine bulgur and water in a large bowl. Cover and let stand 20 minutes or until bulgur is softened.
2. While bulgur stands, combine tomato and next 9 ingredients. Add to bulgur, stirring gently. Add cheese, and toss well. YIELD: 6 servings (serving size: 1 cup).

POINTS: 4; **EXCHANGES:** 2 Starch, 1 Vegetable, 1 Fat; **PER SERVING:** CAL 231 (24% from fat); PRO 10.2g; FAT 6.3g (sat 1.8g); CARB 36.1g; FIB 9.4g; CHOL 7mg; IRON 3.0mg; SOD 481mg; CALC 97mg

FRUITED WILD RICE SALAD

(pictured on page 115)
**prep: 45 minutes • cook: 10 minutes
chill: 4 hours**

1 (6-ounce) package fast-cooking recipe long-grain and wild rice (such as Uncle Ben's)
3 large tangelos
1 cup chopped Gala or Fuji apple
1 cup chopped Granny Smith apple
½ cup dried cranberries
2 green onions, thinly sliced
3 tablespoons chopped fresh parsley
½ teaspoon chopped fresh rosemary
2 tablespoons apple cider vinegar
1 tablespoon olive oil
1 teaspoon dry mustard
½ teaspoon salt
¼ teaspoon pepper
1½ tablespoons pine nuts, toasted
Rosemary sprigs (optional)

1. Cook rice according to package directions, using 2 cups water. Omit salt, fat, and seasoning packet; cool completely.
2. Section tangelos over a bowl; reserve 2 tablespoons juice.

3. Combine cooked rice, tangelo sections, apple, and next 4 ingredients in a large bowl; toss gently.
4. Whisk together 2 tablespoons tangelo juice, vinegar, and next 4 ingredients; drizzle over rice mixture. Sprinkle with pine nuts; toss well. Cover and chill up to 4 hours. Garnish with rosemary sprigs, if desired. YIELD: 12 servings (serving size: ½ cup).

POINTS: 2; **EXCHANGES:** 1 Starch, ½ Fruit; **PER SERVING:** CAL 106 (18% from fat); PRO 2.1g; FAT 2.1g (sat 0.4g); CARB 20.2g; FIB 1.9g; CHOL 0mg; IRON 0.7mg; SOD 285mg; CALC 23mg

SMOKED SALMON AND GOAT CHEESE SALAD

prep: 15 minutes

¼ cup fresh lemon juice
1 tablespoon water
1 tablespoon minced peeled fresh ginger
1 tablespoon honey
1 teaspoon chopped fresh dill
¼ teaspoon salt
¼ teaspoon pepper
2 tablespoons extra-virgin olive oil
8 cups gourmet salad greens
8 ounces smoked salmon, sliced and cut into thin strips
1 (3.5-ounce) package goat cheese, cut into 4 equal slices
¼ cup very thinly sliced red onion

1. Combine first 7 ingredients in a blender; process 30 seconds or until smooth, scraping sides. With blender on, slowly pour oil through food chute; process until thickened.
2. Place salad greens on individual plates; top each evenly with salmon, cheese, and onion; drizzle with

dressing. Serve immediately. **YIELD:** 4 servings (serving size: 1 salad).

POINTS: 5; EXCHANGES: 2 Vegetable, 2 Medium-Fat Meat, 1 Fat; **PER SERVING:** CAL 238 (55% from fat); PRO 17.1g; FAT 14.8g (sat 5.1g); CARB 10.6g; FIB 2.8g; CHOL 24mg; IRON 2.8mg; SOD 714mg; CALC 107mg

MEDITERRANEAN SHRIMP AND RICE SALAD

prep: 15 minutes • chill: 1 hour

i ½ pound peeled cooked shrimp
2 cups cooked long-grain rice, cooled to room temperature
1 cucumber, peeled, seeded, and chopped (about 1¼ cups)
1 cup halved grape tomatoes
½ cup chopped green bell pepper
⅓ cup chopped red onion
½ cup (2 ounces) reduced-fat crumbled feta cheese
12 pitted kalamata olives, chopped
3 tablespoons fresh lemon juice
1 tablespoon olive oil
2 garlic cloves, minced
2 tablespoons chopped fresh mint
½ teaspoon salt
½ teaspoon black pepper

1. Combine first 8 ingredients in a large bowl. Combine lemon juice and remaining 5 ingredients in a small bowl, stirring well. Pour lemon juice mixture over shrimp mixture; toss gently. Chill 1 hour. **YIELD:** 4 servings (serving size: 1½ cups).

POINTS: 5; EXCHANGES: 1 Starch, 2 Vegetable, 1 Very Lean Meat, 1 Fat; **PER SERVING:** CAL 229 (29% from fat); PRO 15.7g; FAT 7.3g (sat 2.0g); CARB 25.1g; FIB 2.3g; CHOL 117mg; IRON 3.3mg; SOD 625mg; CALC 95mg

SHRIMP AND GREEN CHILE SALAD

prep: 35 minutes

If you don't like the crispness of raw corn, the fresh corn can be toasted in a skillet and cooled before tossing with the salad.

1 (4.5-ounce) can green chiles, undrained
½ cup chopped fresh cilantro
2 green onions, sliced
1 teaspoon chili powder
½ teaspoon ground cumin
2 garlic cloves, minced
1 tablespoon vegetable oil
1 tablespoon white wine vinegar
1 pound medium shrimp, cooked and peeled
½ teaspoon chili powder
10 cups torn romaine lettuce
2¼ cups fresh yellow corn kernels (about 4 large ears)
1 pint grape tomatoes, halved
⅔ cup diced peeled avocado
½ cup (2 ounces) crumbled feta cheese

1. Combine first 8 ingredients in a food processor; process until smooth. Set aside.
2. Combine shrimp and ½ teaspoon chili powder; toss well.
3. Toss together shrimp, lettuce, and remaining 4 ingredients. Add chile mixture, and toss well to coat. Serve immediately. **YIELD:** 8 servings (serving size: 2 cups).

POINTS: 3; EXCHANGES: 3 Vegetable, 1½ Very Lean Meat, 1 Fat; **PER SERVING:** CAL 178 (32% from fat); PRO 16.1g; FAT 6.7g (sat 1.8g); CARB 16.1g; FIB 4.0g; CHOL 117mg; IRON 3.5mg; SOD 267mg; CALC 103mg

ASIAN CHICKEN SALAD

prep: 13 minutes • cook: 1 minute

This quick and easy salad is a great way to use leftover roasted chicken.

2 tablespoons rice vinegar
1 tablespoon vegetable oil
1 tablespoon low-sodium soy sauce
1 teaspoon sugar
½ teaspoon grated peeled fresh ginger
⅛ teaspoon freshly ground black pepper
1⅓ cups diagonally halved snow peas
8 ounces ready-to-eat roasted skinless boneless chicken breast halves (such as Tyson), shredded
1 cup chopped cucumber (about 1)
1 (11-ounce) can mandarin orange sections, drained
¼ cup diagonally cut green onions
2 tablespoons chopped fresh cilantro
4 romaine lettuce leaves

1. Combine first 6 ingredients in a small bowl; stir with a whisk.
2. Steam snow peas, covered, 1 to 2 minutes or until crisp-tender. Rinse with cold water; drain well.
3. Combine snow peas and next 5 ingredients in a large bowl. Add dressing, and toss gently.
4. Serve salad immediately over lettuce leaves, or cover and chill until ready to serve. **YIELD:** 4 servings (serving size: 1 lettuce leaf and 1 cup salad).

POINTS: 4; EXCHANGES: ½ Fruit, 1 Vegetable, 2 Lean Meat; **PER SERVING:** CAL 181 (28% from fat); PRO 19.4g; FAT 5.6g (sat 1.1g); CARB 13.2g; FIB 1.8g; CHOL 48mg; IRON 1.9mg; SOD 183mg; CALC 40mg

Sandwiches

TOMATO AND SPINACH BAGUETTES WITH KALAMATA-FETA SPREAD

(pictured on page 134)
prep: 8 minutes

Try the tasty cream cheese mixture on bagel chips for an easy appetizer. One tablespoon of the cream cheese mixture is 1 POINT.

¼ cup (2 ounces) ⅓-less-fat cream cheese, softened
2 tablespoons crumbled feta cheese with basil and tomato
1 tablespoon country-style Dijon mustard
12 chopped pitted kalamata olives
1 garlic clove, minced
1½ tablespoons chopped fresh basil
1 (8-ounce) loaf French bread, cut in half horizontally
2 cups baby spinach
4 (¼-inch-thick) slices tomato

1. Combine first 6 ingredients in a small bowl, mixing well. Spread cream cheese mixture evenly over bottom half of loaf. Place spinach and tomato slices evenly over cream cheese mixture on bottom half of loaf. Top with remaining top half of loaf. Cut into 4 equal sandwiches. YIELD: 4 servings (serving size: 1 sandwich).

POINTS: 5; **EXCHANGES:** 2 Starch, 2 Fat; **PER SERVING:** CAL 250 (34% from fat); PRO 8.0g; FAT 9.2g (sat 3.6g); CARB 32.9g; FIB 2.5g; CHOL 15mg; IRON 2.1mg; SOD 743mg; CALC 99mg

BACON, LETTUCE, AND TOMATO SANDWICHES

prep: 14 minutes

Get back to the basics with these low-POINT B.L.T.s.

4 tablespoons low-fat mayonnaise (such as Hellman's)
8 (1-ounce) slices white or wheat bread, toasted
12 slices 40%-less-fat bacon, cooked (such as Gwaltney's)
8 lettuce leaves
8 (¼-inch-thick) slices tomato
¼ teaspoon salt
¼ teaspoon freshly ground pepper

1. Spread 1 tablespoon mayonnaise over each of 4 bread slices. Top each with 3 pieces bacon, 2 lettuce leaves, and 2 tomato slices. Sprinkle tomatoes evenly with salt and pepper. Top each with a remaining bread slice. YIELD: 4 servings (serving size: 1 sandwich).

POINTS: 4; **EXCHANGES:** 2 Starch, 2½ Lean Meat; **PER SERVING:** CAL 230 (26% from fat); PRO 13.2g; FAT 7.1g (sat 1.8g); CARB 31.7g; FIB 6.5g; CHOL 15mg; IRON 2.9mg; SOD 983mg; CALC 66mg

PICK THE BEST TOMATOES
The flavor of the tomato can either make or break your sandwich. For more flavorful tomatoes:
•Choose well-shaped tomatoes that are heavy for their size.
•Look for tomatoes that are slightly soft when squeezed.
•Keep ripe tomatoes in the refrigerator for only one to two days.

TUNA, CUCUMBER, AND DILL SANDWICHES

prep: 10 minutes

The tuna mixture can be made ahead, covered, and chilled until ready to make into sandwiches.

1 (6-ounce) can albacore tuna in water, drained and flaked
2 tablespoons low-fat mayonnaise (such as Hellman's)
2 tablespoons reduced-fat sour cream
2 teaspoons tarragon vinegar
¾ teaspoon dried dill
⅛ teaspoon salt
⅛ teaspoon pepper
4 (1-ounce) slices whole wheat bread, toasted
⅓ cup thinly sliced peeled cucumber

1. Combine first 7 ingredients in a small bowl.
2. Spread half of tuna mixture on 2 slices of bread. Arrange cucumber slices over tuna mixture. Top with remaining bread slices. Cut sandwiches in half, using a serrated knife. YIELD: 2 servings (serving size: 1 sandwich).

POINTS: 5; **EXCHANGES:** 2 Starch, 2½ Lean Meat; **PER SERVING:** CAL 266 (19% from fat); PRO 22.7g; FAT 5.8g (sat 1.9g); CARB 31.9g; FIB 4.2g; CHOL 27mg; IRON 3.1mg; SOD 810mg; CALC 83mg

CILANTRO SHRIMP SALAD ON SOURDOUGH ROLLS

prep: 12 minutes • cook: 2 minutes

It's easy to confuse fresh parsley and cilantro at the grocery store; they're often displayed side by side. If you're in doubt, press a leaf between your fingers. Parsley has a fresh peppery fragrance while cilantro is more pungent. You'll need both in this recipe.

¼ cup light mayonnaise
3 tablespoons fresh lemon juice
¼ teaspoon dried tarragon
¼ teaspoon salt
¼ teaspoon black pepper
⅛ teaspoon ground red pepper
½ cup finely chopped fresh parsley
¼ cup chopped green onions
¼ cup chopped fresh cilantro
½ pound chopped cooked shrimp
1 cup quartered cherry tomatoes
4 (2-ounce) sourdough rolls (such as Pepperidge Farm)
4 romaine lettuce leaves

1. Combine mayonnaise and next 8 ingredients in a medium bowl; add shrimp to mayonnaise mixture. Gently fold in tomato.
2. Preheat broiler.
3. Split rolls in half lengthwise to, but not through, other side. Place on a baking sheet, and broil 2 minutes or until lightly toasted.
4. Place a lettuce leaf in each toasted roll; spoon ¾ cup shrimp mixture into each roll. YIELD: 4 servings (serving size: 1 sandwich).

POINTS: 5; **EXCHANGES:** 2 Starch, 1 Vegetable, 1 Very Lean Meat, 1 Fat; **PER SERVING:** CAL 266 (25% from fat); PRO 14.6g; FAT 7.3g (sat 1.3g); CARB 35.1g; FIB 2.9g; CHOL 86mg; IRON 3.6mg; SOD 823mg; CALC 79mg

HOT SKILLET SIRLOIN WRAPS WITH BLUE CHEESE

(pictured on page 136)
prep: 12 minutes • cook: 3 minutes

This rolled sandwich is similar to steak fajitas but with a flavor twist—a tangy blue cheese and sour cream sauce.

½ cup plain fat-free yogurt
1 garlic clove, minced
1 tablespoon minced green onions
¼ cup crumbled blue cheese
½ teaspoon salt, divided
1 (¾-pound) sirloin steak, cut into ¼-inch-thick diagonal strips
1½ teaspoons chili powder
½ teaspoon dried oregano
1 teaspoon olive oil
1 green bell pepper, thinly sliced
4 (8-inch) flour tortillas
2 cups torn spinach
¼ teaspoon black pepper

1. Combine first 4 ingredients and ¼ teaspoon salt, stirring well. Set aside.
2. Sprinkle steak with chili powder, oregano, and remaining salt. Heat oil in a large nonstick skillet over high heat. Add steak and green pepper; sauté 2 minutes or until meat is done and pepper strips are tender.
3. Warm tortillas according to package directions. Spoon about ¾ cup steak mixture down center of each tortilla. Top each with ½ cup spinach and 2 tablespoons yogurt mixture. Sprinkle with black pepper; roll up. Serve immediately. YIELD: 4 servings (serving size: 1 wrap).

POINTS: 7; **EXCHANGES:** 2 Starch, 3 Lean Meat; **PER SERVING:** CAL 339 (30% from fat); PRO 27.5g; FAT 11.4g (sat 4.2g); CARB 31.4g; FIB 1.5g; CHOL 63mg; IRON 4.0mg; SOD 738mg; CALC 211mg

ROAST BEEF SANDWICHES WITH HORSERADISH

prep: 10 minutes

Horseradish spices up low-fat mayonnaise and sour cream so that you won't even notice that fat is missing.

¼ cup light sour cream
¼ cup low-fat mayonnaise (such as Hellman's)
1 tablespoon prepared horseradish
4 (2-ounce) French bread rolls, sliced in half horizontally
½ pound thinly sliced deli roast beef
4 curly leaf lettuce leaves
2 small ripe tomatoes, sliced

1. Combine first 3 ingredients in a small bowl; stir well.
2. Spread sour cream mixture evenly over cut sides of rolls. Divide roast beef evenly over 4 bread halves. Top roast beef evenly with lettuce and tomato. Place remaining bread halves, sour cream mixture down, over tomato. YIELD: 4 servings (serving size: 1 sandwich).

POINTS: 5; **EXCHANGES:** 2½ Starch, 1 Medium-Fat Meat; **PER SERVING:** CAL 276 (19% from fat); PRO 16.4g; FAT 5.7g (sat 2.1g); CARB 38.8g; FIB 2.4g; CHOL 28mg; IRON 2.5mg; SOD 937mg; CALC 74mg

HAM AND ARUGULA SANDWICHES WITH CRANBERRY CHUTNEY

(pictured on page 134)
prep: 10 minutes • cook: 5 minutes

Arugula is a green similar to lettuce but with a spicy kick to it. We think it goes well with the sweet chutney.

1 (8-ounce) package Italian-cheese-flavored pizza crusts (such as Boboli)
¼ cup cranberry chutney (such as Crosse & Blackwell)
2 tablespoons Dijon mustard
8 ounces lean cooked ham, sliced
1 cup loosely packed trimmed arugula or chopped romaine lettuce

1. Preheat oven to 450°.
2. Place pizza crusts on a baking sheet. Bake for 5 minutes at 450° or until warm.
3. Spread chutney over bottom side of 1 pizza crust. Spread mustard on bottom side of remaining crust. Arrange sliced ham over mustard-coated crust. Top with arugula. Place chutney-coated side of remaining crust over arugula. Cut into four equal sandwiches. YIELD: 4 servings (serving size: 1 sandwich).

POINTS: 5; **EXCHANGES:** 2 Starch, 1 Lean Meat; **PER SERVING:** CAL 246 (21% from fat); PRO 15.7g; FAT 5.5g (sat 1.5g); CARB 31.4g; FIB 0.7g; CHOL 25mg; IRON 3.0mg; SOD 912mg; CALC 208mg

HAM AND EGG SALAD SANDWICHES

prep: 10 minutes • chill: 15 minutes

Using only three of the six egg yolks helps to keep the fat down without sacrificing the salad's creamy texture.

⅓ cup plain fat-free yogurt
1 tablespoon light mayonnaise
1¼ teaspoons sugar
1 teaspoon Cajun seasoning (such as Spice Island Louisiana Style)
⅛ teaspoon salt
6 hard-cooked large eggs
4 ounces lean deli ham, cut into ¼-inch cubes
½ cup finely chopped celery
⅛ teaspoon pepper
1 (16-ounce) loaf unsliced French bread

1. Combine first 5 ingredients in a medium bowl; stir well.
2. Peel eggs, discarding 3 yolks. Chop egg whites and remaining 3 yolks; stir into yogurt mixture. Add ham and celery; stir gently. Sprinkle with pepper. Cover and chill 15 minutes or until ready to serve.
3. Remove soft bread from center of French bread loaf. Reserve soft bread for another use. Fill center of loaf with salad. Cut into four equal sandwiches, and serve immediately. Yield: 4 servings (serving size: 1 sandwich).

POINTS: 5; **EXCHANGES:** 2 Starch, 1½ Medium-Fat Meat; **PER SERVING:** CAL 245 (27% from fat); PRO 17.1g; FAT 7.3g (sat 2.1g); CARB 27.8g; FIB 1.6g; CHOL 176mg; IRON 1.7mg; SOD 835mg; CALC 83mg

CURRIED CHICKEN SALAD SANDWICHES

prep: 10 minutes

For a 4-POINT meal, serve 1 cup of the salad mixture stuffed in a small tomato or on a bed of salad greens.

2¼ cups chopped cooked chicken breast
2 cups seedless green grapes, halved
¾ cup thinly sliced green onions
¼ cup chopped walnuts
¼ cup low-fat mayonnaise (such as Hellman's)
¼ cup fat-free yogurt
1 teaspoon curry powder
5 lettuce leaves
10 (1-ounce) slices whole wheat bread, toasted

1. Combine first 7 ingredients in a large bowl, tossing well. Cover and chill until ready to serve.
2. Place a lettuce leaf on each of 5 slices bread. Top with 1 cup chicken mixture and remaining slice of bread. Serve immediately. YIELD: 5 servings (serving size: 1 sandwich).

POINTS: 6; **EXCHANGES:** 2 Starch, ½ Fruit, 3 Lean Meat; **PER SERVING:** CAL 304 (22% from fat); PRO 25.9g; FAT 7.8g (sat 1.0g); CARB 37.6g; FIB 8.4g; CHOL 49mg; IRON 2.8mg; SOD 453mg; CALC 83mg

CREAMY CAESAR CHICKEN PITAS

prep: 12 minutes • cook: 7 minutes

Cucumbers, carrots, and onions also make good pita "stuffers" for these quick sandwiches.

½ cup Italian-seasoned breadcrumbs
1 pound skinless, boneless chicken breast halves, cut into thin strips
½ cup fat-free milk
1 tablespoon vegetable oil
3 (6-inch) pita bread rounds, cut in half
3 cups shredded iceberg lettuce
6 (¼-inch-thick) slices tomato, halved
¾ cup low-fat creamy Caesar dressing (such as Kraft's Just 2 Good)

1. Place breadcrumbs in a large heavy-duty zip-top plastic bag. Dip chicken in milk; add chicken to bag. Seal and shake to coat.
2. Heat oil in a large nonstick skillet over medium heat. Add chicken; sauté 7 minutes or until done.
3. Fill each pita half evenly with lettuce, tomato, and chicken. Drizzle each half with 2 tablespoons dressing. YIELD: 6 servings (serving size: 1 pita half).

POINTS: 5; EXCHANGES: 2 Starch, 2½ Lean Meat; PER SERVING: CAL 263 (21% from fat); PRO 22.0g; FAT 6.0g (sat 1.0g); CARB 30.4g; FIB 1.5g; CHOL 54mg; IRON 1.9mg; SOD 627mg; CALC 66mg

CHICKEN AND AVOCADO WRAPS WITH CUMIN-LIME CREAM

prep: 10 minutes • cook: 12 minutes

If you're running short on time, try substituting precooked and seasoned chicken strips, such as Louis Rich's southwestern-flavored chicken breast strips. The cool Cumin-Lime Cream will complement the southwestern flavors.

Cooking spray
3 (4-ounce) skinless, boneless chicken breast halves, cut into thin strips
¾ teaspoon paprika
⅛ teaspoon salt
4 (12-inch) flour tortillas
½ avocado, peeled and chopped
6 cherry tomatoes, quartered
2 tablespoons finely chopped red onion
Cumin-Lime Cream

1. Coat a nonstick skillet with cooking spray. Place over medium-high heat until hot. Add chicken; cook 6 minutes, stirring constantly. Sprinkle with paprika and salt. Cook 2 minutes or until done.
2. Warm tortillas according to package directions.
3. Place chicken evenly on tortillas. Top with avocado, tomato, and onion. Spoon 1½ tablespoons Cumin-Lime Cream evenly over each wrap. Roll up. Cut each wrap in half diagonally. YIELD: 4 servings (serving size: 1 wrap).

POINTS: 6; EXCHANGES: 2 Starch, 2½ Lean Meat; PER SERVING: CAL 284 (22% from fat); FAT 6.8g (sat 1.3g); CARB 30.7g; FIB 2.5g; CHOL 53mg; IRON 2.2mg; SOD 690mg; CALC 40mg

CUMIN-LIME CREAM

prep: 2 minutes

2 tablespoons chopped cilantro
¼ cup fat-free sour cream
2 tablespoons light mayonnaise
1 tablespoon lime juice
¼ teaspoon ground cumin
⅛ teaspoon ground red pepper
¼ teaspoon salt

1. Combine all ingredients in a small bowl. YIELD: 6 tablespoons.

POINTS: 1; EXCHANGE: ½ Fat; PER SERVING: CAL 28 (58% from fat); PRO 0.6g; FAT 1.8g (sat 0.3g); CARB 2.3g; FIB 0.1g; CHOL 3mg; IRON 0.1mg; SOD 145mg; CALC 16mg

BARBECUED CHICKEN AND GRUYÈRE SANDWICHES

prep: 4 minutes • cook: 1 minute

1 (6-ounce) package grilled chicken breast strips (such as Louis Rich)
¼ cup bottled barbecue sauce
4 (2-ounce) onion buns (such as Earthgrains), halved and toasted
½ cup (2 ounces) shredded Gruyère cheese

1. Preheat broiler.
2. Place chicken and barbeque sauce in a bowl. Toss until coated. Place bottom halves of buns on a baking sheet; arrange chicken on bun halves. Sprinkle cheese over chicken. Broil 1 minute or until cheese melts. Cover with top halves of buns. YIELD: 4 servings (serving size: 1 sandwich).

POINTS: 6; EXCHANGES: 2 Starch, 2 Medium-Fat Meat; PER SERVING: CAL 286 (30% from fat); PRO 19.5g; FAT 9.6g (sat 4.8g); CARB 30.4g; FIB 1.3g; CHOL 43mg; IRON 2.1mg; SOD 854mg; CALC 210mg

OPEN-FACED CHICKEN-APPLE SAUSAGE SANDWICHES

prep: 3 minutes • cook: 20 minutes

This hearty sandwich features a unique sausage that's a great lower-fat alternative to regular smoked sausage. It received rave reviews at our kitchen table.

1 (12-ounce) package chicken-apple sausages, cut in half lengthwise (such as Gerhard's)
Cooking spray
2 cups thinly sliced onion
2 tablespoons water
1 teaspoon dark brown sugar
2 tablespoons prepared mustard
4 (1½-ounce) slices pumpernickel bread, toasted

1. Heat a 12-inch nonstick skillet over medium heat. Coat sausage with cooking spray; add sausage to pan, and cook 3 minutes on each side or until browned. Remove sausage from pan; keep warm. Coat pan with cooking spray; add onion. Cook 8 minutes or until browned, stirring frequently; add water and sugar, stirring well. Place sausage over onion mixture; reduce heat to low. Cover and cook 5 minutes.
2. Spread 1½ teaspoons mustard on each slice of bread. Top each with about ¼ cup onion mixture and 2 sausage halves. Serve immediately. YIELD: 4 servings (serving size: 1 sandwich).

POINTS: 5; **EXCHANGES:** 2 Starch, 1 Medium-Fat Meat, 1 Fat; **PER SERVING:** CAL 262 (32% from fat); PRO 14.9g; FAT 9.6g (sat 2.5g); CARB 31.4g; FIB 6.3g; CHOL 62mg; IRON 2.3mg; SOD 795mg; CALC 48mg

TURKEY MEATBALL SUBS WITH MARINARA SAUCE

prep: 20 minutes • cook: 20 minutes

Get your hands around this Italian-style hoagie. Seasonings and sauce spice up the flavor of ground turkey.

1 pound ground turkey
½ cup uncooked quick-cooking oats
1 large egg, lightly beaten
1 tablespoon Italian seasoning
2 teaspoons Worcestershire sauce
½ teaspoon garlic salt
¼ teaspoon freshly ground black pepper
¼ cup Italian-seasoned breadcrumbs
Cooking spray
1½ cups fat-free marinara sauce (such as Colavita)
6 (2-ounce) lite wheat hot dog buns
¾ cup (3 ounces) preshredded part-skim mozzarella cheese

1. Preheat oven to 400°.
2. Combine first 7 ingredients in a large bowl. Roll into 18 (1½-inch) meatballs. Dredge meatballs in breadcrumbs. Arrange meatballs on a jelly roll pan coated with cooking spray. Coat meatballs with cooking spray. Bake at 400° for 15 minutes or until done.
3. Pour marinara sauce into a 2-cup glass measure. Cover and microwave at HIGH 1 minute or until thoroughly heated.
4. Place 3 meatballs on each bun. Spoon ¼ cup marinara sauce over each sandwich; sprinkle each with 2 tablespoons cheese. Place sandwiches on same jelly roll pan. Bake at 400°

for 5 minutes or until cheese melts. Serve immediately. YIELD: 6 servings (serving size: 1 sandwich).

POINTS: 6; **EXCHANGES:** 2 Starch, 2½ Medium-Fat Meat; **PER SERVING:** CAL 316 (30% from fat); PRO 24.7g; FAT 11.2g (sat 3.9g); CARB 33.3g; FIB 6.9g; CHOL 105mg; IRON 2.7mg; SOD 652mg; CALC 241mg

PEPPERY TURKEY SANDWICHES

prep: 6 minutes • cook: 4 minutes

4 (1-ounce) slices multigrain bread
4 tablespoons creamy mustard blend (such as Dijonnaise)
8 ounces thinly sliced cracked black pepper-seasoned turkey breast (such as Sara Lee)
½ cup mild banana pepper rings, drained
4 (¾-ounce) slices Monterey Jack cheese with jalapeño peppers

1. Preheat broiler.
2. Place bread slices on a baking sheet. Toast bread on both sides.
3. Spread 1 tablespoon mustard blend over each bread slice. Place on baking sheet. Arrange 2 ounces turkey on each bread slice. Place banana pepper rings evenly over turkey; top sandwiches with cheese slices. Broil 1 minute or until cheese melts. YIELD: 4 servings (serving size: 1 sandwich).

POINTS: 4; **EXCHANGES:** 1 Starch, 2 Medium-Fat Meat; **PER SERVING:** CAL 221 (36% from fat); PRO 18.2g; FAT 9.6g (sat 5.7g); CARB 20.9g; FIB 3.9g; CHOL 56mg; IRON 0.9mg; SOD 987mg; CALC 177mg

TURKEY STACK-UPS WITH SWEET CURRY MUSTARD SPREAD

(pictured on page 136)
prep: 12 minutes

This sweet curry mixture gives the sandwiches a gourmet flair, while sunflower seeds offer a nutty crunch.

    3 tablespoons light mayonnaise
 1½ tablespoons prepared mustard
 1½ tablespoons honey
    ½ teaspoon curry powder
    8 (1-ounce) slices whole wheat
         bread, toasted
    8 ounces oven-roasted turkey
         breast, thinly sliced
    ½ cup thinly sliced red onion
         (about 1 small)
    ½ green bell pepper, thinly sliced
    ¾ cup alfalfa sprouts
    2 tablespoons sunflower seed kernels

1. Combine first 4 ingredients in a small bowl, stirring with a whisk. Spread mayonnaise mixture evenly over 1 side of each slice of toast.
2. Place 1 slice on each of 4 plates, coated side up. Top each with equal amounts of turkey, onion, bell pepper, and sprouts. Sprinkle 1½ teaspoons sunflower kernels over each sandwich. Top with remaining slices of toast, coated side down. YIELD: 4 servings (serving size: 1 sandwich).

POINTS: 6; EXCHANGES: 2½ Starch, 1 Very Lean Meat, 1 Fat; PER SERVING: CAL 297 (23% from fat); PRO 18.5g; FAT 7.7g (sat 0.8g); CARB 37.5g; FIB 4.7g; CHOL 24.2mg; IRON 1.8mg; SOD 840mg; CALC 16mg

PEPPERONI SALAD-STUFFED PITAS

(pictured on page 135)
**prep: 12 minutes • chill: 1 hour
cook: 4 minutes**

Classic pizza ingredients combine in a pita to make a hand-held salad on the go.

    2 tablespoons cider vinegar
    2 tablespoons olive oil
    1 teaspoon dried basil
    1 teaspoon dried oregano
    ⅛ teaspoon salt
    ⅛ teaspoon black pepper
 28 turkey pepperoni slices, halved
         (such as Hormel)
    8 mushrooms, cut into 8 wedges
         each
    1 small zucchini, cubed
 10 grape tomatoes, halved
    ⅓ cup marinated artichoke hearts,
         drained and coarsely chopped
    6 pepperoncini peppers, coarsely
         chopped
    ¼ cup (1-ounce) preshredded
         part-skim mozzarella cheese
    4 (6-inch) pitas, cut in half
    8 romaine lettuce leaves

1. Preheat oven to 350°.
2. Combine first 6 ingredients in a small bowl, stirring with a whisk.
3. Combine pepperoni and next 6 ingredients in a medium bowl. Pour vinegar mixture over pepperoni mixture, and toss gently. Cover and chill at least 1 hour.
4. Place pitas on a baking sheet, and bake at 350° for 3 to 4 minutes or just until warmed.
5. Place 1 lettuce leaf in each pita half, and spoon ½ cup pepperoni salad into each half. YIELD: 4 servings (servings size: 2 pita halves).

POINTS: 7; EXCHANGES: 2½ Starch, 1 Vegetable, 1 Medium-Fat Meat, 1 Fat; PER SERVING: CAL 324 (30% from fat); PRO 14.5g; FAT 10.9g (sat 2.5g); CARB 42.8g; FIB 3.8g; CHOL 19.4mg; IRON 4.2mg; SOD 1,612mg; CALC 168mg

A Model for Maintenance

JULIE TAYLOR • **HEIGHT** 5'3" • **BEFORE** 158 LBS. • **AFTER** 118 LBS.

Advice: Whatever you do the first day on your weight-loss program is what you need to think about doing for the rest of your life.

If you're looking for a model for weight maintenance look no further than Julie Taylor. Julie, a mother of three and a Weight Watchers leader, has been a lifetime member for 10 years. But maintaining a healthy weight has not always been easy for her.

Julie grew up in a typical Italian family. Pizza, spaghetti, and homemade breads always adorned the table—and adorned it in large quantities. "I was always a little overweight growing up," Julie says. "But my grandmother in her little Italian way would always say that I was cute like that."

Not buying into her grandmother's idea of her ideal weight, Julie decided that she wanted to lose 40 pounds. "I wanted to be comfortable, still have my favorite foods, and not feel deprived," she says. "I knew Weight Watchers offered this and it was something I could stick with long-term." "But the weight didn't come off fast," she recalls. "And it was frustrating. I guess I just expected a quicker loss. Five pounds a month just didn't seem like a lot."

So to stay motivated during what seemed to be a long-drawn-out process, Julie developed a plan.

"There was a cinnamon roll shop near our home, and I decided that for every 10 pounds I lost, I would reward myself with a giant cinnamon roll," she says with a laugh. "But it was funny, because

after every 10 pounds I would say, well, after another 10 pounds I'll eat one. And you know, I just didn't have one."

After 8 months of "stick-to-itiveness" Julie reached her goal. And that was over 10 years ago.

Since then, Julie has incorporated all she learned as a participant in Weight Watchers into her family's lifestyle. She has also become a group leader at her local Weight Watchers center.

"Eating healthfully has become a way of life for our family," she says. "I actually don't have any complaints from the kids because they still get to eat tacos and spaghetti. They will even ask how many **POINTS** are in things. They do laugh sometimes because I don't have ice cream in the house, but I think they really appreciate it."

"Eating healthfully has become a way of life for our family."

As for leading Weight Watchers support groups, Julie has learned that it's an excellent way to maintain her weight. "I really admired my leader when I was losing my weight and wanted to make an impact on others the way she made an impact on me," Julie says. "Helping other people helps me keep my weight in check, too."

133

Tomato and Spinach Baguettes with Kalamata-Feta Spread, page 127

Ham and Arugula Sandwiches with Cranberry Chutney, page 129

Pepperoni Salad-Stuffed
Pitas, page 132

Turkey Stack-Ups with Sweet Curry Mustard Spread, page 132

Hot Skillet Sirloin Wraps with Blue Cheese, page 128

Tomatoes with
Green Onions and
Basil, page 147

Fruited Acorn
Squash, page 146

Sesame Steamed Broccoli, page 143

Risotto with Swiss Chard, page 150

Back in the Game

SANDRA KERNS • **HEIGHT** 5'8" • **BEFORE** 205 LBS. • **AFTER** 155 LBS.

Strategy: Lose weight for yourself, not for anyone else. The benefits will come pouring out, and it will bless you.

For as long as I can remember, even as a small child, I always thought of myself as overweight," homemaker Sandra Kerns says. "I was constantly trying out new fad diets that would work great at first, but then the weight would always come back...and then some."

This fluctuating up and down worked fine for Sandra until she married and began having children. But then the weight just kept climbing. "Being pregnant was a great excuse to not have to think about dieting! It was my license to eat what I wanted. After all, I was eating for two! But five children and 60 pounds later, I was depressed and desperate."

"My weight was constantly on my mind," Sandra recalls. "Not one day would pass by where I didn't worry over it. I felt like I was watching life on the sidelines."

"I now have the tools to keep it (weight) off; I know what to do!"

But then Sandra got back into the game of life. A dear friend approached her and suggested she try Weight Watchers. "My friend had great success with the program. I realized that I had nothing to lose and everything to gain!"

Sandra found that the program was easy to follow and allowed great flexibility—something a mother of five can truly appreciate. "Until Weight Watchers I always felt that I had to 'diet.' Now I realize I can eat the same foods as my family and not feel deprived."

Now 50 pounds lighter, Sandra is excited about sharing her success. For starters, she believes she is giving a wonderful service to her family. "It's great for the kids to learn how to eat so that one day they won't face the same struggles that I faced."

Sandra credits Weight Watchers for giving her life back to her. "Now I'm a participating member of my family instead of just an observer," she says. "I'm no longer a wallflower. Now I'll even ride roller coasters with my kids without being worried or embarrassed about fitting in the seat." And that's not all she no longer fears.

"I don't worry that I'm going to gain the weight back again, either," she says. "Because I know I now have the tools to keep it off; I know what to do!"

Sandra and her husband just recently celebrated their 20th wedding anniversary with a trip to Tahiti. "Bathing suits and all," she says with a laugh. "Several years ago I wouldn't have even considered it. Now I can do anything!"

As a Weight Watchers leader Sandra is able to motivate others who, like her, sought weight-loss success. "It's the ultimate for me to be able to teach someone how to lose weight and keep it off," she says.

Side Dishes

CHUNKY CRANBERRY APPLESAUCE

prep: 10 minutes • cook: 25 minutes

5 Gala apples, peeled and cubed
1 cup fresh or frozen cranberries
½ cup water
¼ cup sugar
1 teaspoon grated orange rind

1. Combine first 3 ingredients in a Dutch oven. Bring to a boil; cover, reduce heat, and simmer 25 minutes or until apples are tender, stirring occasionally.
2. Stir in sugar and orange rind. Remove from heat; mash fruit mixture with a potato masher until chunky. YIELD: 7 servings (serving size: ½ cup).

POINTS: 1; EXCHANGES: ½ Starch, 1 Fruit; PER SERVING: CAL 87 (3% from fat); PRO 0.2g; FAT 0.3g (sat 0.1g); CARB 22.5g; FIB 2.3g; CHOL 0mg; IRON 0.1mg; SOD 1mg; CALC 5mg

ASPARAGUS WITH LEEKS AND PARMESAN

prep: 12 minutes • cook: 6 minutes

1¼ pounds asparagus spears
1 teaspoon olive oil
2 cups thinly sliced leeks (about 2)
3 tablespoons preshredded fresh Parmesan cheese
1 teaspoon grated lemon rind
¼ teaspoon salt
⅛ teaspoon freshly ground black pepper

1. Snap off tough ends of asparagus. Cut asparagus into 2-inch pieces.
2. Heat oil in a large nonstick skillet over medium-high heat. Add

asparagus and leeks; sauté 6 minutes or until asparagus is crisp-tender. Remove from heat. Sprinkle with cheese and remaining ingredients; toss well. Serve immediately. YIELD: 4 servings (serving size: ¾ cup).

POINTS: 1; EXCHANGES: 2 Vegetable, ½ Fat; PER SERVING: CAL 80 (27% from fat); PRO 5.0g; FAT 2.6g (sat 0.9g); CARB 11.4g; FIB 2.7g; CHOL 3mg; IRON 1.8mg; SOD 232mg; CALC 97mg

ROASTED ASPARAGUS SPEARS WITH MUSTARD CREAM

prep: 10 minutes • cook: 8 minutes

The mustard cream can also be used as a tangy salad dressing.

2 pounds asparagus spears
Cooking spray
¾ teaspoon salt, divided
½ teaspoon freshly ground black pepper, divided
¾ cup low-fat buttermilk
⅓ cup low-fat mayonnaise (such as Hellman's)
2 tablespoons Dijon mustard
1 tablespoon fresh lemon juice
1 garlic clove, minced
1 teaspoon dried tarragon leaves

1. Preheat oven to 450°.
2. Snap off tough ends of asparagus.
3. Coat a nonstick baking sheet with cooking spray. Arrange asparagus in a single layer on baking sheet; lightly coat asparagus with cooking spray. Sprinkle asparagus with ¼ teaspoon salt and ¼ teaspoon pepper. Bake at 450° for 8 to 10 minutes or until asparagus is crisp-tender, shaking pan occasionally.

4. Combine remaining ½ teaspoon salt, ¼ teaspoon pepper, buttermilk, and remaining 5 ingredients in a small bowl; stir with a whisk. Cover and chill. Serve asparagus warm or at room temperature with mustard mixture. YIELD: 4 servings (serving size: ¼ asparagus and ⅓ cup mustard mixture).

POINTS: 2; EXCHANGES: ½ Starch, 2 Vegetable, ½ Fat; PER SERVING: CAL 115 (18% from fat); PRO 7.3g; FAT 2.5g (sat 0.4g); CARB 17.5g; FIB 3.5g; CHOL 3mg; IRON 1.6mg; SOD 880mg; CALC 97mg

CITRUSY BEETS

prep: 5 minutes • cook: 35 minutes

Leave the root and part of the stem intact until the beet is cooked. The skin should slip easily off the beet under cold, running water.

6 beets (about 1½ pounds)
2 teaspoons butter
2 teaspoons grated orange rind
⅔ cup fresh orange juice
1 teaspoon fresh lemon juice
⅛ teaspoon salt
⅛ teaspoon pepper
Dash of ground cloves

1. Leave root and 1 inch of stem on beets; scrub with a brush. Place in a large saucepan; cover with water. Bring to a boil; cover, reduce heat, and simmer 25 minutes or until tender. Drain and rinse with cold water. Drain; peel and cut into ¼-inch-thick slices.
2. Melt butter in a large nonstick skillet over medium heat. Add beets, orange rind, and remaining ingredients. Bring to a boil; cook

7 minutes, stirring frequently, until beets are tender and sauce is reduced to ½ cup. YIELD: 6 servings (serving size: ½ cup).

POINTS: 1; EXCHANGES: 2 Vegetable; PER SERVING: CAL 60 (21% from fat); PRO 1.6g; FAT 1.5g (sat 0.8g); CARB 10.9g; FIB 2.4g; CHOL 3mg; IRON 0.7mg; SOD 126mg; CALC 18mg

BEET GREENS WITH OREGANO AND FETA

prep: 5 minutes • cook: 8 minutes

The tangy flavor of the feta cheese enhances the mild flavor of the beet greens.

11 cups coarsely chopped beet greens (about 1 pound beets with greens attached)
1 teaspoon olive oil
¼ teaspoon dried oregano, crushed
⅛ teaspoon pepper
1 teaspoon fresh lemon juice
2 tablespoons crumbled feta cheese

1. Rinse beet greens; drain well. Heat oil in a large nonstick skillet over medium-high heat. Add beet greens; cover and cook, stirring occasionally, 1½ to 2 minutes or until greens are wilted. Reduce heat to low; add oregano and pepper.
2. Cook, uncovered, 5 minutes or until tender, stirring occasionally. Remove from heat; add lemon juice, and stir gently. Sprinkle each serving with feta cheese. YIELD: 6 servings (serving size: ½ cup greens and 1 teaspoon feta cheese).

POINTS: 0; EXCHANGE: 1 Vegetable; PER SERVING: CAL 29 (41% from fat); PRO 1.7g; FAT 1.5g (sat 0.6g); CARB 3.0g; FIB 2.6g; CHOL 3mg; IRON 2.4mg; SOD 175mg; CALC 100mg

BEST BET FOR BEETS

Beets are the jewels of root vegetables because of their intense colors that range from the familiar red-purple to golden yellow, pink, and even white. Like turnips, both the root and greens are edible. Beets are available year-round, but are the freshest during the summer, fall, and winter. Remember these quick tips when purchasing and storing beets:

• Choose firm, medium-sized beets with smooth skins and regularly shaped roots. Large beets tend to be tough and woody.
• Look for bright greens with no sign of wilting or yellowing.
• Remove the greens as soon as you get home. Cover and store both the roots and the greens in the refrigerator. Use the greens within a day or two.

SESAME STEAMED BROCCOLI

(pictured on page 139)
prep: 2 minutes • cook: 6 minutes

Serve as a side dish to fried rice for a quick meal.

1 (12-ounce) package broccoli florets (about 4½ cups)
1½ teaspoons dark sesame oil
2 tablespoons low-sodium soy sauce
⅛ teaspoon salt
¼ teaspoon freshly ground black pepper
2 teaspoons sesame seeds, toasted

1. Steam broccoli, covered, 6 minutes or until crisp-tender. Combine oil and remaining 4 ingredients. Pour oil mixture over broccoli; toss. YIELD: 4 servings (serving size: 1 cup).

POINTS: 1; EXCHANGES: 1 Vegetable, ½ Fat; PER SERVING: CAL 54 (36% from fat); PRO 3.1g; FAT 2.0g (sat 0.3g); CARB 5.0g; FIB 2.6g; CHOL 0mg; IRON 2.9mg; SOD 398mg; CALC 41mg

LEMON-DILL CARROTS

prep: 7 minutes • cook: 9 minutes

8 medium carrots, scraped and diagonally sliced
1 teaspoon cornstarch
1 tablespoon lemon juice
⅓ cup water
2 teaspoons light butter
1 teaspoon chopped fresh dill
¼ teaspoon grated lemon rind
¼ teaspoon salt

1. Arrange carrot in a vegetable steamer over boiling water. Cover; steam 2 to 3 minutes or until crisp-tender. Transfer carrot to a serving bowl, and keep warm.
2. Combine cornstarch and lemon juice in a small saucepan, stirring until smooth. Add water; cook over medium heat, stirring constantly, until thick.
3. Stir in butter and next 3 ingredients. Cook, stirring constantly, until butter melts.
4. To serve, pour lemon juice mixture over carrot, and toss gently. YIELD: 4 servings (serving size: 1 cup).

POINTS: 1; EXCHANGE: 1 Starch; PER SERVING: CAL 74 (14% from fat); PRO 1.7g; FAT 1.3g (sat 0.7g); CARB 15.5g; FIB 1.5g; CHOL 3mg; IRON 0.7mg; SOD 210mg; CALC 40mg

CANDIED CARROTS AND PARSNIPS

prep: 7 minutes • cook: 12 minutes

1 tablespoon butter
3 cups diagonally cut carrot (about ¾ pound)
2 cups diagonally cut parsnip (about ½ pound)
3 tablespoons dark brown sugar
1 teaspoon grated peeled fresh ginger
¼ teaspoon salt
⅛ teaspoon pepper
2 tablespoons chopped fresh flat-leaf parsley

1. Melt butter in a large nonstick skillet over medium-high heat. Add carrot and next 5 ingredients. Cover, reduce heat, and simmer 12 minutes or until tender. Sprinkle with parsley. YIELD: 4 servings (serving size: ½ cup).

POINTS: 3; EXCHANGES: 2 Starch, ½ Fat; **PER SERVING:** CAL 163 (17% from fat); PRO 2.0g; FAT 3.3g (sat 1.9g); CARB 33.5g; FIB 5.7g; CHOL 8mg; IRON 1.3mg; SOD 220mg; CALC 64mg

CAULIFLOWER WITH BUTTERED CRUMBS

prep: 10 minutes • cook: 5 minutes

1 (1-ounce) slice white bread
2 tablespoons light butter, melted and divided
¼ teaspoon salt
⅛ teaspoon freshly ground black pepper
2 tablespoons freshly grated Parmesan cheese
3 cups small cauliflower florets
1 tablespoon chopped fresh parsley

1. Place bread in food processor; pulse 10 times or until coarse crumbs measure ½ cup.
2. Combine crumbs, 1 tablespoon butter, and next 3 ingredients in a small bowl. Set aside.
3. Steam cauliflower, covered, 4 minutes or until crisp-tender.
4. Transfer cauliflower to a serving bowl. Drizzle remaining butter over cauliflower; toss gently to coat. Sprinkle crumb mixture and parsley over cauliflower. Serve immediately. YIELD: 4 servings (serving size: ¾ cup).

POINTS: 2; EXCHANGES: 1 Starch, 1 Vegetable, 1 Fat; **PER SERVING:** CAL 130 (31% from fat); PRO 6.0g; FAT 4.8g (sat 2.8g); CARB 17.6g; FIB 2.6g; CHOL 13mg; IRON 1.1mg; SOD 658mg; CALC 81mg

CHILI-ROASTED CORN

prep: 8 minutes • cook: 20 minutes

4 teaspoons butter, melted
½ teaspoon chili powder
2 teaspoons finely chopped fresh cilantro
3 ears shucked corn
½ teaspoon salt

1. Preheat oven to 450°.
2. Combine butter, chili powder, and cilantro in a small bowl.
3. Cut each ear of corn in half, and place each half on a piece of foil. Brush evenly with butter mixture. Sprinkle with salt; wrap in foil. Bake at 450° for 20 minutes or until corn is tender. YIELD: 6 servings (serving size: ½ ear of corn).

POINTS: 1; EXCHANGES: ½ Starch, ½ Fat; **PER SERVING:** CAL 62 (41% from fat); PRO 1.5g; FAT 3.1g (sat 1.7g); CARB 8.7g; FIB 1.3g; CHOL 7mg; IRON 0.3mg; SOD 230mg; CALC 3mg

CORN PUDDING

prep: 12 minutes • cook: 40 minutes
stand: 5 minutes

If fresh corn is out of season or you're pressed for time, use thawed and drained frozen whole-kernel corn.

3 tablespoons sugar
¼ cup all-purpose flour
2 teaspoons baking powder
¾ teaspoon salt
¼ teaspoon pepper
2 cups fat-free evaporated milk
1½ cups egg substitute
2 tablespoons butter, melted
6 cups fresh corn kernels (about 12 ears)
Cooking spray

1. Preheat oven to 350°.
2. Combine first 5 ingredients in a small bowl.
3. Combine milk, egg substitute, and butter in a large bowl. Gradually add flour mixture, stirring until smooth. Stir in corn. Pour mixture into a 13 x 9-inch baking dish coated with cooking spray.
4. Bake, uncovered, at 350° for 40 to 45 minutes or until deep golden and set. Let stand 5 minutes before serving. YIELD: 12 servings (serving size: ⅔ cup).

POINTS: 4; EXCHANGES: 1½ Starch, 1 Fat; **PER SERVING:** CAL 165 (20% from fat); PRO 9.8g; FAT 4.0g (sat 1.5g); CARB 25.0g; FIB 0.6g; CHOL 7mg; IRON 1.4mg; SOD 364mg; CALC 188mg

GREEN BEAN AND SNOW PEA STIR-FRY

prep: 15 minutes • cook: 14 minutes

1 tablespoon low-sodium soy
  sauce
1 teaspoon cornstarch
½ teaspoon grated peeled fresh
  ginger
¼ teaspoon toasted sesame oil
1 garlic clove, minced
½ cup vegetable broth
1 teaspoon vegetable oil
2 cups (2-inch) diagonally cut
  green beans
½ cup sliced onion (about 1 small)
1 cup trimmed snow peas, cut in
  half diagonally
½ cup red bell pepper strips
  (about 1)
1 teaspoon sesame seeds, toasted

1. Combine first 6 ingredients in a
small bowl; stir with a whisk until
blended.
2. Heat vegetable oil in a large nonstick skillet over medium-high heat.
Add green beans and onion; cook,
stirring occasionally, 8 to 10 minutes
or until beans are crisp-tender and
lightly browned. Add snow peas and
bell pepper strips; cook 3 minutes,
stirring occasionally.
3. Stir soy sauce mixture with a
whisk, and pour over vegetables; cook
1 minute, stirring constantly, until
mixture thickens. Sprinkle with
sesame seeds, and toss gently to coat.
Serve immediately. **YIELD:** 4 servings
(serving size: ¾ cup).

POINTS: 1; **EXCHANGES:** 2 Vegetable, ½ Fat;
PER SERVING: CAL 63 (27% from fat); PRO 2.6g;
FAT 2.0g (sat 0.3g); CARB 10.0g; FIB 3.3g;
CHOL 0mg; IRON 1.4mg; SOD 264mg;
CALC 38mg

MARINATED PORTOBELLOS

prep: 5 minutes • chill: 1 hour
cook: 10 minutes

*Be sure to keep the rich, flavorful juices
that accumulate on the mushrooms as
they cook. This dish is the perfect
accompaniment to grilled beef or pork
and mashed potatoes.*

¼ cup low-sodium teriyaki sauce
2 tablespoons orange juice
1 teaspoon sesame oil
2 teaspoons minced garlic
¼ teaspoon crushed red pepper
4 (4-inch) portobello mushroom
  caps
Cooking spray
Sesame seeds (optional)

1. Combine first 5 ingredients in a
small bowl; stir well. Place mushroom caps, gills up, in a shallow dish.
Pour teriyaki mixture evenly over
gills. Cover and chill at least 1 hour.
2. Prepare grill.
3. Place mushroom caps, gills down,
on a grill rack coated with cooking
spray; grill, covered, 5 minutes on
each side or until tender. Cut mushroom caps into ½-inch-thick slices.
Sprinkle with sesame seeds, if
desired. **YIELD:** 4 servings (serving size:
1 mushroom cap).

POINTS: 1; **EXCHANGE:** 1 Vegetable; **PER SERVING:**
CAL 56 (26% from fat); PRO 1.2g; FAT 1.2g (sat 0.2g);
CARB 6.3g; FIB 1.1g; CHOL 0mg; IRON 0.1mg;
SOD 265mg; CALC 5mg

ROASTED POTATOES WITH MINT AND PARSLEY

prep: 12 minutes • cook: 30 minutes

*Yukon Gold potatoes are usually
boiled and then mashed. We found
that roasting the potatoes created an
equally delicious side dish.*

5 cups cubed Yukon Gold potato
  (about 2 pounds)
Cooking spray
2 teaspoons butter, melted
3 tablespoons finely chopped fresh
  parsley
2 tablespoons finely chopped fresh
  mint
½ teaspoon salt
¼ teaspoon pepper

1. Preheat oven to 425°.
2. Place potato on a jelly roll pan
coated with cooking spray. Bake at
425° for 30 minutes or until tender,
stirring occasionally. Transfer potato
to a large bowl.
3. Add butter and remaining 4
ingredients; toss well. **YIELD:** 6 servings
(serving size: ¾ cup).

POINTS: 2; **EXCHANGE:** 1 Starch; **PER SERVING:**
CAL 102 (12% from fat); PRO 2.5g; FAT 1.4g
(sat 0.8g); CARB 20.7g; FIB 1.9g; CHOL 3mg;
IRON 1.0mg; SOD 217mg; CALC 13mg

CHILI-FRIED POTATOES

prep: 7 minutes • cook: 18 minutes

*Make these spicy spuds for
your next cookout. To save time
and nutrients, leave the skin on
the potatoes. For less spice,
omit the chili powder.*

3 cups cubed unpeeled baking
    potato (about 1 pound)
Olive oil-flavored cooking spray
  ½ teaspoon olive oil
  1 small onion, halved, thinly
    sliced, and separated into rings
  1 teaspoon chili powder
  ½ teaspoon salt
  ½ cup (2 ounces) preshredded
    reduced-fat sharp Cheddar
    cheese

1. Arrange potato in a steamer basket over boiling water. Cover and
steam 10 minutes or until tender.
Remove from heat.
2. Coat a large nonstick skillet with
cooking spray; add oil. Place over
medium-high heat until hot. Add
onion; sauté 3 minutes or until tender. Add potato, chili powder, and
salt. Cook 5 minutes or until potato
is lightly browned, stirring often.
Sprinkle cheese over potato. Cover,
remove from heat, and let stand 1
minute or until cheese melts.
3. Serve immediately. YIELD: 4 servings (serving size: about ¾ cup).

POINTS: 3; **EXCHANGES:** 1½ Starch, 1 Fat;
PER SERVING: CAL 158 (22% from fat); PRO 5.9g;
FAT 3.7g (sat 2.1g); CARB 25.0g; FIB 2.6g;
CHOL 10mg; IRON 1.4mg; SOD 427mg;
CALC 115mg

MEET THE SQUASH FAMILY

Acorn squash, summer squash,
butternut squash—with all the
different types, how do you know
which squash to use?

    Squash are members of the
gourd family and vary widely in
size, shape, and color. Although
they're now available year-round,
squash are generally divided into
two categories: summer squash
and winter squash.

Summer Squash—Yellow (crook-
neck), patty pan, and zucchini
are three common types of
summer squash identified by thin,
edible skins and soft seeds.
Summer squash requires a
short cooking time and is often
steamed, baked, sautéed, and
deep-fried. It's a good source of
Vitamins A, C, and niacin.

Winter Squash—Squash in this
category, which includes acorn,
butternut, and even pumpkin,
have hard, thick skins and seeds
and a deep yellow to orange
flesh that is much firmer than that
of summer squash. Winter squash
may be baked, steamed, or sim-
mered once the seeds are
removed. These squash are good
in both savory and sweet dishes.
Depending on the recipe, the
squash may be peeled before
cooking. Winter squash is an
excellent source of Vitamins A and
C, iron, and riboflavin.

FRUITED ACORN SQUASH

(pictured on page 138)
prep: 15 minutes • cook: 1 hour and
15 minutes

*Oozing with sugary fruit and nuts,
this vitamin-packed squash
is a fun alternative to the usual
green vegetable.*

  2 acorn squash (about 1 pound
    each)
  4 teaspoons light butter
1½ teaspoons light brown sugar
  ¼ teaspoon curry powder
  ⅛ teaspoon ground cinnamon
  ⅛ teaspoon ground nutmeg
  ⅛ teaspoon salt
  ⅛ teaspoon pepper
  2 tablespoons golden raisins
  2 tablespoons dried cranberries
    (such as Craisins)
  2 tablespoons chopped
    pistachios

1. Preheat oven to 350°.
2. Cut a small slice from both ends of
squash so halves sit upright. Cut
squash in half crosswise; discard seeds
and stringy pulp. Place squash halves,
cut sides up, in an 11 x 7-inch baking
dish. Place 1 teaspoon butter in center
of each squash half. Combine brown
sugar and remaining 8 ingredients in a
small bowl; stir well. Sprinkle brown
sugar mixture evenly into center of
each squash half.
3. Cover and bake at 350° for 1 hour
and 15 minutes or until squash is tender. YIELD: 4 servings (serving size: 1
squash half).

POINTS: 2; **EXCHANGES:** 1 Starch, 1 Fat;
PER SERVING: CAL 115 (28% from fat); PRO 2.3g;
FAT 4.0g (sat 1.6g); CARB 20.5g; FIB 2.7g;
CHOL 7mg; IRON 1.1mg; SOD 102mg; CALC 47mg

BUTTERNUT SQUASH WITH MAPLE SYRUP

prep: 10 minutes • cook: 25 minutes

1 (2-pound) butternut squash, peeled and cubed
2½ tablespoons pure maple syrup
1 tablespoon butter, softened
¼ teaspoon salt
⅛ teaspoon pepper

1. Steam squash, covered, 25 minutes or until very tender.
2. Combine squash, syrup, and remaining ingredients in a large bowl; mash squash mixture with a potato masher. YIELD: 4 servings (serving size: ½ cup).

POINTS: 2; **EXCHANGES:** 1 Starch, 1 Vegetable, ½ Fat; **PER SERVING:** CAL 111 (24% from fat); PRO 2.1g; FAT 3.2g (sat 1.9g); CARB 20.9g; FIB 2.1g; CHOL 8mg; IRON 1.0mg; SOD 183mg; CALC 54mg

SQUASH AND MUSHROOM SAUTÉ

prep: 9 minutes • cook: 20 minutes

It's important to cut all the vegetables about the same size and thickness so they cook evenly.

1 large yellow squash
2 medium zucchini
Cooking spray
1 teaspoon olive oil
2 cups halved mushrooms (about 6 ounces)
1 teaspoon toasted sesame oil
3 tablespoons reduced-sodium soy sauce
1 tablespoon minced fresh cilantro

1. Quarter squash and zucchini lengthwise, and cut into slices; set aside.
2. Heat olive oil in a large nonstick skillet coated with cooking spray over high heat. Add mushrooms; sauté 5 minutes, or until mushrooms are tender. Remove from pan, and keep warm.
3. Add squash and zucchini to pan; sauté 13 minutes or until tender and squash is browned in spots. Add mushrooms to squash mixture; cook 1 minute. Add sesame oil, soy sauce, and cilantro. Toss gently. YIELD: 4 servings (serving size: ¾ cup).

POINTS: 1; **EXCHANGES:** 1 Vegetable, ½ Fat; **PER SERVING:** CAL 61 (34% from fat); PRO 3.5g; FAT 2.6g (sat 0.4g); CARB 7.6g; FIB 2.8g; CHOL 0mg; IRON 1.3mg; SOD 405mg; CALC 29mg

TOMATOES WITH GREEN ONIONS AND BASIL

(pictured on page 137)
prep: 5 minutes • cook: 2 minutes

We prefer the natural sweetness of the grape tomatoes, but cherry tomatoes work equally well.

1½ teaspoons olive oil
1 pint grape tomatoes or cherry tomatoes
1½ tablespoons thinly sliced green onions
1 tablespoon minced fresh basil
2 teaspoons balsamic vinegar
¼ teaspoon salt
⅛ teaspoon pepper

1. Heat oil in a large nonstick skillet over medium-high heat. Add tomatoes; sauté 1 to 2 minutes or until tomatoes are heated. Remove from heat, and stir in green onions and remaining ingredients; toss gently. Serve immediately. YIELD: 2 servings (serving size: about ¾ cup).

POINTS: 1; **EXCHANGES:** 2 Vegetable, 1 Fat; **PER SERVING:** CAL 67 (48% from fat); PRO 1.3g; FAT 3.9g (sat 0.5g); CARB 8.2g; FIB 1.9g; CHOL 0mg; IRON 0.8mg; SOD 309mg; CALC 12mg

BAKED TOMATOES

prep: 7 minutes • cook: 20 minutes

These hearty tomatoes are a quick and easy side for grilled chicken breasts or pork chops.

3 tablespoons light mayonnaise
2 tablespoons preshredded fresh Parmesan cheese
¼ teaspoon dried thyme
¼ teaspoon dried rosemary
⅛ teaspoon salt
⅛ teaspoon pepper
2 large tomatoes, cut in half crosswise (about 1 pound)
¼ cup fat-free Caesar-flavored croutons, crushed (such as Brownberry)

1. Preheat oven to 400°.
2. Combine first 6 ingredients in a small bowl. Place tomato halves, cut sides up, in an 8-inch baking dish. Cover tomato halves evenly with mayonnaise mixture. Sprinkle with crushed croutons.
3. Bake at 400° for 20 minutes or until crumbs are lightly browned. YIELD: 4 servings (serving size: 1 tomato half).

POINTS: 2; **EXCHANGES:** 1 Vegetable, 1 Fat; **PER SERVING:** CAL 75 (55% from fat); PRO 2.1g; FAT 4.7g (sat 1.0g); CARB 6.7g; FIB 1.1g; CHOL 6mg; IRON 0.6mg; SOD 235mg; CALC 39mg

BARLEY WITH SWEET RED PEPPER AND PEAS

prep: 6 minutes • cook: 20 minutes
stand: 5 minutes

Using quick-cooking barley cuts the cook-time for this recipe in half. Barley is an excellent source of fiber.

Cooking spray
  1 teaspoon olive oil
  ½ cup chopped celery
  ½ cup chopped red bell pepper
2⅓ cups fat-free, less-sodium
    chicken broth
  1 cup uncooked quick-cooking
    barley
  ½ teaspoon dried basil
  ¼ teaspoon salt
  ⅛ teaspoon black pepper
  1 cup frozen green peas, thawed

1. Heat oil in a large saucepan coated with cooking spray over medium heat. Add celery and bell pepper; sauté 5 minutes. Add broth, and bring to a boil. Add barley and next 3 ingredients; stir well. Cover, reduce heat, and simmer 15 to 17 minutes or until barley is tender. Stir in peas; remove from heat. Cover and let stand 5 minutes. YIELD: 6 servings (serving size: ½ cup).

POINTS: 2; **EXCHANGES:** 2 Starch; **PER SERVING:** CAL 158 (7% from fat); PRO 6.1g; FAT 1.3g (sat 0.2g); CARB 31.4g; FIB 7.2g; CHOL 0mg; IRON 1.5mg; SOD 308mg; CALC 26mg

COUSCOUS WITH GOLDEN RAISINS AND HERBS

prep: 4 minutes • cook: 7 minutes
stand: 5 minutes

Fat-free, less-sodium chicken broth and couscous are key ingredients in a well-stocked pantry. Vary the recipe to suit your personal tastes by substituting another nut or herb.

1⅓ cups fat-free, less-sodium
    chicken broth, divided
  ¼ cup finely chopped onion
  ¼ cup golden raisins
  ¼ teaspoon salt
  ¾ cup uncooked couscous
  2 tablespoons minced fresh parsley
  2 tablespoons chopped fresh basil
  1 tablespoon pine nuts, toasted
  1 tablespoon fresh lime juice
  2 teaspoons extra-virgin olive oil
  ⅛ teaspoon pepper

1. Combine ⅓ cup chicken broth, onion, and raisins in a medium saucepan. Bring to a boil; reduce heat, and simmer, uncovered, 5 minutes or until liquid is absorbed. Add remaining chicken broth and salt; bring to a boil. Stir in couscous. Remove from heat; cover and let stand 5 minutes.
2. Fluff couscous mixture with a fork. Add parsley and remaining ingredients to couscous mixture; toss gently. Serve immediately. YIELD: 4 servings (serving size: ⅔ cup).

POINTS: 4; **EXCHANGES:** 2 Starch, ½ Fat; **PER SERVING:** CAL 194 (17% from fat); PRO 6.2g; FAT 3.6g (sat 0.5g); CARB 34.3g; FIB 2.4g; CHOL 0mg; IRON 0.9mg; SOD 303mg; CALC 21mg

CHEDDAR GRITS SOUFFLÉ

prep: 10 minutes • cook: 25 minutes
stand: 5 minutes

We tested these soufflés in individual custard cups. If you prefer, spoon the mixture into a 1-quart casserole coated with cooking spray, and bake 30 minutes or until puffed and golden.

Cooking spray
  ¼ cup dry breadcrumbs
  2 cups water
  1 tablespoon light butter
  ¼ teaspoon salt
  ¼ teaspoon pepper
  ½ cup uncooked quick-cooking
    grits
  ½ cup (2 ounces) preshredded
    reduced-fat Cheddar cheese
  2 large egg whites

1. Preheat oven to 400°.
2. Coat 5 (6-ounce) custard cups with cooking spray. Dust cups with breadcrumbs; set aside.
3. Bring water and next 3 ingredients to a boil; stir in grits. Reduce heat, and simmer 5 minutes, stirring often. Remove from heat. Stir in cheese. Transfer to a bowl; let stand 5 minutes or until mixture has cooled slightly.
4. Beat egg whites with a mixer at high speed until stiff peaks form; fold egg whites into grits mixture. Spoon into prepared custard cups (cups will be full).
5. Bake at 400° for 20 minutes or until puffed and golden. Serve immediately. YIELD: 5 servings (serving size: 1 soufflé).

POINTS: 3; **EXCHANGES:** 1 Starch, ½ Medium-Fat Meat; **PER SERVING:** CAL 132 (29% from fat); PRO 6.5g; FAT 4.1g (sat 2.5g); CARB 16.5g; FIB 0.4g; CHOL 12mg; IRON 0.5mg; SOD 299mg; CALC 96mg

MEXICAN HOMINY

prep: 11 minutes • cook: 11 minutes

It's always a good idea to wear rubber gloves when seeding any type of pepper. If you prefer, leave the seeds in the jalapeño for an extra peppery punch!

2 teaspoons olive oil
1 cup finely chopped onion
2 teaspoons minced seeded jalapeño pepper
1 teaspoon minced garlic
1 (15-ounce) can golden hominy, drained
1 (14.5-ounce) can Mexican-style stewed tomatoes, drained and chopped
¼ teaspoon salt
⅛ teaspoon black pepper
2 tablespoons chopped fresh cilantro

1. Heat oil in a medium nonstick skillet over medium-high heat. Add onion; sauté 3 minutes. Add jalapeño pepper and garlic; sauté 2 minutes. Stir in hominy; reduce heat to medium, and cook 5 minutes, stirring occasionally. Stir in tomatoes, salt, and black pepper; cook until thoroughly heated. Sprinkle with cilantro. YIELD: 6 servings (serving size: ½ cup).

POINTS: 1; EXCHANGES: 1 Starch; **PER SERVING:** CAL 84 (15% from fat); PRO 2.1g; FAT 1.6g (sat 0.2g); CARB 18.4g; FIB 3.3g; CHOL 0mg; IRON 2.4mg; SOD 627mg; CALC 18mg

ORZO-MUSHROOM PILAF

prep: 10 minutes • cook: 15 minutes

Turn this versatile side dish into an easy vegetarian entrée: Use the pilaf as a stuffing for cabbage rolls or green bell peppers.

1 (3.2-ounce) package shiitake mushrooms
Cooking spray
2 teaspoons butter
2 teaspoons instant minced onion
2 garlic cloves, minced
1 cup uncooked orzo (rice-shaped pasta)
2 cups fat-free, less-sodium chicken broth
⅛ teaspoon pepper
1 tablespoon minced fresh sage

1. Discard mushroom stems, and slice caps into ¼-inch-thick slices.
2. Melt butter in a large saucepan coated with cooking spray over medium-high heat. Add mushrooms, onion, and garlic; sauté 2 minutes. Stir in orzo and broth. Bring to a boil; reduce heat, and simmer, uncovered, 13 to 15 minutes or until orzo is tender and liquid is almost absorbed, stirring frequently. Gently stir in pepper and sage. Serve immediately. YIELD: 4 servings (serving size: about ⅔ cup).

POINTS: 4; EXCHANGES: 2 Starch **PER SERVING:** CAL 189 (13% from fat); PRO 6.3g; FAT 2.6g (sat 1.3g); CARB 34.2g; FIB 1.4g; CHOL 5mg; IRON 2.1mg; SOD 67mg; CALC 16mg

RICE PILAF WITH FENNEL AND CARROTS

prep: 13 minutes • cook: 1 hour

For a more intense fennel flavor, snip some of the fennel greenery (as you would for fresh dill) to stir into the rice.

Cooking spray
1 teaspoon olive oil
1 cup chopped fennel
1 cup chopped carrot
1 cup uncooked brown rice
2½ cups vegetable broth
½ teaspoon fennel seeds
¼ teaspoon salt
⅛ teaspoon pepper
⅓ cup chopped fresh parsley
2 tablespoons grated Parmesan cheese

1. Heat oil in a large saucepan coated with cooking spray over medium heat. Add fennel and carrot; sauté 5 minutes. Add rice and next 4 ingredients. Bring to a boil; cover, reduce heat, and simmer 55 to 60 minutes or until rice is tender.
2. Stir in parsley and cheese. YIELD: 8 servings (serving size: ½ cup).

POINTS: 2; EXCHANGES: 1 Starch, 1 Vegetable; **PER SERVING:** CAL 116 (16% from fat); PRO 3.5g; FAT 2.1g (sat 0.5g); CARB 21.5g; FIB 1.8g; CHOL 1mg; IRON 0.7mg; SOD 429mg; CALC 42mg

WALNUT WILD RICE

prep: 9 minutes • cook: 10 minutes

1 (6.2-ounce) package fast-
  cooking recipe long-grain and
  wild rice (such as Uncle Ben's)
2 cups fat-free, less-sodium
  chicken broth
3 tablespoons chopped walnuts
¼ cup chopped green onions
  (about 1)
1 tablespoon light butter

1. Cook rice according to package
directions, using chicken broth
instead of water, and omitting fat.
2. Combine cooked rice, walnuts,
green onions, and butter. YIELD: 8
servings (serving size: ½ cup).

POINTS: 2; **EXCHANGES:** 1 Starch, ½ Fat;
PER SERVING: CAL 108 (22% from fat); PRO 3.4g;
FAT 2.8g (sat 0.7g); CARB 18.1g; FIB 0.7g;
CHOL 3mg; IRON 0.7mg; SOD 491mg; CALC 10mg

RISOTTO WITH SWISS CHARD

(pictured on page 139)
prep: 10 minutes • cook: 43 minutes

*Chard is usually sold in bunches in the
supermarket. Look for fresh, crisp,
dark green leaves.*

8 cups torn Swiss chard leaves
  (about 9 ounces)
½ cup water
4¾ cups vegetable broth
2 teaspoons olive oil
½ cup finely chopped onion
1 cup uncooked Arborio rice or
  other short-grain rice
3 tablespoons dry vermouth or
  dry white wine
⅛ teaspoon ground nutmeg
3 tablespoons grated Parmesan
  cheese
⅛ teaspoon pepper

1. Combine chard leaves and water
in a large saucepan. Bring to a boil;
cover, reduce heat, and simmer 10 to
15 minutes or until tender. Drain
well, and set aside.
2. Bring broth to a simmer in a
medium saucepan (do not boil).
Keep warm over low heat.
3. Heat oil in a large saucepan over
medium-high heat. Add onion;
cook, stirring occasionally, 5 minutes
or until tender. Add rice; sauté 1
minute. Add vermouth; sauté 30
seconds. Add warm broth, ½ cup at
a time, stirring constantly until each
portion of broth is absorbed before
adding the next (about 25 minutes
total). Add chard leaves, nutmeg,
cheese, and pepper; cook, stirring
constantly, 2 minutes or until thoroughly heated. YIELD: 8 servings (serving size: ½ cup).

POINTS: 3; **EXCHANGES:** 1 Starch, 1 Vegetable,
½ Fat; **PER SERVING:** CAL 137 (17% from fat);
PRO 4.6g; FAT 2.7g (sat 0.7g); CARB 24.0g;
FIB 1.5g; CHOL 2mg; IRON 1.8mg; SOD 716mg;
CALC 54mg

HOW TO COOK RISOTTO

1. Heat oil in a large saucepan
over medium-high heat. Add onion
(and other ingredient if called for);
sauté 5 minutes. Add rice; sauté
1 minute.

2. Add warm broth, ½ cup at a
time, stirring constantly until each
portion of broth is absorbed before
adding the next.

3. The finished product should be
tender and creamy with all the liquid absorbed. Cooking time will be
from 20 to 30 minutes.

WILD MUSHROOM AND HERB RISOTTO

prep: 16 minutes • stand: 20 minutes
cook: 35 minutes

2 (.5-ounce) packages dried
   porcini mushrooms, rinsed
1 cup warm water
2 (14.5-ounce) cans low-salt beef
   broth
2 teaspoons olive oil
1 cup finely chopped onion
1 cup sliced shiitake mushrooms
1 (8-ounce) package presliced
   mushrooms
3 garlic cloves, minced
1½ cups Arborio rice or other
   short-grain rice
½ cup dry red wine
1 teaspoon salt
½ teaspoon freshly ground black
   pepper
1 tablespoon minced fresh sage
2 tablespoons minced fresh
   oregano
½ cup (2 ounces) freshly grated
   Parmesan cheese

1. Combine porcini mushrooms and
water; let stand 20 minutes. Bring
beef broth to a simmer in a medium
saucepan (do not boil). Keep warm
over low heat.
2. Heat oil in a Dutch oven over
medium-high heat. Add onion; cook
5 minutes. Add shiitake mushrooms,
presliced mushrooms, and garlic;
cook 4 minutes. Add rice; cook 1
minute, stirring constantly. Stir in
wine and porcini mushroom mixture; cook over medium heat 5
minutes or until liquid is nearly
absorbed, stirring constantly. Add
warm broth, ½ cup at a time, stirring constantly until each portion
of broth is nearly absorbed before
adding the next (about 20 minutes
total). Stir in salt and remaining
ingredients. Serve immediately. YIELD:
12 servings (serving size: ½ cup).

POINTS: 3; EXCHANGES: 1 Starch, 1 Vegetable,
½ Fat; **PER SERVING:** CAL 146 (15% from fat);
PRO 5.7g; FAT 2.4g (sat 1.0g); CARB 25.3g;
FIB 1.8g; CHOL 3mg; IRON 2.0mg; SOD 406mg;
CALC 70mg

ORIENTAL NOODLES

prep: 6 minutes • cook: 8 minutes

4 ounces uncooked Chinese-style
   noodles
¼ cup chopped green onions
   (about 1)
1 red bell pepper, thinly sliced
2 tablespoons low-sodium soy
   sauce
2 tablespoons water
2 tablespoons peanut butter
2 tablespoons grated peeled fresh
   ginger
¼ teaspoon crushed red pepper

1. Cook noodles according to package directions, omitting salt and fat.
Drain; transfer to a large bowl. Add
green onions and bell pepper; set
aside, and cool slightly.
2. Combine soy sauce and remaining 4 ingredients; stir well. Pour soy
sauce mixture over noodles, tossing
well. Serve warm or at room temperature. YIELD: 4 servings (serving
size: ¾ cup).

POINTS: 3; **EXCHANGES:** 1½ Starch, 1 Vegetable,
1 Fat; **PER SERVING:** CAL 160 (25% from fat);
PRO 5.9g; FAT 4.8g (sat 0.8g); CARB 26.6g;
FIB 5.3g; CHOL 0mg; IRON 1.6mg; SOD 306mg;
CALC 21mg

TOMATO-BASIL PASTA

prep: 22 minutes • cook: 25 minutes

*Vermicelli is a very thin-stranded pasta.
Spaghetti, fettuccine, angel hair, or
other long pasta will also work.*

Cooking spray
1 garlic clove, minced
1 small onion, thinly sliced
2½ cups chopped seeded peeled
   tomato (about 3)
¼ cup no-salt-added tomato sauce
1½ teaspoons olive oil
2 tablespoons minced fresh basil
¼ teaspoon salt
⅛ teaspoon pepper
2 cups hot, cooked vermicelli
3 tablespoons freshly grated
   Parmesan cheese

1. Coat a Dutch oven with cooking
spray; place over medium heat until
hot. Add garlic and onion; sauté 5
minutes or until onion is tender. Stir
in chopped tomato and next 5
ingredients; bring to a boil. Reduce
heat, and simmer, uncovered, 15
minutes, stirring occasionally.
2. Add cooked pasta to tomato mixture; cook, uncovered, until mixture
is thoroughly heated, stirring occasionally. Sprinkle with cheese, and
serve immediately. YIELD: 8 servings
(serving size: ½ cup).

POINTS: 2; **EXCHANGE:** 1 Starch; **PER SERVING:**
CAL 94 (18% from fat); PRO 3.4g; FAT 1.9g
(sat 0.6g); CARB 15.8g; FIB 1.6g; CHOL 2mg;
IRON 1.2mg; SOD 123mg; CALC 39mg

Soups & Stews

CURRIED CARROT SOUP

prep: 13 minutes • cook: 50 minutes

*Pureeing the carrot and broth
mixture gives the soup a thick, silky
texture. Dress up this simple soup
with a sprinkle of chopped fresh
cilantro and a dollop of reduced-fat
sour cream, if you like.*

1 tablespoon butter
1 medium onion, chopped
1 (2-pound) package carrots,
   peeled and coarsely chopped
1 (32-ounce) carton fat-free,
   less-sodium chicken broth
½ cup water
1½ teaspoons curry powder
¼ teaspoon salt
⅛ teaspoon white pepper

1. Melt butter in a large saucepan
over medium heat; add onion, and
cook 3 minutes or until tender, stirring occasionally. Add carrot and
broth. Bring to a boil; reduce heat,
and simmer, uncovered, 45 minutes
or until very tender.
2. Place half of carrot mixture in a
food processor or blender; process
until smooth. Pour pureed mixture
into a large bowl; repeat procedure
with remaining carrot mixture.
3. Return pureed mixture to
saucepan; add water and remaining 3
ingredients. Bring to a simmer over
medium heat, and cook 2 to 3 minutes or until mixture is thoroughly
heated. YIELD: 6 servings (serving size:
1 cup).

POINTS: 1; EXCHANGES: 1 Starch, ½ Fat;
PER SERVING: CAL 100 (17% from fat); PRO 4.2g;
FAT 2.0g (sat 1.2g); CARB 17.3g; FIB 4.2g;
CHOL 5mg; IRON 0.2mg; SOD 606mg; CALC 44mg

CREAM OF CAULIFLOWER SOUP WITH CURRY

(pictured on page 158)
prep: 9 minutes • cook: 26 minutes

*Fresh cauliflower may be substituted
for frozen. Simply steam 1 pound
of fresh cauliflower florets before
they're added in Step #2.*

Cooking spray
1 cup chopped onion
½ cup chopped celery
½ cup chopped carrot
1 (16-ounce) package frozen
   cauliflower florets, thawed
1 (14.5-ounce) can fat-free,
   less-sodium chicken broth
½ teaspoon curry powder
¼ teaspoon pepper
2 cups fat-free milk, divided
¾ teaspoon salt
2 tablespoons light butter
Celery leaves (optional)

1. Heat a Dutch oven coated with
cooking spray over medium–high
heat. Add onion, celery, and carrot;
cook 4 minutes, stirring frequently.
2. Add cauliflower, broth, curry
powder, and pepper; bring to a boil
over high heat. Cover, reduce heat,
and simmer 20 minutes or until carrot is tender.
3. Remove from heat; stir in 1 cup
milk. Place 1 cup cauliflower mixture in a blender; process 10 seconds
or until smooth, and pour into a
large bowl. Repeat procedure with
remaining cauliflower mixture.
4. Return cauliflower mixture to
pan; stir in remaining 1 cup milk
and salt. Cook over medium heat
until thoroughly heated, stirring

frequently. Remove from heat; add
butter, stirring until melted. Garnish
with celery leaves, if desired. YIELD:
6 servings (serving size: 1 cup).

POINTS: 1; EXCHANGES: 2 Vegetable, ½ Fat;
PER SERVING: CAL 85 (24% from fat); PRO 6.1g;
FAT 2.5g (sat 1.5g); CARB 11.7g; FIB 2.8g;
CHOL 8mg; IRON 0.7mg; SOD 577mg; CALC 131mg

WHAT'S THE DIFFERENCE?

Chowder, bisque, chili, stew—these
various dishes all warm you up on a
cold day, are served in a soup
bowl, and are eaten with a spoon.
But what's the real difference between these dishes? To point out the
differences, here are the definitions:
Bisque—a thick, rich soup made of
pureed food and cream or milk. It
may contain vegetables, seafood,
or poultry.
Chowder—a thick, rich, chunky
soup made with seafood or
vegetables.
Chili—a blend of diced or ground
beef, tomatoes, chiles, chili powder,
and often beans. Vegetarian and
chicken chilis are also options.
Gumbo—a thick, stewlike dish that
begins with a dark roux, which
lends a rich flavor. Vegetables found
in gumbo include tomatoes, onions,
and okra, which serves as a thick-
ener. Gumbo also includes a variety
of meats or shellfish, such as chick-
en, sausage, and shrimp.
Soup—a combination of vegetables
and meat cooked in a broth; it may
be served hot or cold.
Stew—a combination of meat, vegetables, and a thick broth created
from the stewing liquid and the natural juices of the food being
cooked.

SWEET POTATO BISQUE

prep: 8 minutes • cook: 40 minutes
cool: 10 minutes

When made with vegetable broth, this bisque is vegetarian. You may substitute fat-free, less-sodium chicken broth, if you prefer.

2 teaspoons olive oil
½ cup finely chopped onion
⅓ cup finely chopped celery
1¼ pounds peeled sweet potatoes, finely chopped (about 4 cups)
1 (14.5-ounce) can vegetable broth
2 cups water
1 teaspoon dried rubbed sage
¼ teaspoon salt
¼ teaspoon pepper

1. Heat oil in a large saucepan over medium heat. Add onion and celery; sauté 4 minutes or until onion is tender. Add potato and next 5 ingredients. Bring to a boil. Cover, reduce heat, and simmer 30 minutes or until potato is tender. Uncover and cool 10 minutes.
2. Place half of potato mixture in a food processor or blender; process until smooth. Pour pureed mixture into a large bowl; repeat procedure with remaining potato mixture. Return pureed mixture to saucepan; cook until thoroughly heated. Yield: 5 servings (serving size: 1 cup).

POINTS: 3; **EXCHANGES:** 2 Starch, 1 Fat; **PER SERVING:** CAL 170 (23% from fat); PRO 3.5g; FAT 4.4g (sat 1.5g); CARB 30.6g; FIB 2.5g; CHOL 8mg; IRON 0.8mg; SOD 760mg; CALC 59mg

FRENCH ONION SOUP

prep: 11 minutes • cook: 49 minutes

Additional beef broth or water may be substituted for the wine.

Cooking spray
2 tablespoons light butter
6 large onions (about 3 pounds), cut into ¼-inch-thick slices
2 (10.5-ounce) cans beef consommé, undiluted
1 (14.25-ounce) can less-salt beef broth
1⅓ cups water
¼ teaspoon pepper
¼ cup dry white wine
8 (1-ounce) slices French bread
½ cup (2 ounces) grated Parmesan cheese

1. Coat a large Dutch oven with cooking spray; add butter. Place over medium-high heat until butter melts. Add onion; sauté 5 minutes. Stir in consommé, broth, water, and pepper; bring to a boil. Reduce heat, and simmer, uncovered, 35 minutes. Add wine, and simmer, uncovered, 5 minutes.
2. Preheat broiler.
3. Place bread on a baking sheet; sprinkle with cheese. Broil 3 inches from heat until cheese is golden. Ladle soup evenly into bowls; top each serving with 1 bread slice. YIELD: 8 servings (serving size: 1½ cups).

POINTS: 4; **EXCHANGES:** 1½ Starch, 1 Vegetable, 1 Fat; **PER SERVING:** CAL 205 (20% from fat); PRO 11.3g; FAT 4.7g (sat 2.5g); CARB 29.3g; FIB 3.8g; CHOL 10mg; IRON 1.6mg; SOD 695mg; CALC 148mg

POTATO-CORN CHOWDER

prep: 14 minutes • cook: 15 minutes

Cooking spray
¾ cup chopped green bell pepper
⅓ cup chopped onion
2¾ cups fat-free, less-sodium chicken broth
2 cups chopped red potato
½ teaspoon salt
¼ teaspoon black pepper
¼ cup cornstarch
2¼ cups 1% milk
2¼ cups frozen whole-kernel corn
1 (2-ounce) jar diced pimiento, drained
4 slices 40%-less-fat bacon (such as Gwaltney's), cooked and crumbled

1. Coat a medium saucepan with cooking spray; place over medium-high heat until hot. Add chopped green pepper and onion; sauté 5 minutes or until tender. Stir in broth and next 3 ingredients. Bring to a boil; reduce heat, and simmer, uncovered, 6 to 8 minutes or until potato is tender.
2. Combine cornstarch and milk, stirring until smooth; gradually add to potato mixture, stirring constantly. Stir in corn and diced pimiento; bring to a boil over medium heat, stirring constantly. Cook, stirring constantly, 1 minute or until mixture is thickened. Sprinkle each serving evenly with bacon crumbles. Serve immediately. YIELD: 5 servings (serving size: 1½ cups).

POINTS: 4; **EXCHANGES:** 2 Starch, 1 Vegetable, ½ Skim Milk; **PER SERVING:** CAL 224 (12% from fat); PRO 11.2g; FAT 3.1g (sat 1.2g); CARB 40.8g; FIB 3.6g; CHOL 8mg; IRON 1.3mg; SOD 756mg; CALC 148mg

CHEESY VEGETABLE CHOWDER

(pictured on page 159)
prep: 6 minutes • cook: 28 minutes

Tossing the shredded Cheddar with a tablespoon of flour helps the cheese melt smoothly. The result is a creamy base for this chunky chowder.

  2 slices 40%-less-fat bacon (such as Gwaltney)
½ cup chopped onion
½ cup chopped red bell pepper
2½ cups refrigerated diced potatoes with onion (such as Simply Potatoes)
  1 (14.5-ounce) can vegetable broth
1½ cups 1% low-fat milk
  1 (15-ounce) can cream-style corn
  1 cup (4 ounces) preshredded reduced-fat Cheddar cheese
  1 tablespoon all-purpose flour
¼ teaspoon black pepper

1. Cook bacon in a Dutch oven over medium-high heat until crisp; remove bacon from pan, reserving drippings in pan. Crumble bacon.
2. Add onion and bell pepper to hot drippings; sauté 5 minutes or until tender. Add potato and broth to pan. Bring to a boil; cover, reduce heat, and simmer 10 minutes or until potatoes are tender.
3. Stir in milk and corn; cook over medium-low heat 5 minutes. Combine cheese and flour, tossing to coat cheese. Add to chowder, stirring until cheese melts. Stir in black pepper. Top each serving evenly with crumbled bacon. YIELD: 7 servings (serving size: 1 cup).

POINTS: 4; **EXCHANGES:** 2 Starch, ½ Medium-Fat Meat; **PER SERVING:** CAL 185 (23% from fat); PRO 9.6g; FAT 5.0g (sat 2.8g); CARB 26.8g; FIB 2.3g; CHOL 16mg; IRON 0.6mg; SOD 721mg; CALC 178mg

THE SECRET TO A CREAMY CHEESE CHOWDER

Combine cheese and flour in a medium bowl, tossing to coat cheese.

Add flour and cheese to chowder, stirring constantly until cheese melts.

WINTER VEGETABLE SOUP

prep: 9 minutes • cook: 49 minutes

You need only 9 spare minutes to get this soup ready to cook. Use a colander to quickly rinse and drain the beans.

  1 tablespoon olive oil
  1 cup finely chopped onion
¾ cup finely chopped carrot (about 2 carrots)
  2 garlic cloves, minced
  1 (14.5-ounce) can diced tomatoes, undrained
  2 (15.5-ounce) cans Great Northern beans, rinsed and drained
  2 cups cubed Yukon Gold potato (about 10 ounces)
2½ cups water
  2 (14.5-ounce) cans vegetable broth
  1 teaspoon dried Italian seasoning
½ teaspoon salt
¼ teaspoon pepper
  1 (10-ounce) package frozen chopped spinach, thawed, drained, and squeezed dry

1. Heat oil in a Dutch oven over medium-high heat. Add onion, carrot, and garlic; cook, stirring occasionally, 4 minutes or until onion is tender. Stir in tomatoes and next 7 ingredients. Bring to a boil; cover, reduce heat, and simmer 40 minutes or until vegetables are tender. Add spinach; cover and cook 5 minutes. YIELD: 10 servings (serving size: 1 cup).

POINTS: 3; **EXCHANGES:** 1½ Starch, 1 Vegetable, ½ Fat; **PER SERVING:** CAL 157 (11% from fat); PRO 9.0g; FAT 2.2g (sat 0.3g); CARB 28.8g; FIB 6.7g; CHOL 0mg; IRON 2.4mg; SOD 549mg; CALC 95mg

LENTIL SOUP WITH KRAUT AND BACON

prep: 8 minutes • cook: 35 minutes

A flavorful combo of sauerkraut and bacon tops this fiber-rich soup.

1 (16-ounce) package dried
  lentils, rinsed
3 cups chopped onion
1 (32-ounce) carton fat-free,
  less-sodium chicken broth
4 cups water
½ teaspoon celery seeds
4 slices 40%-less-fat bacon (such
  as Gwaltney), chopped
1 (14.5-ounce) can shredded
  sauerkraut, drained
¾ teaspoon salt
½ teaspoon pepper

1. Combine first 5 ingredients in a
Dutch oven; bring to a boil. Reduce
heat, and simmer, uncovered, 30
minutes or until lentils are tender.
2. Cook bacon in a nonstick skillet
over medium heat until crisp.
Remove bacon from pan; crumble.
Reserve 1 tablespoon drippings; discard remaining drippings. Combine
bacon and sauerkraut in pan; cook 1
minute or until thoroughly heated.
3. Add reserved drippings, salt, and
pepper to lentil mixture. Spoon soup
into individual bowls; top with
sauerkraut mixture. YIELD: 8 servings
(serving size: 1 cup soup and ½ cup
sauerkraut mixture).

POINTS: 4; EXCHANGES: 2 Starch, 1 Vegetable,
2 Very Lean Meat; PER SERVING: CAL 254 (8% from
fat); PRO 20.7g; FAT 2.2g (sat 0.6g); CARB 39.6g;
FIB 19.9g; CHOL 5mg; IRON 5.5mg; SOD 946mg;
CALC 46mg

"MEATY" MEATLESS DOUBLE-BEAN CHILI

(pictured on page 160)
prep: 8 minutes • cook: 26 minutes

*We gave this vegetarian chili our
highest rating at the taste-testing table.*

1 tablespoon olive oil
2 cups chopped onion
4 garlic cloves, minced
2 drained canned chipotle chiles
  in adobo sauce, minced
1 teaspoon ground cumin
1 teaspoon chili powder
1 (12-ounce) package burger-style
  recipe crumbles
2 cups water
2 (14.5-ounce) cans chili-style
  diced tomatoes, undrained
1 (15-ounce) can black beans,
  rinsed and drained
1 (15-ounce) can dark red kidney
  beans, rinsed and drained
1 (6-ounce) can tomato paste
1 teaspoon dried oregano
1 bay leaf
½ cup sliced green onions
1 (2.5-ounce) can sliced black
  olives, drained
1 cup (4 ounces) preshredded
  reduced-fat Cheddar cheese

1. Heat oil in a Dutch oven over
medium-high heat. Add onion; cook
5 minutes, stirring frequently. Add
garlic and next 3 ingredients; cook 1
minute. Add recipe crumbles and
next 7 ingredients, stirring well;
bring to a boil. Reduce heat to low;
simmer, uncovered, 15 minutes, stirring frequently. Discard bay leaf.
2. Spoon chili into individual bowls.
Top each serving with green onions,

olives, and cheese. YIELD: 10 servings
(serving size: 1 cup chili, 1 tablespoon each green onions and olives,
and about 1½ tablespoons cheese).

POINTS: 5; EXCHANGES: 2 Starch, 1 Medium-Fat
Meat, 1 Fat; PER SERVING: CAL 250 (33% from fat);
PRO 15.8g; FAT 9.3g (sat 2.8g); CARB 28.6g;
FIB 9.8g; CHOL 8mg; IRON 3.4mg; SOD 876mg;
CALC 153mg

BEEF STEW WITH CORN AND FENNEL

(pictured on page 159)
prep: 18 minutes • cook: 2 hours

1 (14.5-ounce) can low-salt beef
  broth
1 cup dry red wine
1 cup water
2 garlic cloves, minced
3 tablespoons tomato paste
1 tablespoon dried basil
1½ teaspoons dried thyme
½ teaspoon salt
¼ teaspoon pepper
2 teaspoons extra-virgin olive oil
1½ pounds lean boneless top round
  steak, cut into 1-inch cubes
2 cups vertically sliced fennel
  (about 2 medium bulbs)
1 large onion, sliced vertically
  (about 1½ cups)
1 (8-ounce) package button
  mushrooms, quartered
2 tablespoons all-purpose flour
3 tablespoons water
1 (10-ounce) package frozen
  whole-kernel corn, thawed
Fennel sprigs (optional)

1. Combine first 9 ingredients in a
medium bowl; stir with a whisk.
2. Heat a Dutch oven over high heat

A New Confidence

SUSAN BONETTI • **HEIGHT** 5'4" • **BEFORE** 166 LBS. • **AFTER** 115 LBS.

Lesson learned: Accountability is the key.

Susan Bonetti has struggled with her weight as long as she can remember. "Gain some, lose some, gain some, lose a little less," she says. "With each passing year, it became harder to get the weight off."

While shopping for a bathing suit in May 1998, Susan realized that her weight had gotten out of control. She knew that she needed help. Susan joined Weight Watchers for the first time and lost 19 pounds in four months. "Excited with my loss and flattered with the compliments I was receiving from friends and coworkers, I decided I didn't need to keep attending meetings and paying the weekly fees," she says. "Sadly, I was mistaken."

> *"I looked at staying within my POINTS as a kind of game or jigsaw puzzle."*

"I stopped counting **POINTS** and exercising, and I regained all the weight I lost—plus more! I needed the encouragement and support I received at the weekly meetings, plus the accountability of getting on that scale each week in front of my leader."

In July 1999, Susan's family relocated to a new city and state. "This was my first move away from home, and I was miserable," she says. "So I consoled myself with food. Fast food was my favorite—especially Taco Bell and Dairy Queen." Overall, Susan felt bad. "My back hurt, my feet ached, and I was tired all the time."

After another year and a half of yo-yo dieting, Susan's friend Nancy asked her to join Weight Watchers with her. Realizing that Weight Watchers was the only weight-loss program that had ever worked for her, Susan agreed.

"This time I was committed wholeheartedly to the program," she says. "I began exercising three days a week, stopped eating fast food, began journaling every day, and attended all the meetings faithfully. I looked at staying within my **POINTS** as a kind of game or jigsaw puzzle. It was fun!"

It was then that Susan began to see results. The weight began coming off weekly. "The encouragement I received from my leader, receptionist, Weight Watchers members, and my friend, Nancy, helped me reach my goal of 130 pounds in March 2001," Susan says. "And I became a lifetime member." She continued to lose weight and is now down to 115 pounds.

Susan's experience with Weight Watchers, especially the sharing and celebrating in the meetings, gave her a new outlook.

"I was a new person," she says. "I found new confidence in myself which was something that I was sadly lacking before. I now want to try new things."

Among those new things is running. Susan recently completed her first 5K run and is now contemplating a half-marathon next year. "The 5K was one of the most exciting things I've ever done," she says. "I've finally found my real self, and it's a nice feeling."

Cream of Cauliflower
Soup with Curry,
page 153

Beef Stew with Corn
and Fennel,
page 156

Cheesy Vegetable
Chowder, page 155

"Meaty" Meatless
Double-Bean Chili,
page 156

Tortilla Chipotle
Chicken Soup,
page 162

until hot; add oil. Add beef; cook 4 minutes or until browned on all sides, stirring occasionally.

3. Reduce heat to medium-high; add fennel, onion, and mushrooms. Cook 5 minutes, stirring occasionally.

4. Add broth mixture; bring to a boil. Cover, reduce heat, and simmer 1½ hours or until beef is tender.

5. Combine flour and water in a small bowl; stir with a whisk until smooth. Stir flour mixture into beef mixture. Add corn. Cover and simmer 8 minutes. Garnish with fennel sprigs, if desired. YIELD: 9 servings (serving size: 1 cup).

POINTS: 4; EXCHANGES: 1 Starch, 3½ Lean Meat; PER SERVING: CAL 211 (22% from fat); PRO 27.3g; FAT 5.2g (sat 1.5g); CARB 14.1g; FIB 2.6g; CHOL 64mg; IRON 3.7mg; SOD 285mg; CALC 46mg

---

SHRINK YOUR STOMACH WITH SOUP

New research indicates that starting each meal with a small cup of soup may actually help you lose weight. How? The warm soup fills your stomach and curbs your appetite so that you consume fewer calories during the rest of the meal. For best results, choose a soup low in fat and sodium, such as a broth or a vegetable-based soup. We recommend Smoked Turkey and Barley Stew on page 163, White Bean-Chicken Chili on page 163, and Lentil Soup with Kraut and Bacon on page 156.

PORK AND VEGETABLE STEW

prep: 20 minutes • cook: 55 minutes

Briefly freezing the pork makes it easier to cut and reduces the preparation time of this perfect-for-fall stew.

Cooking spray
2 teaspoons olive oil
1½ pounds boneless pork loin, cut into 2-inch pieces
1 cup finely chopped onion
1 (28-ounce) can diced tomatoes, undrained
1¼ cups finely chopped celery
1½ cups matchstick-cut carrots
1 (14-ounce) can fat-free, less-sodium chicken broth
1 garlic clove, minced
1 teaspoon dried rubbed sage
½ teaspoon salt
¾ teaspoon pepper
3 cups (1-inch) cubed peeled butternut squash (about 14 ounces)
1 tablespoon grated orange rind

1. Heat oil in a Dutch oven coated with cooking spray over medium-high heat. Add pork; cook 5 minutes, stirring occasionally. Add onion; sauté 5 minutes. Stir in tomatoes and next 8 ingredients. Bring to a boil; cover, reduce heat, and simmer 45 minutes or until squash and pork are tender. Stir in orange rind. YIELD: 9 servings (serving size: 1 cup).

POINTS: 3; EXCHANGES: 2 Vegetable, 2 Lean Meat; PER SERVING: CAL 172 (29% from fat); PRO 18.6g; FAT 5.5g (sat 1.7g); CARB 12.6g; FIB 3.3g; CHOL 45mg; IRON 1.6mg; SOD 537mg; CALC 74mg

---

CHICKEN SUCCOTASH CHOWDER

prep: 5 minutes • cook: 20 minutes

1 tablespoon butter
½ cup finely chopped celery
⅓ cup finely chopped green bell pepper
1½ tablespoons all-purpose flour
1 (14-ounce) can fat-free, less-sodium chicken broth
1 (14.75-ounce) can cream-style corn
1 cup 1% low-fat milk
2 cups frozen diced cooked chicken breast, thawed (such as Tyson's)
1 cup frozen baby lima beans, thawed
½ teaspoon dried thyme
¼ teaspoon salt
⅛ teaspoon black pepper
4 teaspoons chopped fresh parsley

1. Melt butter in a Dutch oven over medium heat. Add celery and green bell pepper; cook, stirring occasionally, 5 minutes or until tender.

2. Combine flour and 2 tablespoons chicken broth; stir with a whisk until smooth. Add flour mixture to remaining broth; stir well. Add broth mixture, corn, and next 6 ingredients to pan; stir well. Bring to a boil; cover, reduce heat, and simmer 10 minutes, stirring occasionally. Ladle chowder into bowls. Sprinkle each serving evenly with parsley. YIELD: 6 servings (serving size: 1 cup).

POINTS: 4; EXCHANGES: 1½ Starch, 2 Lean Meat; PER SERVING: CAL 209 (19% from fat); PRO 20.3g; FAT 4.5g (sat 2.0g); CARB 23.3g; FIB 3.1g; CHOL 46mg; IRON 1.7mg; SOD 576mg; CALC 77mg

FIERY CHICKEN AND RICE STEW

prep: 10 minutes • cook: 25 minutes

You can substitute 2 teaspoons of bottled minced garlic for the garlic cloves.

1 (5-ounce) package yellow rice mix (such as Vigo)
1 pound skinless, boneless chicken thighs, cut into bite-sized pieces
¼ teaspoon salt
½ teaspoon freshly ground black pepper, divided
1 teaspoon olive oil
1 cup chopped onion
½ cup chopped green bell pepper
4 garlic cloves, minced
1 cup fat-free, less-sodium chicken broth
1 (14.5-ounce) can diced tomatoes
1 tablespoon balsamic vinegar
1 teaspoon dried Italian seasoning
¼ teaspoon ground red pepper

1. Prepare rice according to package directions, omitting salt and fat.
2. Sprinkle chicken evenly with salt and black pepper. Heat oil in a Dutch oven over medium-high heat. Add chicken; cook 5 minutes or until browned, turning occasionally. Add onion, green bell pepper, and garlic; cook 5 minutes. Add broth and remaining 4 ingredients; bring to a boil. Cover, reduce heat, and simmer 10 minutes. Serve over rice. YIELD: 4 servings (serving size: 1¼ cups stew and ½ cup rice).

POINTS: 6; **EXCHANGES:** 2 Starch, 1 Vegetable, 3 Lean Meat; **PER SERVING:** CAL 307 (17% from fat); PRO 27.6g; FAT 5.8g (sat 1.3g); CARB 36.1g; FIB 2.1g; CHOL 94mg; IRON 3.6mg; SOD 935mg; CALC 49mg

CREAMY CHICKEN AND MUSHROOM STEW

prep: 11 minutes • cook: 27 minutes

We first tested this recipe using fat-free sour cream, but preferred the flavor and texture of the reduced-fat product.

Cooking spray
¾ pound skinless, boneless chicken breast, cut into bite-sized pieces
2 garlic cloves, minced
2 cups refrigerated diced potatoes with onion (such as Simply Potatoes)
1 (8-ounce) package mushrooms, quartered
1 cup chopped onion
1 (14.5-ounce) can fat-free, less-sodium chicken broth
1 (10.75-ounce) can reduced-fat, 30%-reduced-sodium cream of chicken soup
¼ teaspoon pepper
½ cup reduced-fat sour cream
¼ teaspoon salt
2 tablespoons chopped fresh parsley

1. Heat a Dutch oven coated with cooking spray over medium-high heat. Add chicken; sauté 2 minutes. Add garlic; cook 15 seconds.
2. Stir in potato, mushrooms, and next 4 ingredients. Bring to a boil; cover, reduce heat, and simmer 20 minutes or until potato is tender, stirring occasionally. Remove from heat; stir in sour cream and salt. Sprinkle each serving evenly with parsley. YIELD: 5 servings (serving size: 1⅓ cups).

POINTS: 4; **EXCHANGES:** 1 Starch, 2½ Lean Meat; **PER SERVING:** CAL 192 (19% from fat); PRO 20.9g; FAT 4.0g (sat 2.1g); CARB 17.9g; FIB 2.5g; CHOL 52mg; IRON 1.4mg; SOD 499mg; CALC 61mg

TORTILLA CHIPOTLE CHICKEN SOUP

(pictured on page 160)
prep: 20 minutes • cook: 54 minutes

This soup proves that simple ingredients can provide intense flavor. For an extra taste of Mexico, pair it with low-fat quesadillas and lime sorbet.

Cooking spray
12 ounces skinless, boneless chicken breast, cubed
1 cup finely chopped onion
2 garlic cloves, minced
2 (14-ounce) cans fat-free, less-sodium chicken broth
1 chipotle chile, mashed
2 teaspoons chili powder
1 cup chopped seeded tomato
2 tablespoons fresh lime juice
¼ teaspoon ground cumin
½ teaspoon salt
4 (6-inch) corn tortillas
⅓ cup chopped fresh cilantro

1. Preheat oven to 425°.
2. Heat a Dutch oven coated with cooking spray over medium-high heat. Add chicken, and sauté 2 minutes. Remove chicken; keep warm.
3. Add onion to pan; cook 4 minutes, stirring frequently. Add garlic; sauté 15 seconds. Add broth, chipotle chile, and chili powder. Bring to a boil; cover, reduce heat, and simmer 20 minutes.
4. Stir in tomato and next 3 ingredients; add chicken. Cover, reduce heat, and simmer 20 minutes.
5. While soup simmers, cut tortillas into ¼ x 2-inch strips. Place on a baking sheet in a single layer, and coat lightly with cooking spray. Bake

at 425° for 8 to 10 minutes or until lightly browned. Cool completely. **6.** Ladle soup into bowls; sprinkle servings evenly with cilantro and tortilla strips. YIELD: 4 servings (serving size: 1 cup soup and ¼ cup tortilla strips).

POINTS: 4; EXCHANGES: 1 Starch, 1 Vegetable, 3 Very Lean Meat; PER SERVING: CAL 201 (10% from fat); PRO 24.9g; FAT 2.3g (sat 0.4g); CARB 20.9g; FIB 3.1g; CHOL 49mg; IRON 1.6mg; SOD 983mg; CALC 77mg

WHITE BEAN-CHICKEN CHILI

prep: 7 minutes • cook: 27 minutes

If you have extra POINTS to spare for the day, try topping this delicious chili with chopped green onions and a sprinkle of Monterey Jack cheese.

Cooking spray
1 cup chopped onion (about 1)
1 garlic clove, minced
2 (15-ounce) cans cannellini beans, drained and divided
1 (4-ounce) can chopped green chiles, undrained
2¼ cups fat-free, less-sodium chicken broth
1½ cups chopped cooked chicken breast
1 teaspoon chili powder
⅛ teaspoon salt

1. Coat a large saucepan with cooking spray; place over medium-high heat until hot. Add onion and garlic; sauté until tender. Add 1 can beans and next 5 ingredients.
2. Mash remaining 1 can beans with a fork; add to chicken mixture in pan. Bring to a boil; cover, reduce

heat, and simmer 20 minutes. YIELD: 4 servings (serving size: 1½ cups).

POINTS: 4; EXCHANGES: 1 Starch, 1 Vegetable, 2 Lean Meat; PER SERVING: CAL 207 (18% from fat); PRO 19.4g; FAT 4.3g (sat 1.0g); CARB 19.6g; FIB 3.3g; CHOL 43mg; IRON 3.6mg; SOD 554mg; CALC 121mg

SMOKED TURKEY AND BARLEY STEW

prep: 8 minutes • cook: 40 minutes

Quick-cooking barley can be found in either the breakfast cereal or soup section of the grocery store.

1 tablespoon olive oil
1½ cups sliced carrot (about 3 medium)
2 cups chopped onion
1½ cups sliced celery
1 (8-ounce) package presliced mushrooms
1 cup uncooked quick-cooking barley
1 (32-ounce) carton fat-free, less-sodium chicken broth, divided
2 cups water
2 cups cubed smoked turkey (about 12 ounces)
1 bay leaf
1½ tablespoons chopped fresh thyme
1 (0.88-ounce) package turkey gravy mix (such as French's)
⅓ cup dry sherry
½ teaspoon freshly ground black pepper

1. Heat oil in a 4-quart Dutch oven over medium-high heat. Add carrot, onion, and celery; cook 6 minutes,

stirring frequently. Add mushrooms; cook 2 minutes. Stir in barley, 3 cups broth, water, and next 3 ingredients; bring to a boil. Reduce heat, and simmer, uncovered, 20 minutes or until barley is tender.
2. Combine gravy mix, remaining 1 cup broth, and sherry, stirring with a whisk. Stir gravy mixture into barley mixture; bring to a boil. Reduce heat, and simmer, uncovered, 10 minutes. Stir in pepper. Discard bay leaf. YIELD: 10 servings (serving size: 1 cup).

POINTS: 3; EXCHANGES: 1 Starch, 1 Vegetable, 1½ Lean Meat; PER SERVING: CAL 191 (21% from fat); PRO 14.6g; FAT 4.5g (sat 1.0g); CARB 24.0g; FIB 5.0g; CHOL 26mg; IRON 1.7mg; SOD 407mg; CALC 40mg

BRAWNY BARLEY

Barley has been a staple food for man and beast dating back to the Stone Age. This hardy grain is a good source of fiber and potassium and is used frequently in cereals, breads, and soups.

Two varieties of barley are most often found at markets. The most nutritious form is whole grain barley, which has only the outer husk removed. It's most commonly used to make a thick, oatmeal-like cereal. Pearl barley is less nutritious because the bran has been removed. This type of barley is steamed and polished and is good in soups and stews. Quick-cooking barley, which takes only 20 minutes to prepare, is the most popular form of pearl barley.

One day's menu provides at least two servings of milk and at least five servings of fruits and/or vegetables.

	MONDAY	TUESDAY	WEDNESDAY	THURSDAY
BREAKFAST	**Very Berry Smoothie** (Combine ⅓ cup *each of* fresh or frozen strawberries, blueberries, raspberries; 8 ounces vanilla fat-free yogurt; and ½ cup fat-free milk in a blender. Process until smooth - 4 *POINTS*.) TOTAL *POINTS*: 4	**cooked oatmeal,** 1 cup **brown sugar,** 1 tablespoon **fresh blueberries,** 1 cup **whole wheat toast,** 1 slice, with 1 tablespoon jelly **fat-free milk,** 1 cup TOTAL *POINTS*: 6	**Egg, Cheese, and Tomato Pita** (Fill 1 whole wheat pita pocket half with 1 cooked large egg, 2 tomato slices, and ¼ cup reduced-fat shredded mozzarella cheese. Toast in oven for 3 minutes or until pita is toasted and cheese melts - 5 *POINTS*.) **orange juice,** ½ cup TOTAL *POINTS*: 6	**bran flakes,** 1½ cups **banana,** 1 small **fat-free milk,** 1 cup TOTAL *POINTS*: 5
LUNCH	**hamburger,** 1 fast food **green salad,** 1 fast food **fat-free Italian dressing,** 2 tablespoons **orange,** 1 medium TOTAL *POINTS*: 8	**Barbecue Chicken Pizza** (Spread 2 tablespoons barbecue sauce over a 4-ounce Italian cheese-flavored pizza crust [such as Boboli]. Top with 2 ounces chopped roasted chicken breast, 2 tablespoons chopped red onion, and ¼ cup shredded part-skim mozzarella cheese - 8 *POINTS*.) **carrot sticks,** 1 cup TOTAL *POINTS*: 9	**canned vegetable soup,** 1 cup **saltine crackers,** 6 **apple,** 1 small **fat-free milk,** 1 cup TOTAL *POINTS*: 7	**Grilled Chicken Salad** (Slice a 3-ounce grilled or broiled skinless, boneless chicken breast; place on a bed of 2 cups torn romaine lettuce. Top with ½ cup *each of* diced tomato and cucumber slices and ¼ cup fat-free croutons. Drizzle with 2 tablespoons fat-free ranch dressing, and sprinkle with 2 tablespoons Parmesan cheese - 6 *POINTS*.) **saltine crackers,** 6 TOTAL *POINTS*: 8
DINNER	**Pork Tenderloin with Gingered Cranberries, page 97,** 1 serving **couscous,** 1 cup **sautéed spinach,** 1 cup TOTAL *POINTS*: 8	**Cajun Shrimp and Pasta, page 68,** 1 serving **spinach salad,** 2 cups **fat-free Italian dressing,** 2 tablespoons **fat-free milk,** 1 cup TOTAL *POINTS*: 8	**Chicken with Green Onion Sauce, page 104,** 1 serving **steamed rice,** ½ cup **steamed broccoli,** 1 cup TOTAL *POINTS*: 5	**Santa Fe Meat Loaf, page 87,** 1 serving **mashed potatoes,** ½ cup **steamed green beans,** 1 cup TOTAL *POINTS*: 8
SNACK	**cappuccino fat-free yogurt,** 8 ounces **graham crackers,** 4 (2.5-inch) squares TOTAL *POINTS*: 4	**fresh strawberries,** 1 cup **vanilla fat-free ice cream,** 1 cup TOTAL *POINTS*: 5	**graham crackers,** 4 (2.5-inch) squares **peanut butter,** 1 tablespoon **fat-free milk,** 1 cup TOTAL *POINTS*: 6	**fat-free milk,** 1 cup **chocolate nonfat pudding snack cup,** 1 TOTAL *POINTS*: 4
	POINTS **for the day:** 24 **Exchanges:** 6 Starch, 4 Vegetable, 2 Fruit, 3½ Very Lean Meat, 2 Medium-Fat Meat, 2½ Skim Milk, 1 Fat	*POINTS* **for the day:** 28 **Exchanges:** 9½ Starch, 3 Vegetable, 2 Fruit, 5 Very Lean Meat, 1 Medium-Fat Meat, 2 Skim Milk, 1 Fat	*POINTS* **for the day:** 24 **Exchanges:** 5 Starch, 4 Vegetable, 2 Fruit, 4 Very Lean Meat, 2 Medium-Fat Meat, ½ High-Fat Meat, 2 Skim Milk	*POINTS* **for the day:** 25 **Exchanges:** 8 Starch, 5 Vegetable, 1 Fruit, 3 Very Lean Meat, 3 Lean Meat, 1 Medium-Fat Meat, 2 Skim Milk

	FRIDAY	SATURDAY	SUNDAY
BREAKFAST	**Peanut Butter and Banana Bagel** (Spread 1 tablespoon peanut butter on 1 whole wheat bagel. Top with 1 sliced banana - 6 *POINTS*.) **fat-free milk,** 1 cup TOTAL *POINTS*: 8	**bran flakes,** 1½ cups **blueberries,** 1 cup **fat-free milk,** 1 cup TOTAL *POINTS*: 5	**Lemon Poppy Seed Scones, page 30,** 1 serving **orange juice,** ½ cup **fat-free milk,** 1 cup TOTAL *POINTS*: 8
LUNCH	**Veggie Burger** (Heat veggie burger according to package directions. Spread 2 teaspoons *each of* fat-free mayonnaise, ketchup, and mustard on 1 cut side of hamburger bun. Layer with patty, 2 lettuce leaves, and 2 tomato slices. Top with remaining half of bun - 5 *POINTS*.) **peach,** 1 medium **fat-free milk,** 1 cup TOTAL *POINTS*: 8	**Portobello Sandwich** (Brush 1 teaspoon *each of* olive oil, balsamic vinegar, and soy sauce over 1 large portobello mushroom cap. Broil 2 minutes on each side. Place mushroom, 2 tomato slices, 1 red onion slice, and a 1-ounce slice reduced-fat cheese on a 2-ounce hamburger bun - 5 *POINTS*.) **fat-free milk,** 1 cup TOTAL *POINTS*: 7	**lasagna with meat sauce,** 1 low-fat frozen entrée **fat-free milk,** 1 cup **celery sticks,** 1 cup TOTAL *POINTS*: 9
DINNER	**Grilled Halibut with Lemon Sauce, page 59,** 1 serving **roasted potato wedges,** 1 cup **steamed asparagus,** 12 spears TOTAL *POINTS*: 7	**Meatless Stroganoff, page 83,** 1 serving **steamed greens beans,** 1 cup TOTAL *POINTS*: 8	**Skillet Ham with Ginger-Peach Glaze, page 98,** 1 serving **baked sweet potato,** 1 medium **steamed broccoli** TOTAL *POINTS*: 6
SNACK	**vanilla fat-free ice cream,** ½ cup **chocolate syrup,** 1 tablespoon TOTAL *POINTS*: 3	**Bagel Chips** (Preheat oven to 400°. Slice day-old bagel into small, thin pieces. Top with fat-free garlic butter spray and bake until crisp.) TOTAL *POINTS*: 3	**chocolate nonfat pudding snack cup,** 1 **banana,** 1 small TOTAL *POINTS*: 3
	POINTS **for the day: 26** **Exchanges:** 8 Starch, 3 Vegetable, 2 Fruit, 7 Very Lean Meat, ½ High-Fat Meat, 2 Skim Milk	*POINTS* **for the day: 23** **Exchanges:** 9 Starch, 4 Vegetable, 1 Fruit, 3 Medium-Fat Meat, 2 Skim Milk, ½ Fat	*POINTS* **for the day: 26** **Exchanges:** 7½ Starch, 3 Vegetable, 2 Fruit, 2 Lean Meat, 2 Medium-Fat Meat, 2 Skim Milk, 1 Fat

One day's menu provides at least two servings of milk and at least five servings of fruits and/or vegetables.

	MONDAY	TUESDAY	WEDNESDAY	THURSDAY
BREAKFAST	**Banana-Oatmeal Muffins, page 30**, 2 servings **orange juice**, ½ cup **fat-free milk**, 1 cup TOTAL *POINTS*: 7	**bagel**, 1 small **light cream cheese**, 2 tablespoons **fresh strawberries**, 1 cup **fat-free milk**, 1 cup TOTAL *POINTS*: 7	**cooked oatmeal**, 1 cup **raisins**, 2 tablespoons **honey**, 1 tablespoon **blueberry fat-free yogurt**, 8 ounces TOTAL *POINTS*: 6	**Egg and Cheese Sandwich** (Combine 1 large egg and 2 tablespoons shredded reduced-fat sharp Cheddar cheese; stir well. Cook in a nonstick skillet over medium heat until set, stirring occasionally. Spoon egg mixture between 2 slices high-fiber bread - 5 *POINTS*.) **fat-free milk**, 1 cup TOTAL *POINTS*: 7
LUNCH	**Tomato-Avocado Bagel Sandwich** (Top ½ bagel with 2 tablespoons mashed avocado; ¼ cup shredded reduced-fat sharp Cheddar cheese; 1 small tomato, sliced; ⅛ teaspoon each of salt and pepper; and the other ½ bagel - 6 *POINTS*.) **orange sections**, 1 cup TOTAL *POINTS*: 7	**Chicken Salad Wrap** (Combine ½ cup chopped cooked chicken, ¼ cup *each of* finely diced celery and onion, 3 tablespoons low-fat mayonnaise, and a dash *each of* salt and pepper. Chill until serving. Top 1 [10-inch] fat-free flour tortilla with mixture and roll up - 6 *POINTS*.) **fresh tomato slices**, 1 cup **mixed berry fat-free yogurt**, 8 ounces TOTAL *POINTS*: 8	**turkey submarine sandwich** (with no cheese or mayonnaise), 1 6-inch **baked chips**, 1½ ounce bag TOTAL *POINTS*: 7	**Tuna Salad Pita** (Combine ½ cup canned tuna packaged in water, drained; 4 teaspoons light mayonnaise, and ⅛ teaspoon each of dried dill and pepper; mix well. Cut 1 [2-ounce] pita in half; line each half with 2 lettuce leaves and 2 tomato slices. Stuff halves evenly with tuna mixture - 5 *POINTS*.) **carrot sticks**, 1 cup **fat-free ranch dressing**, 2 tablespoons TOTAL *POINTS*: 7
DINNER	**Sicilian Chicken, page 106**, 1 serving **sauteed spinach**, 1 cup **fat-free milk**, 1 cup TOTAL *POINTS*: 7	**Dijon Pork Cutlets, page 95** **baked sweet potato**, 1 serving **steamed squash and zucchini**, 1 cup TOTAL *POINTS*: 7	**Szechuan Salmon Stir-Fry, page 61**, 1 serving **mixed fruit salad**, ¾ cup **fat-free milk**, 1 cup TOTAL *POINTS*: 8	**Chicken, Spinach, and Feta Pizza, page 101**, 1 serving **green salad**, 2 cups **fat-free Italian dressing**, 2 tablespoons TOTAL *POINTS*: 9
SNACK	**banana**, 1 small **angel food cake**, 2 ounces . TOTAL *POINTS*: 3	**Banana-Oatmeal Muffin, page 30**, 1 serving **peach**, 1 TOTAL *POINTS*: 3	**angel food cake**, 2 ounces **fresh strawberries**, 1 cup TOTAL *POINTS*: 3	**vanilla fat-free yogurt**, 8 ounces **orange juice**, ½ cup TOTAL *POINTS*: 3
	POINTS **for the day: 24** **Exchanges:** 9 Starch, 3 Vegetable, 3 Fruit, 3½ Very Lean Meat, 1 Medium-Fat Meat, 2 Skim Milk,1 Fat	*POINTS* **for the day: 25** **Exchanges:** 8 Starch, 3 Vegetable, 2 Fruit, 3 Very Lean Meat, 3½ Lean Meat, 1 Medium-Fat Meat, 2 Skim Milk, 1 Fat	*POINTS* **for the day: 26** **Exchanges:** 11 Starch, 2 Vegetable, 3 Fruit, 3 Very Lean Meat, 3 Lean Meat, 2 Skim Milk, ½ Fat	*POINTS* **for the day: 26** **Exchanges:** 7 Starch, 4 Vegetable, 1 Fruit, 3 Very Lean Meat, 3 Lean Meat, 1½ Medium-Fat Meat, 2 Skim Milk, 1 Fat

	FRIDAY	SATURDAY	SUNDAY
BREAKFAST	low-fat granola, ½ cup blueberries, 1 cup fat-free milk, 1 cup TOTAL *POINTS*: 6	Chunky Apple Pancakes, page 19, 1 serving maple syrup, 1 tablespoon orange juice, ½ cup fat-free milk, 1 cup TOTAL *POINTS*: 8	Southwestern Omelet (Combine ¾ cup egg substitute and 1 tablespoon fat-free milk. Pour into a small nonstick skillet and place over medium heat; cover and cook until set. Add 2 tablespoons *each of* chopped green bell pepper, onion, and tomato; 2 teaspoons fresh cilantro; and ¼ cup reduced-fat Cheddar cheese. Fold in half and heat through - 5 *POINTS*.) fat-free milk, 1 cup TOTAL *POINTS*: 7
LUNCH	Chicken-Veggie Wrap (Top 1 [10-inch] fat-free flour tortilla with 3 ounces chopped chicken and ¼ cup e*ach of* sliced bell pepper, spinach, yellow squash, chopped tomato, and shredded carrot. Sprinkle with 3 tablespoons crumbled feta cheese; roll up - 7 *POINTS*.) grapes, 1 cup TOTAL *POINTS*: 8	grilled chicken sandwich, 1 fast food (without mayonnaise) side salad, 1 fast food fat-free dressing, 2 tablespoons blueberries, 1 cup TOTAL *POINTS*: 9	canned low-sodium chicken noodle soup, 1 cup saltine crackers, 6 reduced-fat sharp Cheddar cheese, 1 ounce carrot sticks, 1 cup TOTAL *POINTS*: 8
DINNER	Refried Bean and Mushroom Burritos, page 81, 1 serving fat-free strawberry yogurt, 8 ounces TOTAL *POINTS*: 8	Marinated Flank Steak with Lime Chipotle Glaze, page 87, 1 serving mashed potatoes, ½ cup sautéed zucchini, 1 cup TOTAL *POINTS*: 7	Pan-Seared Scallops with Cilantro, page 65, 1 serving angel hair pasta, 1 cup steamed snow peas, 1 cup TOTAL *POINTS*: 9
SNACK	prepared hummus, ¼ cup pita bread, ½ round carrot sticks, 1 cup TOTAL *POINTS*: 4	reduced-fat vanilla wafers, 6 fat-free milk, 1 cup TOTAL *POINTS*: 4	apple, 1 small lemon chiffon fat-free yogurt, 8 ounces TOTAL *POINTS*: 3
	POINTS for the day: 26 Exchanges: 7½ Starch, 3 Vegetable, 2 Fruit, 3 Very Lean Meat, 1½ Medium-Fat Meat, 2 Skim Milk, 2 Fat	*POINTS* for the day: 28 Exchanges: 8 Starch, 4 Vegetable, 3 Fruit, 5 Lean Meat, 2 Skim Milk	*POINTS* for the day: 27 Exchanges: 4 Starch, 4 Veg, 1 Fruit, 5 Very Lean Meat, 3 Medium-Fat Meat, 2 Skim Milk

One day's menu provides at least two servings of milk and at least five servings of fruits and/or vegetables.

	MONDAY	TUESDAY	WEDNESDAY	THURSDAY
BREAKFAST	**Mango Smoothie** (Combine 1 small frozen banana; ½ cup diced, peeled mango; ⅔ cup strawberry low-fat yogurt; and ½ cup orange juice in a blender. Process until smooth - 4 *POINTS*.) TOTAL *POINTS*: 4	**cooked oatmeal**, 1 cup with 1 teaspoon artificial sweetener **fresh cranberries**, 1 cup **fat-free milk**, 1 cup TOTAL *POINTS*: 5	**fat-free frozen waffles**, 2 **maple syrup**, 2 tablespoons **sliced apple**, 1 small **fat-free milk**, 1 cup TOTAL *POINTS*: 7	**Peanut Butter-Raisin Toast** (Spread 1 tablespoon peanut butter over 1 slice raisin bread - 3 *POINTS*.) **grapefruit**, ½ **fat-free milk**, 1 cup TOTAL *POINTS*: 6
LUNCH	**canned tomato soup**, 1 cup **saltine crackers**, 6 **green salad**, 2 cups **fat-free ranch dressing**, 2 tablespoons **fat-free milk**, 1 cup TOTAL *POINTS*: 7	**Turkey Barbecue Sandwich** (Cook ¼ lb. turkey and ¼ cup onion in a non-stick skillet over medium-high heat for 4-5 minutes. Stir in 2 ounces tomato sauce and 1 ounce red bell pepper. Simmer 5 minutes. Stir in BBQ sauce, salt, and pepper. Spoon turkey mixture onto bottom half of 2-ounce bun, then place top half - 7 *POINTS*.) **baked potato chips**, 1 ounce TOTAL *POINTS*: 9	**bean burrito**, fast food **carrot sticks**, 1 cup **orange**, 1 TOTAL *POINTS*: 10	**Veggie Pita Pocket** (Fill 1 pita half with ¼ cup *each of* tomatoes, cucumbers, bell peppers, and squash. Sprinkle 3 tablespoons grated Parmesan cheese in pocket and drizzle with 2 tablespoons fat-free Italian dressing - 4 *POINTS*.) **blueberry fat-free yogurt**, 8 ounces **baked chips**, 1 ounce TOTAL *POINTS*: 8
DINNER	**Blackened Catfish Fillets, page 58**, 1 serving **saffron rice**, 1 cup **steamed broccoli**, 1 cup TOTAL *POINTS*: 8	**Spicy Ginger Chicken, page 102**, 1 serving **couscous**, 1 cup **steamed asparagus**, 12 spears TOTAL *POINTS*: 8	**Smothered Sirloin Patties with Veggies and Horseradish Sour Cream, page 87**, 1 serving **baked potato**, 1 medium **steamed green beans**, 1 cup TOTAL *POINTS*: 7	**Pasta with Zucchini, Parsley, and Feta, page 79**, 1 serving **green salad**, 2 cups **fat-free Italian dressing**, 2 tablespoons **breadstick**, 1 TOTAL *POINTS*: 8
SNACK	**reduced-fat chocolate sandwich cookies**, 3 **fat-free milk**, 1 cup TOTAL *POINTS*: 5	**nonfat mixed berry yogurt**, 8 ounces **low-fat granola**, 2 tablespoons TOTAL *POINTS*: 3	**peach**, 1 small **fat-free milk**, 1 cup TOTAL *POINTS*: 3	**reduced-fat vanilla wafers**, 6 **fat-free milk**, 1 cup TOTAL *POINTS*: 4
	POINTS for the day: 24 **Exchanges:** 6 Starch, 3 Vegetable, 3 Fruit, 4 Lean Meat, 2½ Skim Milk, 1 Fat	**POINTS for the day: 25** **Exchanges:** 8 Starch, 4 Vegetable, 1 Fruit, 1 Lean Meat, 2 Skim Milk, 1 Fat	**POINTS for the day: 27** **Exchanges:** 7 Starch, 3 Vegetable, 3 Fruit, 5 Lean Meat, 2 Skim Milk, 1 Fat	**POINTS for the day: 26** **Exchanges:** 7 Starch, 4 Vegetable, 1 Fruit, 1 Medium-Fatat Meat, ½ High-Fat Meat, 3 Skim Milk, 2 Fat

	FRIDAY	SATURDAY	SUNDAY
BREAKFAST	**bran flakes,** 1½ cups **cranberries,** 1 cup **fat-free milk,** 1 cup **TOTAL** *POINTS*: 5	**Extra Cheesy Toast** (Place ½ cup shredded reduced-fat Cheddar cheese on 1 slice whole wheat bread. Broil until bubbly - 5 *POINTS*.) **fat-free milk,** 1 cup **apple,** 1 small **TOTAL** *POINTS*: 8	**Hearty Wheat and Oat Pancakes, page 20,** 1 serving **maple syrup,** 2 tablespoons **fat-free milk,** 1 cup **TOTAL** *POINTS*: 8
LUNCH	**Kalamata Cucumber Sandwich** (Cut off ends from 1 small cucumber and slice thinly. Combine ¼ cup [⅓ less-fat] cream cheese, 6 chopped and pitted kalamata olives, and 1 minced garlic clove. Spread evenly on 1 slice pumpernickel bread. Arrange 2 slices cucumber on olive spread. Top with other slice of bread - **7** *POINTS*.) **grapes,** 1 cup **TOTAL** *POINTS*: 8	**Spinach Stuffed Potato** (Split a medium baked potato and stuff with ½ cup fresh chopped spinach, ¼ cup shredded Cheddar cheese, and 1 tablespoon fat-free sour cream. Add a dash *each of* salt and pepper. Bake at 350° for 10 minutes - 4 *POINTS*.) **grapefruit,** ½ **TOTAL** *POINTS*: 5	**grilled chicken sandwich,** 1 fast food (without mayonnaise) **green salad,** 1 fast food **fat-free ranch dressing,** 2 tablespoons **apple,** 1 small **TOTAL** *POINTS*: 9
DINNER	**Shrimp-Andouille Creole, page 65,** 1 serving **low-fat deli coleslaw,** ½ cup **TOTAL** *POINTS*: 7	**Spiced Pork Chops with Pineapple Salsa, page 96,** 1 serving **black beans,** ½ cup **steamed broccoli,** 1 cup **TOTAL** *POINTS*: 8	**Black Bean, Spinach, and Cheese Quesadillas, page 81,** 1 serving **mixed fruit salad,** ¾ cup **TOTAL** *POINTS*: 6
SNACK	**key lime pie fat-free yogurt,** 8 ounces **pretzels,** 15 small **TOTAL** *POINTS*: 4	**reduced-fat vanilla wafers,** 6 **fat-free milk,** 1 cup **TOTAL** *POINTS*: 4	**peach fat-free yogurt,** 8 ounces **low-fat granola,** 2 tablespoons **TOTAL** *POINTS*: 3
	POINTS for the day: 24 **Exchanges:** 7 Starch, 3 Vegetable, 2 Fruit, 2 Lean Meat, 1 Medium-Fat Meat, 2 Skim Milk, 2 Fat	*POINTS* for the day: 25 **Exchanges:** 5 Starch, 4 Vegetable, 3 Fruit, 3 Lean Meat, 3 Medium-Fat Meat, 2 Skim Milk, ½ Fat	*POINTS* for the day: 26 **Exchanges:** 7 Starch, 4 Vegetable, 2 Fruit, 3 Lean Meat, 1 Medium-Fat Meat, 2 Skim Milk, 2 Fat

One day's menu provides at least two servings of milk and at least five servings of fruits and/or vegetables.

	MONDAY	TUESDAY	WEDNESDAY	THURSDAY
BREAKFAST	**English muffin,** 1 (2-ounce), split and toasted **light butter,** 2 teaspoons **vanilla fat-free yogurt,** 8 ounces **strawberries,** 1 cup TOTAL *POINTS*: 6	**Honey-Raisin Oatmeal** (Combine 1 cup cooked oatmeal with 2 tablespoons raisins and 1 tablespoon honey - 4 *POINTS*.) **fat-free milk,** 1 cup TOTAL *POINTS*: 8	**bagel,** 1 small **light cream cheese,** 2 tablespoons **blueberries,** 1 cup **fat-free milk,** 1 cup TOTAL *POINTS*: 6	**Banana-Peanut Butter Smoothie** (Combine 1 cup fat-free milk, 1 tablespoon peanut butter, and 1 peeled banana in a blender; process until smooth - 4 *POINTS*.) **whole wheat English muffin,** ½ muffin TOTAL *POINTS*: 5
LUNCH	**Tuna Sandwich** (Combine ½ cup drained water-packed tuna tuna in water; 4 teaspoons light mayonnaise; dried dill; dash of pepper. Stir well. Spread on 1 slice whole wheat bread; top with ½ cup fresh spinach leaves, 2 slices tomato, and another slice of bread - 6 *POINTS*.) **dill pickle spear,** 1 **celery sticks,** 1 cup **baked potato chips,** 1 ounce TOTAL *POINTS*: 8	**canned vegetable soup,** 1 cup **saltine crackers,** 6 **orange,** 1 **fat-free milk,** 1 cup TOTAL *POINTS*: 7	**thin-crust cheese pizza,** 1 fast food slice **apple,** 1 small **fat-free milk,** 1 cup TOTAL *POINTS*: 8	**Carrot-Raisin Salad** (Combine ¾ cup grated carrot, 2 tablespoons raisins, 2 tablespoons fat-free mayonnaise, and a dash *each of* salt and pepper - 2 *POINTS*.) **baked potato chips,** 1 ounce **fat-free milk,** 1 cup TOTAL *POINTS*: 6
DINNER	**Shrimp Fried Rice, page 67,** 1 serving **blueberries,** 1 cup **fat-free milk,** 1 cup TOTAL *POINTS*: 8	**Pork with Curried Fruit, page 97,** 1 serving **steamed green beans,** 1 cup TOTAL *POINTS*: 7	**Sicilian Chicken, page 106,** 1 serving **mixed salad greens,** 2 cups **fat-free Italian dressing,** 2 tablespoons TOTAL *POINTS*: 6	**Flounder Fillets with Béarnaise Sauce, page 58,** 1 serving **hot cooked wild rice,** 1 cup **sautéed spinach,** 1 cup **blueberries,** 1 cup TOTAL *POINTS*: 8
SNACK	**Tortilla Chips** (Cut 1 [8-inch] fat-free flour tortilla into 8 wedges. Coat wedges with cooking spray. Place on baking sheet; bake at 400° for 8 minutes - 1 *POINT*.) **prepared hummus,** ¼ cup TOTAL *POINTS*: 3	**popcorn (94%-fat-free microwave), popped,** 1 large bag **apple,** 1 small TOTAL *POINTS*: 3	**angel food cake,** 2 ounces **strawberries,** 1 cup **fat-free whipped topping,** 2 tablespoons TOTAL *POINTS*: 3	**Apple Pie Parfait** (Layer 8 ounces apple pie à la mode fat-free yogurt alternately with 4 gingersnaps crumbled in a parfait glass - 4 *POINTS*.) TOTAL *POINTS*: 4
	POINTS for the day: 25 **Exchanges:** 9 Starch, 4 Vegetable, 2 Fruit, 2 Very Lean Meat, 2 Lean Meat, 2 Skim Milk	*POINTS* for the day: 25 **Exchanges:** 8 Starch, 4 Vegetable, 3 Fruit, 3 Lean Meat, 2 Skim Milk, 1 Fat	*POINTS* for the day: 23 **Exchanges:** 8 Starch, 3 Vegetable, 3 Fruit, 3½ Very Lean Meat, 2 Medium-Fat Meat, 2 Skim Milk, 1 Fat	*POINTS* for the day: 24 **Exchanges:** 5 Starch, 3 Vegetable, 2 Fruit, 4 Very Lean Meat, ½ High-Fat Meat, 3 Skim Milk, 1½ Fat

FRIDAY	SATURDAY	SUNDAY	
Open-Faced Egg Sandwich (Scramble one egg in a small nonstick skillet over medium heat. Spoon egg onto 1 slice whole wheat bread. Top with 1 slice fat-free American cheese, tomato - 4 *POINTS*.) **fat-free milk**, 1 cup **peach**, 1 small **TOTAL** *POINTS*: 7	**Cinnamon-Raisin Sticky Buns, page 19,** 1 serving **fat-free milk,** 1 cup **blueberries,** 1 cup **TOTAL** *POINTS*: 6	**Peanut Butter Toast** (Spread 2 tablespoons peanut butter evenly over 2 slices whole wheat toast - 4 *POINTS*.) **peach,** 1 small **lemon chiffon fat-free yogurt,** 8 ounces **TOTAL** *POINTS*: 7	**BREAKFAST**
Hummus Veggie Wrap (Spread 2 tablespoons hummus over 1 [8-inch] flour tortilla; top with ¼ cup *each of* sliced red bell pepper, spinach leaves, zucchini, and yellow squash. Sprinkle with 3 tablespoons feta cheese. Roll up - 4 *POINTS*.) **seedless red grapes,** 1 cup **baked potato chips,** 1 ounce **TOTAL** *POINTS*: 7	**grilled chicken sandwich,** 1 fast food (without mayonnaise) **side salad,** 1 fast food **fat-free dressing,** 2 tablespoons **TOTAL** *POINTS*: 8	**Tuna Stuffed Tomato** (Combine 2 ounces drained water-packed tuna, 2 tablespoons chopped carrot, 2 teaspoons reduced-fat mayonnaise, 1 teaspoon Dijon mustard, and a dash of celery seeds. Stir well. Cut tomato into 4 wedges, cutting to, but not through, bottom of tomato; stuff with tuna salad - 3 *POINTS*.) **pretzels,** 15 sticks **fat-free milk,** 1 cup **TOTAL** *POINTS*: 7	**LUNCH**
Flank Steak with Tomato-Avocado Salsa, page 88, 1 serving **Garlic Mashed Potatoes** (Stir 2 teaspoons light butter and ¼ teaspoon garlic powder into ½ cup cooked mashed potatoes - 3 *POINTS*.) **steamed green beans,** 1 cup **TOTAL** *POINTS*: 9	**Potato and Yellow Squash Frittata, page 76,** 1 serving **strawberries,** 1 cup **fat-free milk,** 1 cup **TOTAL** *POINTS*: 8	**Maple-Barbecued Drumsticks, page 107,** 1 serving **wild rice,** ¾ cup **sauteed squash and zucchini,** 1 cup **TOTAL** *POINTS*: 8	**DINNER**
cherry-vanilla fat-free yogurt, 8 ounces **TOTAL** *POINTS*: 2	**angel food cake,** 2 ounces **fat-free whipped topping,** 2 tablespoons **TOTAL** *POINTS*: 2	**animal crackers,** 13 **fat-free milk,** 1 cup **TOTAL** *POINTS*: 4	**SNACK**
POINTS **for the day: 25** **Exchanges:** 4 Starch, 4 Vegetable, 2 Fruit, 1 Very Lean Meat, Lean Meat, 5 Medium-Fat Meat, 2 Skim Milk, 1 Fat	*POINTS* **for the day: 24** **Exchanges:** 7 Starch, 3 Vegetable, 2 Fruit, 3 Lean Meat, 3 Medium-Fat Meat, 2 Skim Milk, ½ Fat	*POINTS* **for the day: 26** **Exchanges:** 7 Starch, 4 Vegetable, 1 Fruit, 6 Very Lean Meat, 1 High-Fat Meat, 3 Skim Milk, 1 Fat	

171

One day's menu provides at least two servings of milk and at least five servings of fruits and/or vegetables.

	MONDAY	TUESDAY	WEDNESDAY	THURSDAY
BREAKFAST	**Fruit and Cheese** (⅓ cup 1% low-fat cottage cheese spooned into ½ cantaloupe - 2 *POINTS*.) **fat-free milk**, 1 cup TOTAL *POINTS*: 4	**bran flakes**, 1½ cups **strawberries**, 1 cup **fat-free milk**, 1 cup TOTAL *POINTS*: 5	**Cinnamon Toast** (Spread 1 teaspoon light butter over 1 slice whole wheat bread; sprinkle with 1 teaspoon cinnamon-sugar. Broil until toasted - 2 *POINTS*.) **banana**, 1 small **fat-free milk**, 1 cup TOTAL *POINTS*: 5	**Brown Sugar-Walnut Oatmeal** (Stir 1 teaspoon walnuts and 2 teaspoons brown sugar in 1 cup hot cooked oatmeal - 4 *POINTS*.) **fat-free milk**, 1 cup **orange juice**, 1 cup TOTAL *POINTS*: 8
LUNCH	**Ham and Egg Bagel Sandwich** (Cook ¼ cup fat-free egg substitute in a nonstick skillet coated with cooking spray until firm, stirring constantly. Spread 2 teaspoons reduced-fat mayonnaise over bottom half of 1 [2-ounce] bagel; top with egg, 1 ounce sliced lean ham, and other half of bagel - 6 *POINTS*.) **orange juice**, 1 cup TOTAL *POINTS*: 7	**hamburger**, 1 fast food **green salad**, 1 **fat-free ranch dressing,** 2 tablespoons **seedless red grapes**, 1 cup TOTAL *POINTS*: 8	**Quick Vegetable Pizza** (Spread ¼ cup low-fat tomato pasta sauce over top of 1 [6-inch] pita. Top with ¼ cup *each of* chopped tomato, mushrooms, and zucchini. Sprinkle with ¼ cup part-skim mozzarella cheese. Bake at 450° for 6 minutes or until golden brown - 4 *POINTS*.) **apple slices**, 1 cup **fat-free milk**, 1 cup TOTAL *POINTS*: 7	**Sloppy Joe** (Cook 4 ounces ground round, ¼ cup chopped onion, and 1 minced garlic clove over medium-high heat until beef is browned, stirring to crumble. Stir in ½ cup tomato sauce and ½ teaspoon chili powder; cook until thoroughly heated. Serve on a 2-ounce hamburger bun - 7 *POINTS*.) **steamed broccoli**, 1 cup TOTAL *POINTS*: 7
DINNER	**Citrus-Beef Stir-Fry with Carrots, page 93**, 1 serving **steamed rice**, ½ cup **steamed broccoli**, 1 cup **fat-free milk**, 1 cup TOTAL *POINTS*: 10	**Sweet Tequila-Lime Chicken, page 103**, 1 serving **black beans**, ½ cup **low-fat deli coleslaw**, ½ cup TOTAL *POINTS*: 8	**Honey-Glazed Salmon, page 61**, 1 serving **orzo**, 1 cup **roasted or steamed asparagus spears**, 1 cup TOTAL *POINTS*: 9	**Salsa Omelet with Roasted Peppers and Cheese, page 77**, 1 serving **mixed green salad**, 2 cups **fat-free ranch dressing,** 2 tablespoons **French bread roll**, 1 (2-ounce) TOTAL *POINTS*: 7
SNACK	**part-skim mozzarella string cheese**, 1 stick **apple**, 1 small TOTAL *POINTS*: 3	**fat-free peach yogurt**, 8 ounces **orange juice**, ½ cup TOTAL *POINTS*: 3	**banana**, 1 small **peanut butter**, 1 tablespoon TOTAL *POINTS*: 3	**fat-free cereal bar**, 1 **fat-free milk**, 1 cup TOTAL *POINTS*: 4
	POINTS for the day: 25 **Exchanges:** 4½ Starch, 2 Vegetable, 4 Fruit, 1 Very Lean Meat, 4 Lean Meat, 1 Medium-Fat Meat, 2 Skim Milk, 1 Fat	*POINTS* for the day: 24 **Exchanges:** 5½ Starch, 3 Vegetable, 3 Fruit, 5 Very Lean Meat, 2 Medium-Fat Meat, 2 Skim Milk, 1 Fat	*POINTS* for the day: 24 **Exchanges:** 6 Starch, 3 Vegetable, 3 Fruit, 5 Very Lean Meat, 1 Medium-Fat Meat, 1 High-Fat Meat, 1 Fat	*POINTS* for the day: 26 **Exchanges:** 7 Starch, 5 Vegetable, 2 Fruit, 5 Medium-Fat Meat, 2 Skim Milk

	FRIDAY	SATURDAY	SUNDAY
BREAKFAST	**Fruit and Cheese Bagel** (Spoon ⅓ cup 1% low-fat cottage cheese evenly over a split 2-ounce bagel. Top with ½ cup sliced strawberries; drizzle with 2 teaspoons honey - 5 *POINTS*.) **fat-free milk**, 1 cup **TOTAL *POINTS*: 7**	**Marmalade Swirl Biscuits, page 29**, 1 serving **strawberries**, 1 cup **fat-free milk**, 1 cup **TOTAL *POINTS*: 7**	**1% low-fat cottage cheese**, ⅓ cup **raisin bread**, 1 slice toasted **light butter**, 2 teaspoons **fat-free milk**, 1 cup **TOTAL *POINTS*: 5**
LUNCH	**Beef and Blue Sandwich** (Spread 2 teaspoons light mayonnaise and 1 teaspoon Dijon mustard over 2 slices whole wheat bread. Layer 2 ounces thinly sliced roast beef, 2 tomato slices, 2 lettuce leaves, and 3 tablespoons crumbled blue cheese between bread slices - 6 *POINTS*.) **seedless red grapes**, 1 cup **TOTAL *POINTS*: 7**	**Minted Couscous** (Gently stir 1 tablespoon fresh mint and 1 teaspoon light butter into 1 cup hot cooked couscous - 5 *POINTS*.) **steamed asparagus**, 1 cup **apple**, 1 small **baked ham**, 3 ounces **TOTAL *POINTS*: 9**	**Peanut Butter and Banana Sandwich** (Spread 2 tablespoons peanut butter over 1 slice whole wheat bread; top with 1 sliced banana and another slice of bread - 5 *POINTS*.) **carrot and celery sticks**, 1 cup **blueberry fat-free yogurt**, 8 ounces **TOTAL *POINTS*: 7**
DINNER	**Quick Pork with Sweet Bourbon Sauce, page 95**, 1 serving **couscous**, ½ cup **steamed carrots**, 1 cup **TOTAL *POINTS*: 8**	**Curried Sea Scallops, page 64**, 1 serving **hot cooked angel hair pasta**, ½ cup **steamed sugar snap peas**, 1 cup **TOTAL *POINTS*: 6**	**Barbecued Duck with Mango Salsa, page 108**, 1 serving **mashed potatoes**, ½ cup **low-fat deli coleslaw**, ½ cup **TOTAL *POINTS*: 9**
SNACK	**Strawberries and Cream** (Serve 1 cup fresh strawberries with ⅓ cup frozen reduced-calorie whipped topping, thawing, and 4 animal crackers - 2 *POINTS*.) **fat-free milk**, 1 cup **TOTAL *POINTS*: 4**	**French vanilla fat-free yogurt**, 8 ounces **TOTAL *POINTS*: 2**	**vanilla fat-free ice cream**, ½ cup **sliced strawberries**, ½ cup **TOTAL *POINTS*: 3**
	POINTS for the day: 26 **Exchanges:** 6 Starch, 3 Vegetable, 3 Fruit, 6 Very Lean Meat, 1 Medium-Fat Meat, 2 Skim Milk, 1 Fat	**POINTS for the day: 24** **Exchanges:** 6 Starch, 4 Vegetable, 2 Fruit, 3 Very Lean Meat, 3 Lean Meat, 2 Skim Milk, 1 Fat	**POINTS for the day: 24** **Exchanges:** 5 Starch, 2 Vegetable, 3 Fruit, 1 Very Lean Meat, 3 Lean Meat, 1 High-Fat Meat, 2 Skim Milk, 2 Fat

One day's menu provides at least two servings of milk and at least five servings of fruits and/or vegetables.

	MONDAY	TUESDAY	WEDNESDAY	THURSDAY
BREAKFAST	**Cinnamon-Raisin Bread** (Spread 1½ teaspoons light whipped butter on *each of* two slices raisin bread. Sprinkle with cinnamon-sugar. Place under broiler 1 to 2 minutes or until toasted - 5 *POINTS*.) **strawberries**, 1½ cups **fat-free milk**, 1 cup TOTAL *POINTS*: 8	**scrambled eggs**, 1 large egg and 3 large egg whites **reduced-fat bacon**, 2 slices **orange juice**, ½ cup TOTAL *POINTS*: 5	**cooked oatmeal**, 1 cup **raisins**, 2 tablespoons **brown sugar**, 1 tablespoon **fat-free milk**, 1 cup TOTAL *POINTS*: 6	**bran flakes**, 1½ cups **fat-free milk**, 1 cup **blueberries**, 1 cup TOTAL *POINTS*: 5
LUNCH	**Broccoli Salad** (Combine 1 cup small broccoli florets, ¼ cup shredded reduced-fat sharp Cheddar cheese, 2 tablespoons raisins, 2 teaspoons *each of* reduced-fat mayonnaise and fat-free sour cream, and ½ teaspoon Dijon mustard; toss well - 4 *POINTS*.) **banana**, 1 small TOTAL *POINTS*: 5	**Turkey and Swiss Bagel Sandwich** (Spread 1 tablespoon reduced-fat mayonnaise and 2 teaspoons Dijon mustard evenly over whole wheat bagel halves. Place 2 ounces thinly sliced smoked turkey, 1 [¾-ounce] slice Swiss cheese, 2 tomato slices, and 2 lettuce leaves on 1 bagel half; top with remaining bagel half - 8 *POINTS*.) **fat-free milk**, 1 cup TOTAL *POINTS*: 10	**low-fat lasagna with meat sauce**, 1 frozen entrée **tossed green salad**, 2 cups **fat-free Italian dressing**, 2 tablespoons **fat-free milk**, 1 cup TOTAL *POINTS*: 9	**Peanut Butter and Jelly Sandwich** (Spread 2 tablespoons *each of* peanut butter and jelly between 2 slices of reduced-calorie bread - 7 *POINTS*.) **apple**, 1 small **peach fat-free yogurt**, 8 ounces TOTAL *POINTS*: 8
DINNER	**Cuban Brisket, page 94**, 1 serving **saffron rice**, ½ cup **steamed green beans**, 1 cup TOTAL *POINTS*: 8	**Herbed Shrimp and Pasta with Feta, page 68**, 1 serving **sautéed spinach**, 1 cup TOTAL *POINTS*: 6	**Omelet with Zucchini and Onion, page 76**, 1 serving **French bread**, 2 ounces **fresh fruit salad**, 1 cup TOTAL *POINTS*: 6	**Cheese-Stuffed Italian Chicken, page 106**, 1 serving **risotto**, ½ cup **roasted asparagus**, 14 spears TOTAL *POINTS*: 7
SNACK	**reduced-fat vanilla wafers**, 6 **fat-free milk**, 1 cup TOTAL *POINTS*: 4	**Strawberry Smoothie** (Combine 1 cup sliced strawberries, ½ cup milk, and 8 ounces fat-free yogurt in a blender; process until smooth - 4 *POINTS*.) TOTAL *POINTS*: 4	**fat-free milk**, 1 cup **reduced-fat vanilla wafers**, 6 **peanut butter**, 1 tablespoon TOTAL *POINTS*: 6	**reduced-fat chocolate sandwich cookies**, 3 **apple**, 1 small TOTAL *POINTS*: 4
	POINTS for the day: 25 **Exchanges:** 6 Starch, 3 Vegetable, 2 Fruit, 3 Lean Meat, 1 Medium-Fat Meat, 2 Skim Milk, 1½ Fat	*POINTS* for the day: 25 **Exchanges:** 7 Starch, 3 Vegetable, 2 Fruit, 3 Very Lean Meat, 3 Lean Meat, 2 Medium-Fat Meat, 2½ Skim Milk, 2 Fat	*POINTS* for the day: 27 **Exchanges:** 8 Starch, 3 Vegetable, 2 Fruit, 2 Lean Meat, 1½ Medium-Fat Meat, 1 High-Fat Meat, 2 Skim Milk	*POINTS* for the day: 24 **Exchanges:** 8 Starch, 2 Vegetable, 3 Fruit, 4½ Very Lean Meat, 2 High-Fat Meat, 2 Skim Milk, 1 Fat

	FRIDAY	SATURDAY	SUNDAY
BREAKFAST	**whole wheat bagel,** 1 small **light cream cheese,** 2 tablespoons **orange juice,** 1 cup TOTAL *POINTS*: 7	**Waffles with Blueberry Syrup** (In a microwave-safe bowl, heat 2 tablespoons blueberry jelly or jam at HIGH until melted; stir in 1 tablespoon maple syrup. Add ½ cup blueberries. Pour over 2 heated fat-free frozen waffles - 6 *POINTS*.) **fat-free milk,** 1 cup TOTAL *POINTS*: 8	**whole wheat English muffin,** 1 (2 ounce), split and toasted **light butter,** 1 teaspoon **vanilla fat-free yogurt,** 1 cup **orange juice,** ½ cup TOTAL *POINTS*: 6
LUNCH	**Chicken Salad** (Combine ½ cup chopped cooked chicken, ¼ cup *each of* finely diced celery and onion, 3 tablespoons low-fat mayonnaise, and a dash *each of* salt and pepper. Chill until serving - 4 *POINTS*.) **fresh tomato slices,** 1 cup **saltine crackers,** 6 **fat-free milk,** 1 cup TOTAL *POINTS*: 8	**Veggie Pizza** (Spread ¼ cup prepared low-fat tomato sauce over a whole wheat bagel half. Top with ¼ cup sliced mushrooms, 2 tablespoons diced green or red bell peppers, and ¼ cup preshredded part-skim mozzarella cheese. Bake at 450° for 6 minutes or until cheese melts - 5 *POINTS*.) **celery sticks,** 1 cup **apple,** 1 small TOTAL *POINTS*: 6	**Bean Burrito** (Warm ½ cup canned fat-free refried beans; spread over 1 [8-inch] low-fat flour tortilla. Top with ¼ cup shredded lettuce, ¼ cup chopped tomato, ¼ cup reduced fat Cheddar cheese, and 1 tablespoon fat-free sour cream; roll up - 6 *POINTS*.) **salsa,** ½ cup **mango chunks,** 1 cup TOTAL *POINTS*: 7
DINNER	**Gemelli with White Beans and Artichokes, page 79,** 1 serving **spinach salad,** 2 cups **fat-free Italian dressing,** 2 tablespoons TOTAL *POINTS*: 8	**Baked Snapper with Tomato-Orange Sauce, page 61,** 1 serving **white rice,** ½ cup **steamed broccoli,** 1 cup TOTAL *POINTS*: 7	**Sausage and Rice Casserole, page 99,** 1 serving **low-fat deli coleslaw,** 1 cup **fat-free milk,** 1 cup TOTAL *POINTS*: 8
SNACK	**Cinnamon Apples with Raisins** (Sprinkle 1 sliced apple and 2 tablespoons raisins with ½ teaspoon cinnamon-sugar. Broil 2-3 minutes - 2 *POINTS*.) **fat-free milk,** 1 cup TOTAL *POINTS*: 4	**reduced-fat chocolate sandwich cookies,** 3 **fat-free milk,** 1 cup TOTAL *POINTS*: 5	**Cookies and Cream** (Let ¾ cup vanilla low-fat ice cream soften at room temperature. Crumble 2 reduced-fat chocolate sandwich cookies, and sprinkle on softened ice cream - 5 *POINTS*.) TOTAL *POINTS*: 5
	POINTS for the day: 27 **Exchanges:** 6 Starch, 3 Vegetable, 3 Fruit, 2 Very Lean Meat, 2 Medium-Fat Meat, 2 Skim Milk, 2 Fat	*POINTS* for the day: 26 **Exchanges:** 10 Starch, 4 Vegetable, 1½ Fruit, 5 Very Lean Meat, 1 Medium-Fat Meat, 2 Skim Milk, 1 Fat	*POINTS* for the day: 26 **Exchanges:** 9 Starch, 3 Vegetable, 2 Fruit, 2 Very Lean Meat, 1 Medium-Fat Meat, 2 Skim Milk, 2 Fat

One day's menu provides at least two servings of milk and at least five servings of fruits and/or vegetables.

	MONDAY	TUESDAY	WEDNESDAY	THURSDAY
BREAKFAST	**cooked grits,** 1 cup **lean Canadian bacon,** 1 slice **apple juice,** 1 cup TOTAL *POINTS*: 5	**fruit-filled cereal bar,** 1 **fat-free milk,** 1 cup **honeydew melon,** 1 cup TOTAL *POINTS*: 5	**low-fat pancakes,** 2 (4-inch) **strawberries,** ½ cup sliced **low-calorie syrup,** 2 tablespoons **fat-free milk,** 1 cup TOTAL *POINTS*: 6	**Bacon, Mushroom and Cheese Omelet** (Combine 1 egg, 1 egg white, 2 tablespoons water, and a dash *each of* salt and pepper; pour into a small nonstick skillet and cook over medium heat 1 minute or until almost set. Top with ¼ cup diced lean Canadian bacon, ¼ cup sliced mushrooms, and ¼ cup shredded reduced-fat Cheddar cheese; fold in half - 5 *POINTS*.) TOTAL *POINTS*: 6
LUNCH	**Mexican Pizza** (Top 1 [8-inch] flour tortilla with ¼ cup *each of* fat-free refried beans, chopped tomato, and shredded reduced-fat sharp Cheddar cheese. Broil 2 minutes or until cheese melts. Top with ½ cup shredded lettuce, 2 tablespoons salsa, and 1 tablespoon *each of* chopped fresh cilantro, sliced ripe olives, and fat-free sour cream - 6 *POINTS*.) **fat-free milk,** 1 cup TOTAL *POINTS*: 8	**Chicken Ceasar Salad** (Combine 2 cups sliced romaine lettuce; 1 chopped plum tomato; 2 ounces thinly sliced roasted chicken breast, and 2 tablespoons fat-free Caesar dressing; toss well. Sprinkle with 3 tablespoons shredded part-skim mozzarella cheese - 5 *POINTS*.) **crème caramel fat-free yogurt,** 8 ounces TOTAL *POINTS*: 7	**Peanut Butter-Banana Pita Pocket** (Split 1 small pita in half. Save 1 half for future use. Spread 1 tablespoon peanut butter in remaining half; stuff with 1 sliced banana, and drizzle with 1 teaspoon honey - 5 *POINTS*.) **fat-free milk,** 1 cup **honeydew melon,** 1 cup TOTAL *POINTS*: 8	**Turkey-Spinach Roll Up** (Spread 2 teaspoons light mayonnaise over 1 [8-inch] low-fat tortilla; layer 2 ounces shaved deli turkey breast, ½ cup fresh spinach leaves, ¼ cup diced tomato, and 3 tablespoons crumbled blue cheese. Roll up tightly - 6 *POINTS*.) **peach,** 1 medium **fat-free milk,** 1 cup TOTAL *POINTS*: 8
DINNER	**Mussels in Piquant Broth, page 63,** 1 serving **French bread,** 2 ounces **green salad,** 2 cups **low-fat ranch dressing,** 2 tablespoons TOTAL *POINTS*: 8	**Seared Rosemary Beef Tenderloin, page 93,** 1 serving **roasted potato wedges,** 1 cup **steamed asparagus,** 14 spears TOTAL *POINTS*: 8	**Roasted Chicken and Corn Risotto, page 101,** 1 serving **fresh fruit salad,** 1 cup TOTAL *POINTS*: 8	**Pork Chops with Sweet Potatoes and Apples, page 96,** 1 serving **steamed carrots,** 1 cup **fat-free milk,** 1 cup TOTAL *POINTS*: 9
SNACK	**Tropical Smoothie** (Combine 1 cup fat-free milk, ¾ cup cubed peeled ripe mango, and 1 peeled banana; process until smooth - 4 *POINTS*.) TOTAL *POINTS*: 4	**vanilla reduced-fat ice cream,** ½ cup **banana,** 1 small TOTAL *POINTS*: 3	**whole wheat English muffin,** 1, split and toasted **honey,** 1 tablespoon **apple juice,** ½ cup TOTAL *POINTS*: 4	**Strawberry Shortcake** (Top 1 [1-ounce] slice angel food cake with ¾ cup sliced strawberries and ¼ cup lite whipped topping - 3 *POINTS*.) TOTAL *POINTS*: 3
	POINTS for the day: 25 **Exchanges:** 7 Starch, 3 Vegetable, 4 Fruit, 3 Lean Meat, 1 Medium-Fat Meat, 2 Skim Milk, 1 Fat	**POINTS for the day: 23** **Exchanges:** 6 Starch, 4 Vegetable, 2 Fruit, 2 Very Lean Meat, 3 Lean Meat, 1 Medium-Fat Meat, 2 Skim Milk	**POINTS for the day: 26** **Exchanges:** 10 Starch, 1 Vegetable, 4 Fruit, 4 Lean Meat, 1 High-Fat Meat, 2 Skim Milk	**POINTS for the day: 26** **Exchanges:** 4 Starch, 3 Veg, 2 Fruit, 3 Very Lean Meat, 4½ Lean Meat, 3 Medium-Fat Meat, 2 Skim Milk, 1 Fat

	FRIDAY	SATURDAY	SUNDAY
BREAKFAST	**Honeydew-Banana Smoothie** (Combine 1 banana and 1 cup chopped fresh honeydew melon, 8 ounces vanilla fat-free aspartame-sweetened yogurt, and ¼ cup fat-free milk in a blender; process until smooth - 4 *POINTS*.) **TOTAL** *POINTS*: 4	**low-fat granola,** ½ cup **fat-free milk,** 1 cup **apple,** 1 small **TOTAL** *POINTS*: 6	**Cheese Toast** (Sprinkle ¼ cup shredded reduced-fat sharp Cheddar cheese over 1 slice high-fiber whole wheat bread; broil until cheese melts - 3 *POINTS*.) **fat-free milk,** 1 cup **strawberries,** 1½ cups **TOTAL** *POINTS*: 5
LUNCH	**Veggie Burger** (Heat veggie burger according to package directions. Spread 2 teaspoons *each of* fat-free mayonnaise, ketchup, and mustard on 1 cut side of hamburger bun. Layer with patty, 2 lettuce leaves, and 2 tomato slices. Top with remaining piece of bun - 5 *POINTS*.) **cantaloupe chunks,** 1 cup **fat-free milk,** 1 cup **TOTAL** *POINTS*: 8	**canned tomato soup,** 1½ cups **Spinach Salad** (Combine 1 cup torn fresh spinach, ½ cup red bell pepper strips, ¼ cup shredded carrot, and 2 tablespoons fat-free Catalina dressing; toss well - 1 *POINT*.) **saltine crackers,** 6 **TOTAL** *POINTS*: 6	**Hummus-Veggie Pita** (Spread ¼ cup prepared hummus on 1 [8-inch] low-fat flour tortilla; top with ⅓ cup *each of* sliced red bell pepper, zucchini, and yellow squash. Sprinkle with 3 table-spoons crumbled feta cheese - 6 *POINTS*.) **cantaloupe chunks,** 1 cup **blueberry fat-free yogurt,** 8 ounces **TOTAL** *POINTS*: 9
DINNER	**Pizza with Tomatoes, Asparagus, and Basil, page 75,** 1 serving **spinach salad,** 2 cups **low-fat ranch dressing,** 2 tablespoons **TOTAL** *POINTS*: 9	**Grilled Tuna with Herbed Mayonnaise, page 62,** 1 serving **wild rice,** ½ cup **steamed broccoli,** 1 cup **TOTAL** *POINTS*: 8	**Pan-Fried Cornmeal Chicken with Corn and Onions, page 105,** 1 serving **mashed potatoes,** ½ cup **steamed green beans,** 1 cup **TOTAL** *POINTS*: 7
SNACK	**Pita Chips** (Cut 1 [8-inch] low-fat pita into 8 wedges. Coat wedges with cooking spray. Place on a baking sheet and bake at 400° for 6 to 8 minutes or until toasted - 2 *POINTS*.) **prepared hummus,** ¼ cup **TOTAL** *POINTS*: 4	**Peach Crisp** (Place 1 cup sliced peaches in a 10-ounce custard cup coated with cooking spray. Combine 2 teaspoons *each of* regular oats, all-purpose flour, brown sugar, and light butter; crumble over peaches. Bake at 350° for 5 minutes - 4 *POINTS*.) **TOTAL** *POINTS*: 4	**Frozen Vanilla Parfait** (Layer ½ cup vanilla reduced-fat ice cream and 3 tablespoons graham cracker crumbs in a parfait glass - 4 *POINTS*.) **TOTAL** *POINTS*: 4
	POINTS **for the day: 25** **Exchanges:** 7 Starch, 4 Vegetable, 3 Fruit, 2 Very Lean Meat, 2½ Medium-Fat Meat, 2 Skim Milk, 1 Fat	*POINTS* **for the day: 24** **Exchanges:** 6 Starch, 5 Vegetable, 3 Fruit, 5 Lean Meat, 1 Fat	*POINTS* **for the day: 26** **Exchanges:** 7 Starch, 3 Vegetable, 2 Fruit, 4 Very Lean Meat, 3 Medium-Fat Meat, 2 Skim Milk, ½ Fat

One day's menu provides at least two servings of milk and at least five servings of fruits and/or vegetables.

	MONDAY	TUESDAY	WEDNESDAY	THURSDAY
BREAKFAST	**Egg-Sausage Burrito** (Combine 1 egg, 1 egg white, and 1 tablespoon fat-free milk; cook 30 seconds in a nonstick skillet. Stir in 1 cooked, crumble meatless breakfast patty; cook until set. Spoon onto an 8-inch low-fat flour tortilla; roll up - 5 *POINTS*.) **orange juice,** 1 cup **keylime pie fat-free yogurt,** 8 ounces **TOTAL** *POINTS*: 8	**cooked oatmeal,** 1 cup **fat-free milk,** 1 cup **chopped walnuts,** 1 tablespoon **brown sugar,** 1 tablespoon **TOTAL** *POINTS*: 6	**whole wheat bagel,** 1 small, split and toasted **peanut butter,** 1 tablespoon **fat-free milk,** 1 cup **orange juice,** 1 cup **TOTAL** *POINTS*: 7	**Breakfast Sandwich** (Combine 1 egg, 1 egg white, and 1 tablespoon water; cook 30 seconds in a nonstick skillet. Stir in 1 cooked, crumbled meatless breakfast patty; cook until set. Spoon over bottom half of 1 [2-ounce] whole wheat bagel; top with remaining bagel half - 5 *POINTS*.) **fat-free milk,** 1 cup **TOTAL** *POINTS*: 7
LUNCH	**Quick Jambalaya** (Place a skillet over medium-high heat. Add 1 ounce sliced turkey kielbasa, ½ cup *each of* chopped onion and green bell pepper, and 1 minced garlic clove. Stir in 1 cup cooked rice, ¾ cup undrained canned diced tomatoes, ½ teaspoon Cajun seasoning, and a dash of hot sauce; cook 5 minutes - 5 *POINTS*.) **apple,** 1 small **TOTAL** *POINTS*: 6	**Roast Beef Sandwich** (Spread 2 teaspoons horseradish mustard over bottom half of 1 [2-ounce] hamburger bun. Fill with 2 ounces shaved deli roast beef, 2 tomato slices, 4 cucumber slices, and ¼ cup alfalfa sprouts - 4 *POINTS*.) **red grapes,** 1 cup **baked chips,** 1 ounce **TOTAL** *POINTS*: 7	**Bow-Tie Pasta Pepper Toss** (Combine 1 cup cooked bow-tie pasta, ½ cup *each of* drained canned chick-peas [garbanzo beans], chopped red bell pepper, chopped green bell pepper, ¼ cup chopped tomato, 3 tablespoons crumbled feta cheese, and 2 tablespoons fat-free balsamic vinaigrette; toss to coat - 7 *POINTS*.) **papaya chunks,** 1 cup **TOTAL** *POINTS*: 8	**White Bean-and-Tomato Salad** (Combine 1 cup navy or white beans with ½ cup chopped tomato. Add 2 tablespoons each of light balsamic vinaigrette and crumbled feta cheese; mix well. Sprinkle with pepper; serve over lettuce - 6 *POINTS*.) **pretzels,** 15 small **peach fat-free yogurt,** 8 ounces **TOTAL** *POINTS*: 10
DINNER	**Sirloin Steak with Sherry-Soy Sauce, page 93,** 1 serving **baked potato,** 1 medium **fat-free sour cream,** 2 tablespoons **steamed green beans,** 1 cup **TOTAL** *POINTS*: 7	**Indian Curried Shrimp, page 67,** 1 serving **steamed broccoli,** 1 cup **TOTAL** *POINTS*: 6	**Marinated Greek Kebabs, page 102,** 1 serving **couscous,** ½ cup **fresh tomato slices,** 1 cup **fat-free Italian dressing,** 2 tablespoons **TOTAL** *POINTS*: 7	**Pork Marsala, page 97,** 1 serving **egg noodles,** ½ cup **steamed squash,** 1 cup **TOTAL** *POINTS*: 6
SNACK	**fat-free cereal bar,** 1 **fat-free milk,** 1 cup **TOTAL** *POINTS*: 4	**Yogurt Crunch** (Stir 3 tablespoons low-fat granola into 1 [8-ounce] container vanilla fat-free yogurt - 3 *POINTS*.) **orange juice,** 1 cup **TOTAL** *POINTS*: 5	**graham crackers,** 4 (2.5-inch) squares **fat-free milk,** 1 cup **TOTAL** *POINTS*: 4	**orange juice,** 1 cup **fat-free cereal bar,** 1 **TOTAL** *POINTS*: 4
	POINTS for the day: 25 **Exchanges:** 7 Starch, 4 Vegetable, 3 Fruit, 1 Very Lean Meat, 4½ Lean Meat, 1 Medium-Fat Meat, 2 Skim Milk	*POINTS* for the day: 24 **Exchanges:** 10 Starch, 3 Vegetable, 3 Fruit, 2 Very Lean Meat, 3 Lean Meat, 2 Skim Milk, 2 Fat	*POINTS* for the day: 26 **Exchanges:** 9 Starch, 4 Vegetable, 1 Fruit, 4 Very Lean Meat, 1 Medium-Fat Meat, 1 High-Fat Meat, 2 Skim Milk	*POINTS* for the day: 27 **Exchanges:** 8 Starch, 3 Vegetable, 2 Fruit, 3 Very Lean Meat, 3 Lean Meat, 2 Medium-Fat Meat, 2 Skim Milk, 1 Fat

FRIDAY	SATURDAY	SUNDAY	
Garlic-Cheese Grits (Stir ¼ cup shredded reduced-fat Cheddar cheese and ¼ teaspoon garlic salt into 1 cup hot cooked grits; stir until smooth - 4 *POINTS*.) **orange juice,** ½ cup TOTAL *POINTS*: 5	**French Toast** (Combine 3 tablespoons fat-free milk, 2 large egg whites, and a dash *each of* salt, cinnamon, and vanilla; stir well. Dip 2 slices high-fiber bread in mixture. Melt 1 tablespoon light whipped butter in a nonstick skillet over medium heat; add bread. Cook 7 minutes, turning after 3 minutes. Serve with 2 tablespoons maple syrup - 6 *POINTS*.) **fat-free milk,** 1 cup TOTAL *POINTS*: 8	**whole wheat bagel,** 1 small, split and toasted **light cream cheese,** 1 tablespoon **blueberries,** 1 cup TOTAL *POINTS*: 4	**BREAKFAST**
Ham-Swiss Sandwich (Spread 2 teaspoons *each of* fat-free mayonnaise and Dijon mustard over 2 slices high-fiber bread. Place 2 ounces thinly sliced smoked deli ham, 1 ounce Swiss cheese, 2 lettuce leaves, and 2 tomato slices on 1 bread slice; top with remaining slice - 5 *POINTS*.) **blueberry fat-free yogurt,** 8 ounces **red grapes,** 1 cup TOTAL *POINTS*: 8	**Tuna Salad in Tomato** (Combine 4 ounces drained canned tuna in water with 1 tablespoon chopped celery, 2 teaspoons light mayonnaise, and 1 teaspoon Dijon mustard; stir well. Spoon into a tomato - 4 *POINTS*.) **saltine crackers,** 6 **orange juice,** 1 cup TOTAL *POINTS*: 8	**French Onion Soup** (Heat 1 teaspoon olive oil in a small saucepan over medium heat. Add ¾ cup thinly sliced onion; sauté 15 minutes. Add 1 cup beef broth; bring to a boil. Reduce heat, and simmer 15 minutes. Spoon into a bowl; top with 1 [1-ounce] slice French bread, and sprinkle with ¾ ounce shredded Swiss cheese and freshly ground black pepper - 4 *POINTS*.) **apple,** 1 small **fat-free milk,** 1 cup TOTAL *POINTS*: 7	**LUNCH**
Broiled Salmon with Citrus Salsa, page 60, 1 serving **couscous,** ½ cup **roasted asparagus,** 14 spears TOTAL *POINTS*: 8	**Vegetarian Chili Dogs, page 83,** 1 serving **baked chips,** 1 ounce **celery sticks,** 1 cup TOTAL *POINTS*: 8	**Chicken and Sausage Ragoût, page 102,** 1 serving **salad greens,** 2 cups **fat-free Italian dressing,** 2 tablespoons TOTAL *POINTS*: 6	**DINNER**
graham crackers, 4 (2½-inch) squares **peanut butter,** 1 tablespoon **fat-free milk,** 1 cup TOTAL *POINTS*: 6	**Papaya Smoothie** (Combine ¾ cup chopped papaya, ¼ cup *each of* chopped fresh pineapple and fat-free milk, and 8 ounces vanilla fat-free yogurt in a blender; process until smooth - 4 *POINTS*.) TOTAL *POINTS*: 4	**Sugared Pineapple** (Sprinkle 1 tablespoon brown sugar over 2 pineapple slices; broil. Top with ½ cup vanilla fat-free ice cream - 4 *POINTS*.) **fat-free milk,** 1 cup TOTAL *POINTS*: 6	**SNACK**
POINTS for the day: 27 **Exchanges:** 8 Starch, 3 Vegetable, 2 Fruit, 7 Very Lean Meat, 2 Medium-Fat Meat, 1 High-Fat Meat, 2 Skim Milk	*POINTS* for the day: 28 **Exchanges:** 9 Starch, 2 Vegetable, 4 Fruit, 4 Very Lean Meat, 2 Lean Meat, 2 Skim Milk, 2 Fat	*POINTS* for the day: 23 **Exchanges:** 8 Starch, 5 Vegetable, 3 Fruit, 4 Very Lean Meat, 2 Medium-Fat Meat, 2 Skim Milk, 1 Fat	

One day's menu provides at least two servings of milk and at least five servings of fruits and/or vegetables.

	MONDAY	TUESDAY	WEDNESDAY	THURSDAY
BREAKFAST	**poached egg,** 1 large **high-fiber toast,** 1 slice **light whipped butter,** 1 tablespoon **orange juice,** ½ cup **TOTAL** *POINTS:* 5	**Banana-Nut Pancakes** (Top 2 [4-inch] pancakes with ½ cup sliced banana and 1 tablespoon *each of* toasted walnuts and maple syrup - 6 ***POINTS***.) **fat-free milk,** 1 cup **TOTAL** *POINTS:* 8	**low-fat granola,** ½ cup **fat-free milk,** 1 cup **kiwifruit,** 1 **TOTAL** *POINTS:* 6	**high-fiber toast,** 2 slices **grape jelly,** 2 tablespoons **fat-free milk,** 1 cup **watermelon chunks,** 1 cup **TOTAL** *POINTS:* 7
LUNCH	**hamburger,** 1 small fast food **side salad,** 1 fast food **fat-free Italian dressing,** 2 tablespooons **fat-free milk,** 1 cup **TOTAL** *POINTS:* 9	**Broccoli-and-Cheese-Stuffed Potato** (Split a large baked potato, and stuff with ¾ cup steamed broccoli florets, ¼ cup shredded reduced-fat sharp Cheddar cheese, and 1 tablespoon *each of* fat-free sour cream and chopped green onions - 5 ***POINTS***.) **orange sections,** 1 cup **TOTAL** *POINTS:* 6	**Grilled Chicken Salad** (Top 2 cups sliced romaine lettuce with 3 ounces thinly sliced grilled chicken breast, 2 tomato slices, ¼ cup *each of* fat-free croutons, shredded carrot, and sliced cucumber, and 3 large ripe olives. Serve with 2 tablespoons low-fat ranch dressing - 6 ***POINTS***.) **watermelon chunks,** 1 cup **fat-free milk,** 1 cup **TOTAL** *POINTS:* 9	**Philly Swiss Melt** (Place a nonstick skillet coated with cooking spray over medium heat; sauté ½ cup *each of* sliced onion and red bell pepper 4 minutes. Spread 2 teaspoons reduced-fat mayonnaise over cut sides of 2 [1-ounce] slices French bread. Layer 2 ounces thinly sliced lean deli-style roast beef, sautéed vegetables, and 1 [¾-ounce] slice Swiss cheese on 1 slice bread. Broil until cheese melts. Top with remaining bread slice - 7 ***POINTS***.) **carrot sticks,** 1 cup **TOTAL** *POINTS:* 8
DINNER	**Pork with Dried Plums and Onions, page 95,** 1 serving **couscous,** ½ cup **steamed green beans,** 1 cup **TOTAL** *POINTS:* 8	**Tamale Pie, page 82,** 1 serving **low-fat deli coleslaw,** ½ cup **carrot sticks,** 1 cup **TOTAL** *POINTS:* 8	**Louisiana Deviled Crab Cakes with Hot Peppered Sour Cream, page 63,** 1 serving **green salad,** 2 cups **fat-free Italian dressing,** 2 tablespoons **TOTAL** *POINTS:* 7	**Fresh Salsa Chicken, page 103,** 1 serving **risotto,** ½ cup **sautéed zucchini,** 1 cup **TOTAL** *POINTS:* 5
SNACK	**high-fiber toast,** 1 slice **peanut butter,** 1 tablespoon **fat-free milk,** 1 cup **TOTAL** *POINTS:* 5	**Berry-Yogurt Parfait** (Place ½ cup blueberries in bottom of a tall glass; top with half of an 8-ounce carton of raspberry fat-free yogurt. Add another ½ cup blueberries and remaining yogurt. Sprinkle with 2 tablespoons low-fat granola - 4 ***POINTS***.) **TOTAL** *POINTS:* 4	**vanilla low-fat ice cream,** ¾ cup **TOTAL** *POINTS:* 3	**low-fat granola,** ½ cup **fat-free milk,** 1 cup **TOTAL** *POINTS:* 5
	POINTS **for the day: 27** **Exchanges:** 5 Starch, 4 Vegetable, 4 Fruit, 3½ Lean Meat, 3 Medium-Fat Meat, 1 High-Fat Meat, 2 Skim Milk, 1 Fat	*POINTS* **for the day: 26** **Exchanges:** 9 Starch, 4 Vegetable, 3 Fruit, 2 Medium-Fat Meat, 2 Skim Milk, 2 Fat	*POINTS* **for the day: 26** **Exchanges:** 7 Starch, 4 Vegetable, 1 Fruit, 6 Very Lean Meat, 2 Skim Milk, 4 Fat	*POINTS* **for the day: 25** **Exchanges:** 8 Starch, 4 Vegetable, 1 Fruit, 6 Very Lean Meat, 1 Medium-Fat Meat, 2 Skim Milk, 2 Fat

	FRIDAY	SATURDAY	SUNDAY
BREAKFAST	**Waffles with Apple Syrup** (Melt 1 teaspoon light butter in a nonstick skillet. Add ½ cup chopped apple; sauté 3 minutes. Stir in 2 tablespoons maple syrup and a dash of cinnamon. Spoon over 2 warmed fat-free frozen waffles - 6 *POINTS*.) **fat-free milk,** 1 cup TOTAL *POINTS*: 8	**scrambled eggs,** 1 egg and 3 egg whites **high-fiber toast,** 1 slice **fat-free milk,** 1 cup TOTAL *POINTS*: 7	**Cheese Bagel** (Sprinkle 2 tablespoons shredded reduced-fat sharp Cheddar cheese over cut sides of a split whole wheat bagel; broil until cheese melts - 5 *POINTS*.) **orange juice,** 1 cup **strawberry fat-free yogurt,** 8 ounces TOTAL *POINTS*: 9
LUNCH	**canned vegetable soup,** 1 cup **saltine crackers,** 6 **kiwifruit,** 1 TOTAL *POINTS*: 5	**Beef and Bean Tortilla** (Cook 3 ounces ground round and ¼ cup chopped onion in a nonstick skillet until browned, stirring to crumble. Stir in ¼ cup fat-free refried beans and 3 tablespoons *each of* salsa and shredded reduced-fat sharp Cheddar cheese. Spoon over 1 [8-inch] low-fat flour tortilla. Serve with ¼ cup salsa and 1 tablespoon fat-free sour cream - 7 *POINTS*.) **watermelon chunks,** 1 cup TOTAL *POINTS*: 8	**Greek Pasta Salad** (Combine ½ cup *each of* cannellini beans and chopped tomato; add ½ cup *each of* shredded romaine lettuce and cooked penne pasta and 2 tablespoons light olive oil vinaigrette. Top with 1 tablespoon grated Parmesan cheese - 4 *POINTS*.) **fat-free milk,** 1 cup TOTAL *POINTS*: 6
DINNER	**Grilled Pork Tenderloin with Black Bean Salad, page 98,** 1 serving **saffron rice,** ½ cup **low-fat deli coleslaw,** ½ cup TOTAL *POINTS*: 9	**Greek Pasta with Shrimp and Artichokes, page 68,** 1 serving **spinach salad,** 2 cups **low-fat ranch dressing,** 2 tablespoons TOTAL *POINTS*: 7	**Hoisin Chicken, page 104,** 1 serving **rice,** 1 cup **steamed sugar snap peas,** 1 cup TOTAL *POINTS*: 7
SNACK	**raspberry fat-free yogurt,** 8 ounces **orange sections,** 1 cup TOTAL *POINTS*: 3	**Blueberry-Peach Parfait** (In a tall glass, layer ½ cup *each of* peach fat-free yogurt, blueberries, and ¼ cup low-fat granola. Repeat layers once - 6 *POINTS*.) TOTAL *POINTS*: 6	**low-fat ice cream,** ¾ cup TOTAL *POINTS*: 3
	POINTS for the day: 25 **Exchanges:** 8 Starch, 3 Vegetable, 3 Fruit, 4 Lean Meat, 2 Skim Milk, 2 Fat	**POINTS for the day: 28** **Exchanges:** 6 Starch, 3 Vegetable, 2 Fruit, 6 Very Lean Meat, 2 Medium-Fat Meat, 2 Skim Milk, 1 Fat	**POINTS for the day: 27** **Exchanges:** 8 Starch, 3 Vegetable, 2 Fruit, 4 Very Lean Meat, 1 Medium-Fat Meat, 2 Skim Milk, 1 Fat

General Recipe Index

POINTS Recipe Index

All recipes are listed under the **POINTS** value for the recipe.

VEGETABLE COOKING CHART

Vegetable	Servings	Preparations	Cooking Instructions
Asparagus	3 to 4 per pound	Snap off tough ends. Remove scales, if desired.	To steam: Cook, covered, on a rack above boiling water 8 to 12 minutes. To boil: Cook, covered, in a small amount of boiling water 6 to 8 minutes or until crisp-tender.
Broccoli	3 to 4 per pound	Remove outer leaves and tough ends of lower stalks. Wash; cut into spears.	To steam: Cook, covered, on a rack above boiling water 15 to 18 minutes.
Carrots	4 per pound	Scrape; remove ends, and rinse. Leave tiny carrots whole; slice large carrots, or cut into strips.	Cook, covered, in a small amount of boiling water 8 to 10 minutes (slices) or 12 to 15 minutes (strips).
Cauliflower	4 per medium head	Remove outer leaves and stalk. Wash. Leave whole, or break into florets.	Cook, covered, in a small amount of boiling water 10 to 12 minutes (whole) or 8 to 10 minutes (florets).
Corn	4 per 4 large ears	Remove husks and silks. Leave corn on the cob, or cut off tips of kernels, and scrape cob with dull edge of knife.	Cook, covered, in boiling water to cover 10 minutes (on cob) or in a small amount of boiling water 8 to 10 minutes (cut).
Green beans	4 per pound	Wash; trim ends, and remove strings. Cut into 1½-inch pieces.	Cook, covered, in a small amount of boiling water 12 to 15 minutes.
Potatoes	3 to 4 per pound	Scrub; peel, if desired. Leave whole, slice, or cut into chunks.	To cook: Cook, covered, in a small amount of boiling water 30 to 40 minutes (whole) or 15 to 20 minutes (slices or chunks). To bake: Bake at 400° for 1 hour or until done.
Snow peas	4 per pound	Wash; trim ends, and remove tough strings.	Cook, covered, in a small amount of boiling water 3 to 5 minutes. Or cook over high heat in reduced-calorie margarine or in pan coated with cooking spray 3 to 5 minutes, stirring constantly.
Squash, summer	3 to 4 per pound	Wash; trim ends. Leave whole, slice, or chop.	To steam: Cook, covered, on a rack over boiling water 10 to 12 minutes (sliced or chopped). To boil: Cook, covered, in a small amount of boiling water 8 to 10 minutes (slices) or 15 minutes (whole).
Squash, winter (including acorn, butternut, hubbard, and spaghetti)	2 per pound	Rinse; cut in half, and remove all seeds.	To boil: Cook, covered, in boiling water 20 to 25 minutes. To bake: Place cut side down in shallow baking dish; add ½ inch water. Bake, uncovered, at 375° for 30 minutes. Turn and season, or fill; bake 20 to 30 minutes or until tender.